MATHS IN ACTION

Statistics FOR Higher MATHEMATICS

Ralph Riddiough
Deanne Thomas

Thomas Nelson & Sons Ltd
Nelson House
Mayfield Road
Walton-on-Thames
Surrey KT12 5PL
United Kingdom

I(T)P® Thomas Nelson is an International Thomson Company

I(T)P® is used under licence

First Published by Thomas Nelson & Sons Ltd 1998
ISBN 0-17-431496-5
9 8 7 6 5 4 3 2 1
02 01 00 99 98

Project Manager: Lesley Wiseman
Editor: Margaret Cameron

Typeset by Upstream, London
Printed in Croatia by Zrinski, Cakovec

Preface

This book provides complete coverage of the optional Statistics unit within the Mathematics course at Higher level as specified in the Arrangements documents published for the Higher Still Development Programme (May 1997), and has been written as a companion to ***Higher Mathematics*** in the **Maths in Action series**.

The inclusion of statistics within Higher Still mathematics courses is a significant new development. It is recognised that some of the students undertaking this unit on statistics at Higher level may possess Standard Grade qualifications which do not include the study of statistics. Furthermore, many teachers have requested help with the statistics content of the new syllabus. Because of these considerations, every effort has been made to support students and teachers through the inclusion of additional explanatory text, illustrative examples and informative answers. This approach should also enable the book to be used for self-study and as a resource to assist those students who have a Higher Mathematics qualification which does not include statistics, enabling them to progress to the Statistics 1 (AH) unit as part of a programme of study at Advanced Higher level.

Chapter 1 provides a review of the data handling content of Intermediate 1 and Intermediate 2. It focuses on the techniques of organising, displaying and summarising data which are essential for Exploratory Data Analysis (EDA). Outcome 1 of the Statistics unit at Higher level requires students to interpret the results of an EDA and the emphasis in Chapter 2 shifts from data handling techniques to the interpretation of data in the context of real statistical problems. Interpretation is a skill which students need to develop through practice and the inclusion of real data from actual designed statistical investigations is intended to motivate this. The authors recommend a practical approach to learning statistics and firmly believe that students should be given the opportunity to collect their own data. 'Statistics in action' panels are included at appropriate points early in the text to encourage teachers to take this approach and to use the data gathered to illustrate various statistical methods throughout the unit. These activities follow a simple pattern – pose a question, collect some data, analyse the data, interpret the results – and promote an understanding of the inferential nature of statistics.

The variability of the data collected leads to an inevitable difficulty – how sure are we that our subjective interpretation of the data is reliable? An agreed set of rules is required which enables decisions to be made in the face of such uncertainty. The ability to use these rules requires an understanding of how uncertainty is measured and how mathematical models which describe uncertainty are used. Recognising that some students may be confronting these ideas for the first time, Chapter 3 provides a carefully graded introduction to probability and Chapter 4 develops these ideas further through an introduction to discrete and continuous random variables. Considerable effort has been made to present these concepts clearly without lengthy and sometimes difficult proofs. Although complete mathematical rigour is not required by the syllabus at this level, care has been taken to present the material in a way which will not compromise more advanced study at a later stage. Students will be required to make use of the calculus learned in Mathematics Units 1 and 2.

Chapter 5 discusses linear models for data and emphasises the importance of always displaying the data in a scatter plot before attempting to interpret a correlation coefficient or fit a linear model by simple least squares regression. In addition to both simulated and real data sets, students are invited to collect some measurements for themselves, and examine the relationship between variables.

Particular attention has been paid to providing a differentiated course, thus enabling teachers to respond to the needs of individual students. Exercises have been numbered to distinguish basic work necessary for all from that of a more extensive or challenging nature provided for those who wish to develop their competence beyond the minimum. In Chapter 5 for example, the topic of fitting a linear model using linear regression (with the associated Exercise 5.4) is basic work for all at this level, while the topic of using a linear model for prediction is followed by two exercises where Exercise 5.5A is required practice for all and Exercise 5.5B provides an opportunity to develop understanding and competence beyond the minimum requirement. These more challenging questions are also indicated by a purple square behind the question number.

Calculators with statistical features are widely available. An icon is used throughout the book to indicate where advice on their use is given and to prompt students to find out what their calculator can do. Some calculators allow data to be stored for future use – a feature which can save time since many of the data sets in the book are used more than once.

For those with access to a computer, the data used in this book can be entered into software packages. The extent to which teachers can make use of computers in the classroom will vary greatly depending on local circumstances. As a general rule, once the basic techniques have been mastered, there are considerable benefits to be derived from using spreadsheets and statistical packages to process the data which feature substantially in Chapters 1, 2 and 5. For example, using a computer to produce the required graphical displays and numerical summaries of the data in Chapter 2 would allow students to concentrate on interpretation which is the essential skill in Outcome 1 at Higher level.

Ralph Riddiough
Deanne Thomas

Contents

1 Organising, Displaying and Summarising Data

Types of data

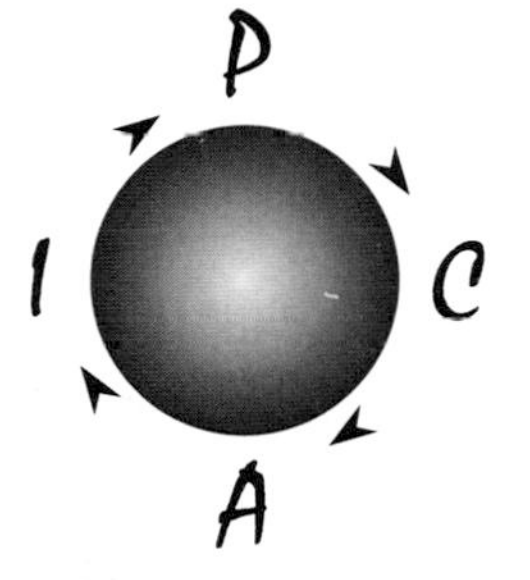

A statistical investigation follows a certain pattern:

P Pose a question.
C Collect some data.
A Analyse the data.
I Interpret the results.

Examples of the sorts of questions we might ask are:

What proportion of the patients attending a doctor's clinic belong to blood group AB?
What proportion of the senior pupils believe Britain should remain a monarchy?
How many pups are there in litters of a certain breed of dog?
How far will a certain model of car travel on 1 gallon of petrol?

The replies given to such questions will vary from one situation to another. Evidence in the form of numerical data will need to be collected and analysed. Analysis includes organising, displaying and summarising the data. Eventually a mathematical description – a model – may be proposed which attempts to explain the variability in the data. The data are the values taken by the variables which feature in the model. The methods used to do the analysis will depend in part on the types of variable being observed.

Qualitative variables:
Observations record a quality or attribute of the object that interests us.
Observations put or classify objects into categories.

A sample of a person's blood is observed and may belong to one of four main blood groups: O, A, B or AB. In this case we are simply naming the type of blood a person has. Blood type is a **nominal** variable.

In a survey, people may be asked to react to the statement 'Britain should remain a constitutional monarchy' by ticking one of the following options: strongly disagree, disagree, indifferent, agree, strongly agree. In this case the categories can be put in an order. These replies are the values taken by an **ordinal** variable.

Observations such as a person's blood type, or a person's response to a question, have no numerical meaning by themselves. However, it is usual to produce numerical data by counting how many observations belong to each category. In this way we can answer questions such as:

'What proportion of those attending the clinic had blood group AB?'

or 'What proportion of those surveyed felt strongly that Britain should remain a monarchy?'

Quantitative variables:

Observations describe the amount or quantity of something.
Observations are the result of counting or measuring and are numerical.

The number of puppies in a litter is *counted.* In this case it is only possible to have a whole number answer. Litter size is an example of a **discrete** variable.

The distance travelled by a certain model of car on 1 gallon of petrol is *measured.* This measurement could be any value within some range or interval of values. Distance is an example of a **continuous** variable. Although any value is possible, such as 33.126 407 miles, it is doubtful that we would want to measure the distance with such accuracy. We may simply record the distance as 33.1 miles or perhaps 33 miles.

Often, the values taken by a variable – the data – are described as nominal, ordinal, discrete, or continuous.

Qualitative data		Quantitative data	
Nominal	**Ordinal**	**Discrete**	**Continuous**
Flavours of ice-cream	Colours of Olympic medals	Class sizes in primary schools	Vehicle tyre pressures
Makes of wristwatch	Travel class of airline tickets	Number of passengers in cars	Lifetimes of light bulbs

EXERCISE 1.1

1 Identify the type of data in each of the following situations:

- **a** The ages of students in your maths class.
- **b** The colour of table wines: red, white and rose.
- **c** The scores on a recent maths test.
- **d** The number of road accidents per week.
- **e** The commissioned ranks in the British army.
- **f** The weekly wages of skilled manual workers.
- **g** The sex of kittens in a litter.
- **h** The number of children in a family who are under the age of 16 years.
- **i** The geographic regions: North, South and Central.

2 'Latest opinion polls show main candidates neck and neck in local by-election ...'
What type of data have the pollsters collected?

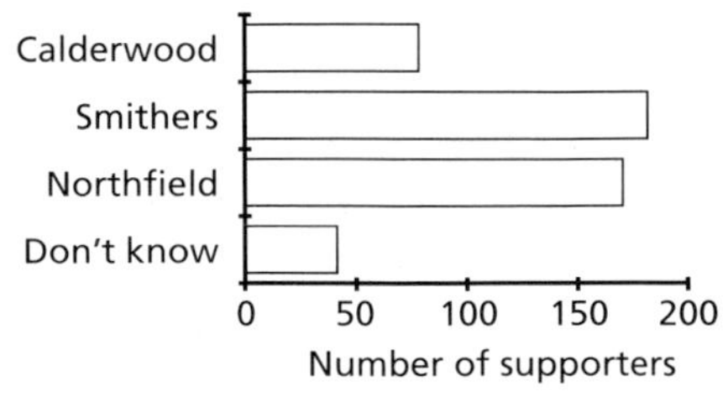

3 A doctor's patients were asked which of the following they thought best described their general state of health: Very good – Good – Average – Poor – Very poor.
Describe the type of data their replies would produce.

4 During a study into the effect of a diet supplement on the growth of guinea pigs, the body weight of each guinea pig was recorded at regular intervals, as shown in the table.
What type of data is being recorded?

Vitamin E Supplement – Experimental Results (Body weight in grams)			
Guinea pig	Week 1	Week 2	Week 3
1	235	245	260
2	225	240	254
3	233	247	266
:	:	:	:

5 Triage is a method of sorting the casualties of major disasters and accidents into categories of priority for treatment, such as critical, moderate, minor. During these emergencies, hospitals will keep records of how many patients fall into each category. What type of data are they collecting?

6 Houses heated by electricity were used in a study to compare the effectiveness of two methods of house insulation. The total electricity consumption for these houses was measured in kWh for one year. What type of data are these?

7 A social survey plans to interview a sample of 1000 employed persons, and one of the questions will ask each person what type of work he or she does.
What type of data will be produced by this question?

Survey briefing
The following occupation types should be used:
1 professional
2 managers and employers
3 intermediate and junior non-manual
4 skilled manual
5 semi-skilled manual
6 unskilled manual.

8 Describe the type of data collected in a study of driving performance, where the number of steering corrections the driver had to make was recorded.

9 The survival times of patients suffering from a certain fatal disease were recorded in days from the time of diagnosis:

7	47	58	74	177	232	273	285	317	429	440	445
455	468	495	497	532	571	579	581	650	702	715	779
881	900	930	968	1077	1109	1314	1334	1367	1534	1712	1784
1877	1886	2045	2056	2260	2429	2509					

What type of data are these?

Organising and displaying qualitative and discrete data

An important first step when trying to answer the question(s) posed in a statistical investigation is to organise and display the data. An efficient way to record the data is to use a **recording sheet** which once completed gives a frequency table.

Example 1 The blood type of a sample of 40 patients attending a clinic was noted on a recording sheet. What proportion of patients have blood type AB? Display these nominal data.

Blood type	Tally	Frequency
O	~~||||~~ ~~||||~~ ~~||||~~ ~~||||~~	20
A	~~||||~~ ~~||||~~ ////	14
B	////	4
AB	//	2
	Total	40

Proportion with blood type AB $= \frac{2}{40} = 0.05$

A **bar diagram** gives a picture which shows clearly that O and A were the most frequently occurring blood types amongst these patients and that type AB was comparatively rare. A further line of enquiry might be to question whether this pattern is typical of the population as a whole.

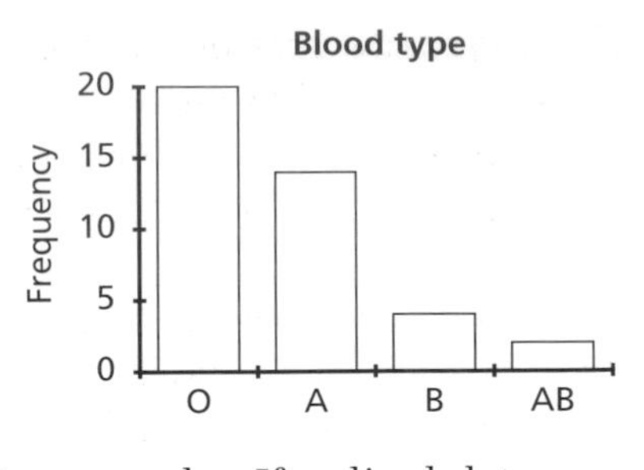

For nominal data such as these, the categories (blood types) along the horizontal axis can be arranged in any order. If ordinal data are being illustrated however, the categories will have a definite order.

An alternative which is ideal for illustrating nominal data is a **pie chart** as it shows the proportions in each category.
The angle at the centre of the AB sector is:

$$\text{proportion of AB} \times 360° = 0.05 \times 360 = 18°$$

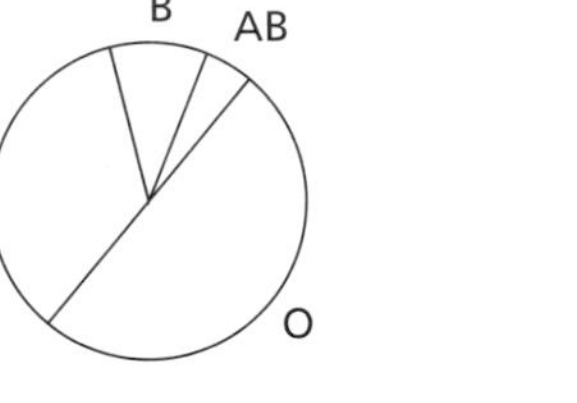

Similarly, the angles at the centre for the other types of blood are:

B: $\frac{4}{40} \times 360 = 36°$

A: $\frac{14}{40} \times 360 = 126°$

O: $\frac{20}{40} \times 360 = 180°$

Example 2 How many paper clips are in each box?

Counting the contents of 50 boxes of paper clips produced the following data.

53	53	51	50	49	51	45	46	52	52
50	49	50	48	46	51	48	53	49	51
50	51	54	53	48	52	52	48	52	55
54	47	50	51	52	55	51	52	53	49
46	51	51	51	50	47	53	50	50	49

Recording in this way makes it difficult to answer the question posed.

A **frequency table** organises the data. Notice that half the boxes contain 50, 51 or 52 paper clips. Also notice that there is considerable variability in the contents of the boxes: one box contained as few as 45 paper clips; two boxes contained as many as 55 clips.

Contents	Tally	Frequency
45	/	1
46	///	3
47	//	2
48	////	4
49	~~////~~	5
50	~~////~~ ///	8
51	~~////~~ ~~////~~	10
52	~~////~~ //	7
53	~~////~~ /	6
54	//	2
55	//	2
	Total	50

The frequency distribution can be shown in a **bar diagram**.
The bars are all the same width, and the height of the bars indicates the frequency.
There is a definite order to the numbers along the horizontal axis.
The gaps between the bars emphasise that the data are discrete.

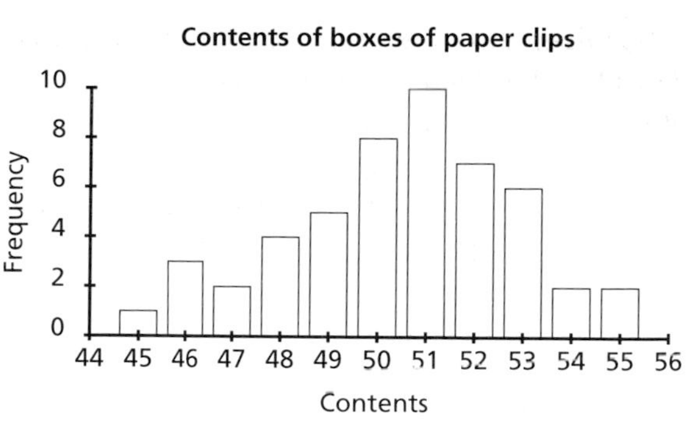

If discrete data are distributed over a wide range of values they may be **grouped**.

Contents	Frequency
44–46	4
47–49	11
50–52	25
53–55	10

Contents of boxes of paper clips

Frequency: 0, 5, 10, 15, 20, 25

Contents: 44–46, 47–49, 50–52, 53–55

The appearance of the resulting bar diagram will vary, depending on how the values are grouped.

As a quick alternative to a bar diagram these data could be displayed using a **dotplot**.

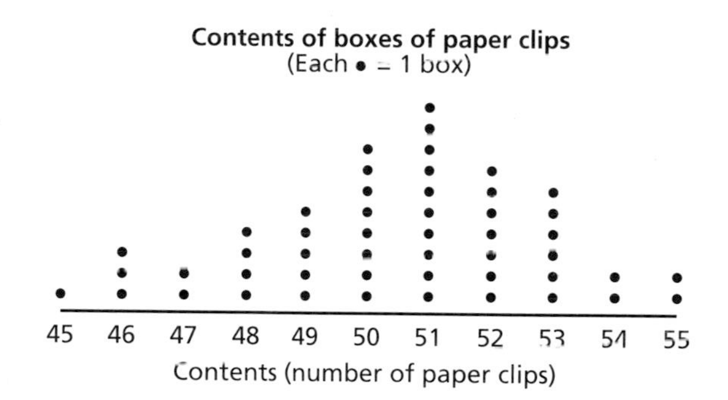

EXERCISE 1.2

1 A survey of the operations performed on children at a local hospital showed that:
21 had general surgery;
15 had plastic surgery;
36 had ENT (ear, nose and throat) surgery;
18 had other surgical procedures.
Represent the data in a pie chart.

2 A class of 12-year-olds was asked how many fast food meals had been eaten by each pupil during the previous week.

7	1	3	1	2	2	2	4	2	1
2	3	7	5	1	3	3	2	5	2
2	1	1	6	2					

Illustrate their responses with a dotplot.

3 The makers of a certain brand of matches claim the average contents of their boxes are 85 matches. The number of matches in a sample of 50 boxes was counted. The data are:

83 89 85 91 82 85 89 88 85 90 86 81 92 92 83 87 85 87
81 81 83 82 90 86 86 80 89 91 81 84 88 84 86 88 86 94
86 87 86 87 86 91 82 83 84 82 87 80 88 90

a Organise the data in an ungrouped frequency table and draw a bar diagram.
b Using the groups 78–80, 81–83, 84–86, and so on, re-tabulate the data and draw a new bar diagram. Compare its appearance with the bar diagram in part **a**.

4 In an opinion poll people were asked to react to the statement 'Britain should remain a constitutional monarchy' by choosing one of these options:

Strongly agree	Agree	Indifferent	Disagree	Strongly disagree
☐	☐	☐	☐	☐

When tabulating the results, these ordinal data were coded as follows:

Strongly agree = 2
Agree = 1
Indifferent = 0
Disagree = −1
Strongly disagree = −2

The survey produced the following responses in coded form:

1	1	0	−2	1	−1	0	−2	1	−1
−2	−1	0	1	1	1	−2	0	2	1
1	0	1	−1	0	1	1	0	−2	2

Organise and display the data using a bar diagram.

Stem and leaf diagrams

A supermarket's brand of potato crisps come in packets which claim to contain 25 grams. The contents of a selection of 50 packets were weighed to the nearest 0.1 g:

26.4 25.2 25.7 26.3 26.0 24.1 25.3 26.3 25.6 26.0 26.2 25.2 27.8 24.5 25.0 27.5 27.1
26.1 27.3 26.3 25.3 28.5 26.5 25.8 26.1 25.2 24.4 27.0 24.8 25.8 27.7 26.7 25.8 25.5
27.1 26.9 27.6 26.6 26.3 25.5 24.7 26.4 27.0 25.5 26.0 25.8 26.2 25.7 26.0 25.8

Questions we may ask include:
How many packets in the sample contain more than 25 g?
What proportion of the packets in the sample contain less than 25 g?
By how much are some packets under or over the stated weight?

To find answers to these questions, first organise the data. A stem and leaf diagram is one way to do this.

The whole number part of the weights can be used to form the stem shown to the left of the vertical line, and the decimal fraction part of the weights forms the leaves on the right.

The leaves on each **level** or row in the diagram increase in value outwards from the stem.

Contents of packets of crisps (g)

Stem	Leaves
24	14578
25	02223355567788888
26	000011223333445679
27	001135678
28	5

$n = 50$ 24 | 1 represents 24.1 g

The statement '24 | 1 represents 24.1 g' is very important because '24 | 1' could mean 241, or 24.1, or 2.41, etc., depending on the quantities being displayed.
The diagram has a title and the sample size $n = 50$ is noted.

To build a stem and leaf diagram:

- Choose the stems.
- Scan the data one value at a time.
- Place the leaves on their stem.

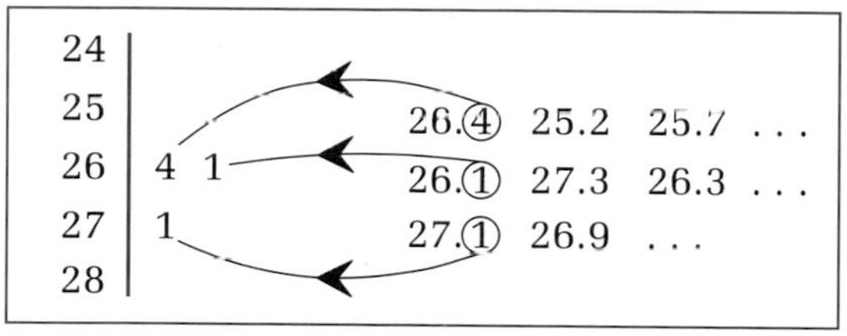

24				
25		26.④	25.2	25.7 ...
26	4 1	26.①	27.3	26.3 ...
27	1	27.①	26.9	...
28				

Finally:

- Redraw the diagram with the leaves increasing in value outwards from the stem.
- Show the units and sample size.
- Give the diagram a title.

The above stem and leaf diagram can be stretched by choosing the stems to represent more levels as shown here:

24.0 to 24.4
24.5 to 24.9
25.0 to 25.4
25.5 to 25.9
etc.

The choice of stems changes the appearance of a stem and leaf diagram.

Contents of packets of crisps (g)

Stem	Leaf
24	14
24	578
25	022233
25	55567788888
26	00001122333344
26	5679
27	00113
27	5678
28	
28	5

$n = 50$ 24 | 1 represents 24.1 g

EXERCISE 1.3

1 The weekly earnings of a sample of women who were in full-time employment are shown.
Copy and complete the stem and leaf diagram.
Data:

148	147	145	103	113
135	93	87	111	110
119	107	113	110	104

Weekly earnings

Stem	Leaf
8	
9	
10	
11	
12	
13	
14	

14 | 8 represents £148

2 A sample of eggs was taken from one day's production and weighed in grams.
Draw a stem and leaf diagram for the data, using stems 4, 4, 5, 5, ... etc.

40	50	72	51	60	55	67	46	57	53	55	42	51
59	49	52	46	64	43	66	54	64	48	58	52	

3 The pupils in Class 1B measured their heights to the nearest centimetre. They ranged from a minimum of 135 cm to a maximum of 177 cm. Display their heights using a stem and leaf diagram.

157	145	159	143	142	152	147	135	141	155	150	145	152	142
166	154	136	145	154	160	177	158	155	157	152	147	159	

4 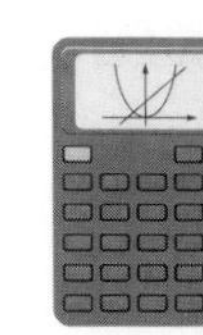
A random number generator is supposed to produce numbers that are evenly distributed across the range $0 \le x < 1$. The following data were produced using *rand*, the random number function on a graphics calculator, rounded to 2 decimal places using the formula: int(rand*100)/100.

0.23	0.62	0.24	0.84	0.76	0.46	0.64	0.04	0.01	0.11
0.68	0.15	0.88	0.65	0.88	0.88	0.05	0.63	0.76	0.51
0.03	0.23	0.34	0.85	0.30	0.26	0.60	0.47	0.76	0.99
0.84	0.81	0.53	0.99	0.30	0.24	0.51	0.82	0.68	0.02

Show the data in a stem and leaf diagram where 9 | 9 represents 0.99. Using your calculator, produce 100 random numbers rounded to 2 decimal places. (A spreadsheet or tables of random numbers are other sources.) Display your data in a stem and leaf diagram and compare them with the above data.

Histograms

The contents of a sample of crisp packets were weighed and the results are shown in this stem and leaf diagram.
These data are continuous. Although the weights have been recorded to the nearest 0.1 g any quantity is possible within a certain range of values around 25 g.

Contents of packets of crisps (g)

24	14578
25	02223355567788888
26	000011223333445679
27	001135678
28	5

$n = 50$ 28 | 5 represents 28.5 g

The **class interval** $25.0 \le x < 26.0$ refers to all the possible weights x g between 25.0 g and 26.0 g. and has:

- a **class width** of $26.0 - 25.0 = 1.0$ g
- a **lower limit** of 25.0 g which is included in the interval
- an **upper limit** of 26.0 g which is not included in the interval
- a **mid-point** of 25.5 g.

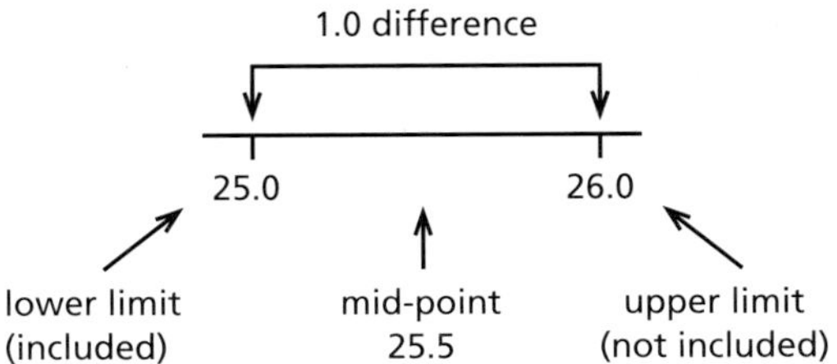

Net weight (x g)	Tally	Frequency
$24.0 \le x < 25.0$	~~////~~	5
$25.0 \le x < 26.0$	~~////~~ ~~////~~ ~~////~~ //	17
$26.0 \le x < 27.0$	~~////~~ ~~////~~ ~~////~~ ///	18
$27.0 \le x < 28.0$	~~////~~ ////	9
$28.0 \le x < 29.0$	/	1
	Total	50

A **frequency table** can be constructed for the above continuous data by tabulating into which interval each weight belongs. Other choices for the class intervals are possible.

A suitable diagram to show the frequency distribution of these weights is a **histogram** like the one shown.

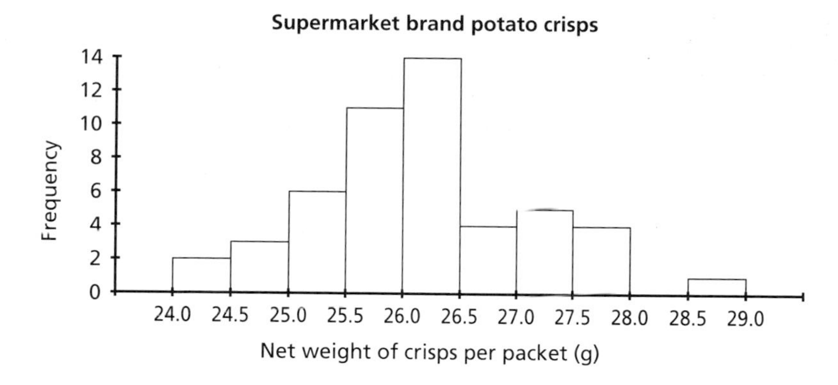

This histogram uses ten intervals as follows:

$24.0 \leq x < 24.5$

$24.5 \leq x < 25.0$

$25.0 \leq x < 25.5$

etc.

Notice that the choice of class intervals has an effect on the appearance of the histogram.

Hint

When grouping quantitative data, between five and ten intervals or groups are usually sufficient.

Note that The bars are touching, emphasising the continuous nature of the data.
The markings on the horizontal scale show the limits of the class intervals.

A histogram is a diagram consisting of rectangles whose *areas* are proportional to frequency. The total area of all the rectangles represents the sample size. The importance of areas will become clear later. For class intervals of equal width, the height of the rectangle is proportional to the frequency:

$$\begin{aligned} &\text{frequency} \propto \text{area of rectangle} \\ \Rightarrow \quad &\text{frequency} \propto \text{height} \times \text{width.} \end{aligned}$$

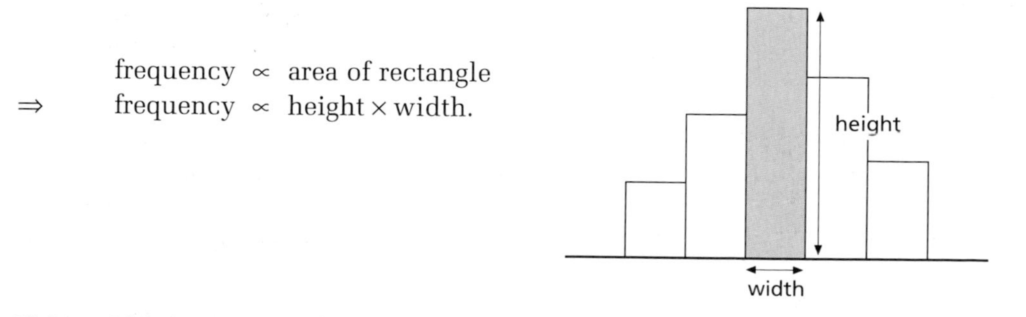

If the width is constant then the frequency is proportional to the height of the rectangle.

EXERCISE 1.4

1 A police speed check recorded these vehicle speeds in miles per hour.

41 48 60 40 72 44 59 21 49 46 50 42 33 43 43 49 47
47 49 56 46 45 44 52 48 54 68 51 50 47 60 55 46 38

Organise these speeds in a frequency table using intervals $20 \le s < 30$, $30 \le s < 40$, etc.
Draw a histogram and comment on its appearance.

2 The contents of 50 packets of a supermarket's brand of crisps were weighed and the results in grams were:

26.4 25.2 25.7 26.3 26.0 24.1 25.3 26.3 25.6 26.0 26.2 25.2 27.8 24.5 25.0 27.5 27.1 26.1
27.3 26.3 25.3 28.5 26.5 25.8 26.1 25.2 24.4 27.0 24.8 25.8 27.7 26.7 25.8 25.5 27.1 26.9
27.6 26.6 26.3 25.5 24.7 26.4 27.0 25.5 26.0 25.8 26.2 25.7 26.0 25.8

Group the data using class intervals $23.5 \le x < 24.5$, $24.5 \le x < 25.5$, etc., and draw the histogram.

3 This stem and leaf diagram shows the results of the October maths test.
Draw the corresponding histogram.

October maths test

Stem	Leaf
1	68
2	1368
3	1122335589
4	01122345689
5	0025667899
6	345699
7	0139
8	09
9	4

$n = 50$ 1 | 6 represents 16 marks

4 These data show the number of days that patients with a certain disease survived from the time their condition was first diagnosed.

7 47 58 74 177 232 273 285 317 429 440
445 455 468 495 497 532 571 579 581 650 702
715 779 881 900 930 968 1077 1109 1314 1334 1367
1534 1712 1784 1877 1886 2045 2056 2260 2429 2509

Using intervals of width 365 days, draw a histogram to represent the data.
How many patients survived more than five years?

5

Some calculators have features which allow data to be stored for future use and displayed. Find out what your calculator can do. Find out how to:

a enter and store for future use the data in question **2** above
b sort the data into increasing order
c set the X and Y scales so that this range of values will fit on the screen
d draw a histogram for the data.

Organising and displaying data - Further topics

Relative frequency

In 1882, R. Wolf reported the results of tossing a die 20 000 times. The frequency table shows his results.

Face	Frequency	Relative frequency
1	3407	0.170 35
2	3631	0.181 55
3	3176	0.158 80
4	2916	0.145 80
5	3448	0.172 40
6	3422	0.171 10
Total frequency	20 000	1.000 00

The relative frequency is calculated by dividing each individual frequency by the total frequency. For example, the relative frequency for a '6' is:

$$\frac{3422}{20\,000} = 0.171\,10$$

Note that the relative frequencies add up to 1.

Each relative frequency is the proportion of times that a particular face was showing. In the long run, a fair die would be expected to produce equal frequencies of each face, so the proportion of times that each face would be showing is $\frac{1}{6} = 0.166\,666\,6...$

Comparing this proportion with the relative frequencies in the above table shows a slight variation from the ideal. Face '4', for example, seems to have occurred less often than expected, while face '2' has occurred more often than expected. It is possible that this variability is due to chance. On the other hand it could be the result of some bias in the die.

Frequency polygons

The following frequency table summarises the net contents of 50 packets of a supermarket's brand of potato crisps.

Net weight (x g)	Mid-point	Frequency
$23.5 \leq x < 24.5$	24.0	2
$24.5 \leq x < 25.5$	25.0	9
$25.5 \leq x < 26.5$	26.0	25
$26.5 \leq x < 27.5$	27.0	9
$27.5 \leq x < 28.5$	28.0	4
$28.5 \leq x < 29.5$	29.0	1
	Total	50

A frequency polygon is drawn by plotting the frequency for each interval against the mid-point of the interval, and joining the points with straight line segments. There are no observations in the intervals $22.5 \leq x < 23.5$ or $29.5 \leq x < 30.5$ so the points (23.0, 0) and (30.0, 0) are included.

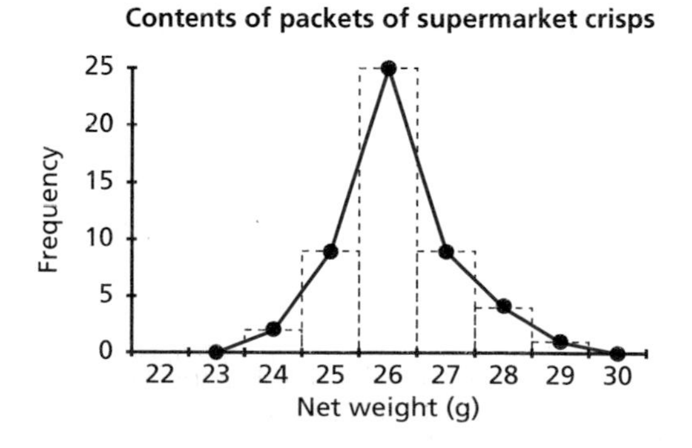

Cumulative frequency

The **cumulative frequency table** shown here summarises the results of the October maths test and has an extra column which shows a running total of the frequencies for these marks. For example, the cumulative frequency in the $20 \le x < 30$ row of the table is 6 which can be interpreted as: '6 pupils scored less than 30 marks'.

October maths test		
Class interval	Frequency	Cumulative frequency
$0 \le x < 10$	0	0
$10 \le x < 20$	2	2
$20 \le x < 30$	4	6
$30 \le x < 40$	10	16
$40 \le x < 50$	11	27
$50 \le x < 60$	10	37
$60 \le x < 70$	6	43
$70 \le x < 80$	4	47
$80 \le x < 90$	2	49
$90 \le x < 100$	1	50

A **cumulative frequency diagram** is drawn by plotting the cumulative frequency against the upper class limit as follows.

There are 0 observations less than 10 marks; plot the point (10, 0).
There are 2 observations less than 20 marks; plot the point (20, 2).
There are 6 observations less than 30 marks; plot the point (30, 6), etc.

The points are then joined by straight line segments.

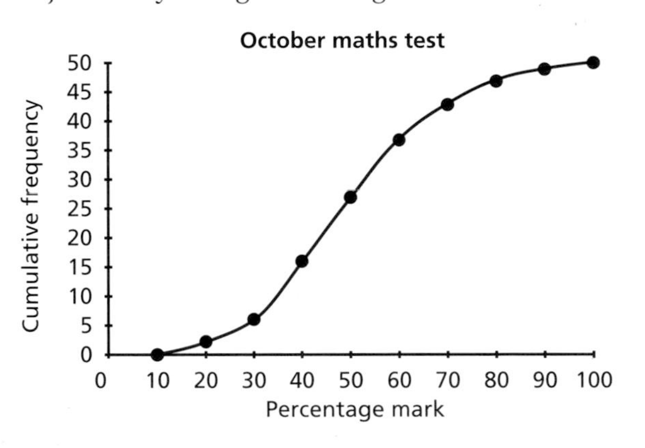

EXERCISE 1.5A

1 A sample of 40 unrelated pupils was asked 'How many children are there in your family?' The responses were as follows:

2	2	3	3	2	2	3	4	1	2	4	3	2	4	4	2	6	2	2	3
2	1	2	2	4	2	2	2	3	2	2	4	2	3	1	3	3	3	3	1

a Construct a relative frequency table for the data.
b Which size of family has the largest relative frequency?
c What is the relative frequency of families with three or more children?

2 800 employed people were asked about their jobs and the following frequency table shows how many of the sample were in each category of employment. The researchers were interested in the proportion of the sample in each type of job.

a Copy and complete the table.

Type of employment	Frequency	Relative frequency
1. professional	47	0.059
2. managers and employers	93	0.116
3. intermediate and junior non-manual	228	
4. skilled manual	113	
5. semi-skilled manual	147	
6. unskilled manual	172	
Total	800	1.000

b Use the relative frequencies to construct a pie chart for the data.

c If one of these people was picked at random, what type of work is that person most likely to do?

3 The heights (in centimetres) of a sample of pupils put in order are:

130 132 134 135 136 137 137 137 138 138 139 141 141 142 142 142 142 143
144 144 144 145 145 145 146 146 147 148 148 148 149 149 150 151 151 152
152 152 153 154 154 155 156 157 158 158 159 159 161 164

a Construct a frequency table and draw a histogram for these continuous data using intervals of width 5 cm commencing with $130 \le x < 135$.

b On the same diagram, draw the frequency polygon for the data.

c Extend the frequency table to include cumulative frequencies and draw a cumulative frequency diagram. (Remember to include the point (130, 0) as 0 pupils were < 130 cm tall.)

4 This frequency table summarises the contents of 50 boxes of paper clips.

a Copy and complete the table, including a cumulative frequency column, e.g. the third row shows there are 6 boxes containing ≤ 47 paper clips.

b Draw a cumulative frequency diagram for these data. (Remember to include the point (44, 0) because no boxes had ≤ 44 paper clips. Think carefully how to join the points.)

Contents	Frequency	Cumulative frequency
45	1	1
46	3	4
47	2	6
48	4	
49	5	
50	8	
51	10	
52	7	
53	6	
54	2	
55	2	
Total	50	

5 Sixty vehicles were inspected and their mileage noted. Draw a cumulative frequency diagram and use it to estimate how many vehicles had travelled less than 36 000 miles. (Include (0, 0) to show that 0 vehicles travelled < 0 miles.)

Mileage (1000s miles)	Number of vehicles
$0 \le x < 10$	2
$10 \le x < 20$	8
$20 \le x < 30$	14
$30 \le x < 40$	17
$40 \le x < 50$	10
$50 \le x < 60$	5
$60 \le x < 70$	3
$70 \le x < 80$	1
Total	60

EXERCISE 1.5B

1 The random number generator in a statistics computer package is supposed to produce numbers that are evenly distributed across the range $0 \le x < 1$. The following random numbers were printed out by the computer package:

0.066984	0.107615	0.961191	0.072400	0.268400	0.752890	0.334382
0.362620	0.171727	0.066707	0.660066	0.003300	0.535033	0.639328
0.984140	0.941553	0.821712	0.822860	0.383846	0.426547	0.776413
0.006368	0.099980	0.095688	0.276944	0.733812	0.309576	0.490665
0.276614	0.656822	0.634420	0.232832	0.265009	0.229375	0.264649

a Tabulate the data in the intervals $0 \le x < 0.1$, $0.1 \le x < 0.2$, $0.2 \le x < 0.3$, etc.

b Calculate the relative frequencies of random numbers in these intervals and comment.

c In the long run, what relative frequency would you expect (i) in each interval (ii) for numbers less than 0.5?

d Calculate the relative frequencies of numbers (i) less than 0.5 (ii) greater than or equal to 0.5, and comment on your results.

The same random number generator produced 1000 random numbers between 0 and 1 and these are shown in the histogram and frequency table below.

e Calculate the relative frequency of random numbers in each interval and comment.

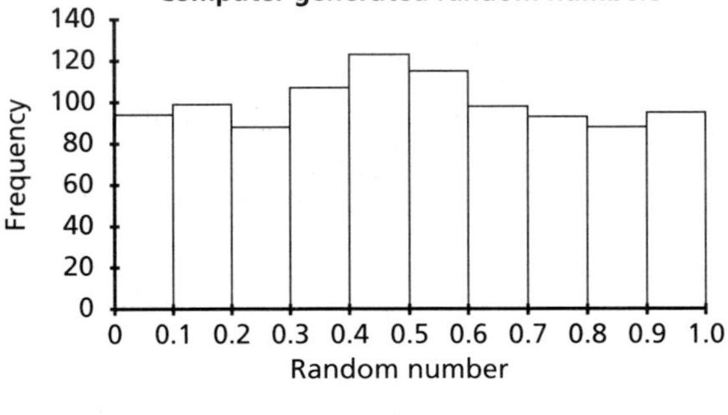

Interval	Frequency
$0.0 \le x < 0.1$	94
$0.1 \le x < 0.2$	99
$0.2 \le x < 0.3$	88
$0.3 \le x < 0.4$	107
$0.4 \le x < 0.5$	123
$0.5 \le x < 0.6$	115
$0.6 \le x < 0.7$	98
$0.7 \le x < 0.8$	93
$0.8 \le x < 0.9$	88
$0.9 \le x < 1.0$	95
Total	1000

2 These data give the duration of pregnancy for 1585 women who gave birth in a large maternity hospital, and compare women admitted on a planned basis with those admitted on an emergency basis. The durations were recorded to the nearest week.

Duration (weeks)	Planned	Emergency
33	8	6
34	22	7
35	27	11
36	45	13
37	84	16
38	140	35
39	274	38
40	352	32
41	239	27
42	119	25
43	45	8
44	7	5
Total	1362	223

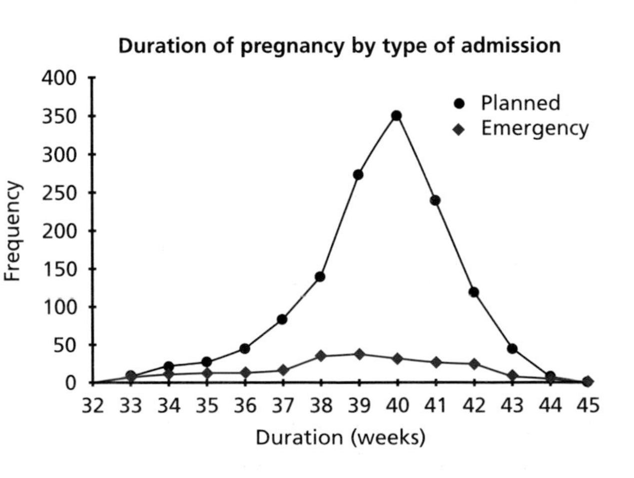

It is difficult to compare the duration of pregnancy for these two groups of women because the sample sizes are very different. However, relative frequencies make comparisons easier.

a Calculate the relative frequencies of each duration for planned and emergency admissions.

b Draw relative frequency polygons on the same axes for planned and emergency admissions.

c For women whose admission was planned, which duration has the greatest relative frequency?

d If a woman who was admitted as an emergency is chosen at random what would be the most likely duration of her pregnancy?

e What proportion of the women who had (i) planned (ii) emergency admission to hospital completed their pregnancy in 39 weeks or less?

f Percentage frequency = relative frequency × 100. Prepare a table of cumulative percentage frequencies for planned and emergency admissions.

g Draw cumulative percentage diagrams for planned and emergency admissions on the same axes and compare them.

Summarising data – Averages

How many paper clips are in a box?

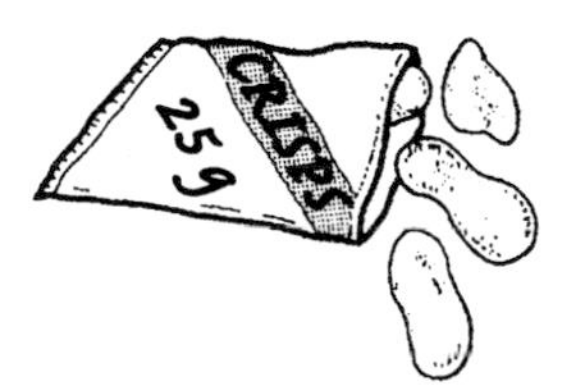

What is the weight of the contents of a packet of crisps?

The statistical investigations to find answers to these questions may produce lots of data and show considerable variation. If the mass of data collected could be reduced to one representative value which is in the centre of the collected data then this may provide a suitable answer for the question posed. Such a typical value is called an **average** or **measure of central location**. Commonly used averages are the **mean**, **median** and **mode**.

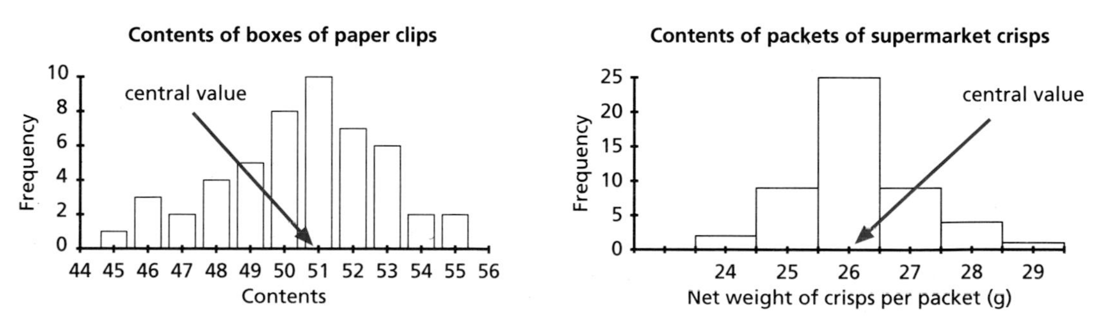

The mean

Example 1 The labels on boxes of paper clips claim 'average contents 50'. The contents of a sample of 10 boxes were counted:

52 48 52 50 55 50 49 53 51 52.

Find the mean number of paper clips per box.

$$Mean = \frac{\textit{total of observations}}{\textit{number of observations}} = \frac{52+48+52+50+55+50+49+53+51+52}{10}$$

$$= \frac{512}{10} = 51.2 \text{ paper clips}$$

The mean often turns out to be a value that is not the same as any of the observations. For example, in this case it is not possible to have a box containing 51.2 paper clips. However, do not quote the mean to more accuracy than one decimal place beyond that in the data.

A formula for the mean:

$$\bar{x} = \frac{x_1 + x_2 + \ldots + x_n}{n} = \frac{\Sigma x_i}{n}$$

x_i represents one of the observations

n represents the number of observations

Σx_i represents the total or sum of all the observations

$\bar{x}$ represents the mean of the observations
($\bar{x}$ is read as 'x bar', and Σ is pronounced 'sigma'.)

The mean is the only average which is influenced by the numerical value of each and every observation.

Example 2 The net contents (in grams) of a sample of 15 packets of a supermarket's brand of potato crisps are:

26.9 24.1 26.0 27.8 26.2 24.8 28.5 25.8 24.4 24.9 25.2 25.5 27.3 26.5 26.4

The label shows the contents are supposed to be 25 g. Calculate the mean weight.
Adding up all the weights gives $\Sigma x_i = 390.3$ g, $n = 15$, so the mean is

$$\bar{x} = \frac{\Sigma x_i}{n} = \frac{390.3}{15} = 26.02 \text{ g.}$$

The median

A simple way to determine a typical or central value is to place all the values in increasing order and to choose 'the middle value' which splits the data into two equal halves. This value is called the median.

Example 3 Find the median of the net contents of the 15 packets of crisps in Example 2.
Rank the data in increasing order:

24.1 24.4 24.8 24.9 25.2 25.5 25.8 26.0 26.2 26.4 26.5 26.9 27.3 27.8 28.5
↑ (26.0)

The median is the value in the middle.

In this case the mean, 26.02 g, and the median, 26.0 g, are almost identical.

Example 4 Find the median of the contents of the 10 boxes of paper clips in Example 1.
Rank the data in increasing order:

48 48 49 50 51 52 52 52 53 55
↑ ↑ (51, 52)

Median = 51.5

This time there are an even number of boxes and there are two values in the middle. In this case the median is the value halfway between 51 and 52.

A rule for finding the median: Sort the data into increasing order. Recall that a stem and leaf diagram is an efficient way to do this.
If n represents the number of observations then the median is the value in the $\frac{n+1}{2}$th position.

How the rule works: When n is odd: in Example 3 above, $n = 15$ so the median is in the $\frac{15+1}{2} = 8$th position.
Count in from either end of the sorted list and choose the 8th value.
When n is even: in Example 4 above, $n = 10$ so the median is in the $\frac{10+1}{2} = 5.5$th position.
5.5 is halfway between 5 and 6.
Count in from either end of the sorted list and calculate the value halfway between the 5th and 6th value.

Check this rule works with the data in Example 3 and in Example 4.

The mode

The most frequently occurring observation of a data set is called the mode. For example, the contents of 50 boxes of paper clips were counted and the results are displayed in this bar diagram. The tallest bar represents the mode, which is 51 clips per box.

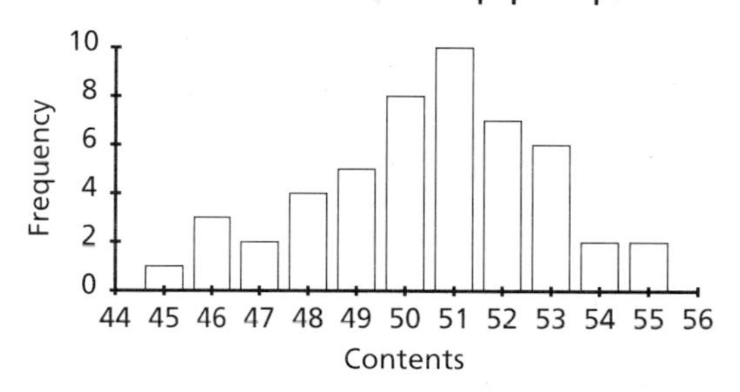

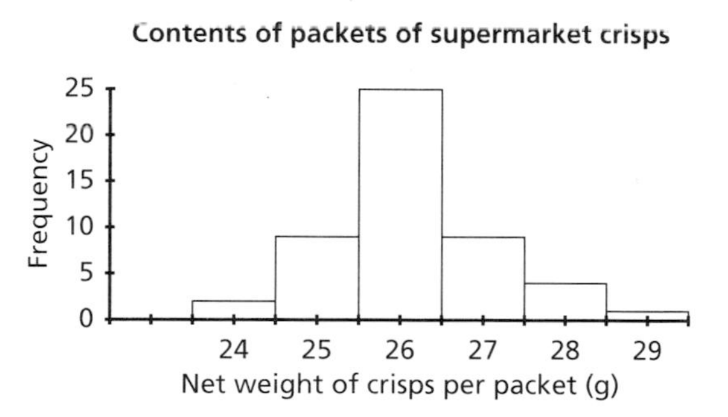

This histogram illustrates the data resulting from weighing the contents of 50 packets of crisps.
The **modal class interval** is $25.5 \leq x < 26.5$ g.

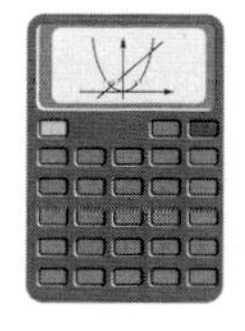

Does your calculator have special statistical features built in? Some calculators can:

- store a data set
- store a frequency table
- calculate the mean of a stored data set
- arrange a data set in order
- find the median.

Learning how to use these features will allow you to do many of the tasks throughout this book more efficiently. Start using them now!

EXERCISE 1.6A

1 The number of fast food meals each pupil in a class had eaten during the previous week was recorded. Calculate the mean, median and mode of the data.

7	1	3	1	2	2	2	4	2	1
2	3	7	5	1	3	3	2	5	2
2	1	1	6	2					

2 Calculate the mean and median of these weights (grams) of a sample of flower bulbs:

40	50	72	51	60	55	67	46	57	52	55	42
51	59	49	52	46	64	43	66	54	64	48	58

3 The contents of 50 boxes of paper clips were counted and the following table summarises the results. Copy the table and complete the last column.

Σf represents the total frequency, 50 boxes.

Σxf represents the total number of paper clips.

Contents x	Frequency f	Number of paper clips xf
45	1	45
46	3	138
47	2	
48	4	
49	5	
50	8	
51	10	
52	7	
53	6	
54	2	
55	2	
Total	$\Sigma f = 50$	$\Sigma xf =$

The mean contents is obtained by dividing the total number of paper clips by the total number of boxes. Write down a formula using this Σ-notation for the mean number of paper clips per box and use it to calculate the mean.
Find the median number of paper clips per box from the frequency table.

4 The net weight of potato crisps in each of 50 packets is shown in this stem and leaf diagram.

a Find the mean and median of the data from the stem and leaf diagram.

Contents of packets of crisps (g)

Stem	Leaf
24	14
24	578
25	022233
25	55567788888
26	00001122333344
26	5679
27	00113
27	5678
28	
28	5

$n = 50$ 24 | 1 represents 24.1 g

b These same data have been grouped in the following frequency table.

Net weight	Mid-point (x g)	Frequency f	xf
$23.5 \le x < 24.5$	24.0	2	48.0
$24.5 \le x < 25.5$	25.0	9	225.0
$25.5 \le x < 26.5$	26.0	25	
$26.5 \le x < 27.5$	27.0	9	
$27.5 \le x < 28.5$	28.0	4	
$28.5 \le x < 29.5$	29.0	1	
		Total 50	

Each mid-point value listed is used to represent all the values in the corresponding interval. Copy the table and complete the last column. Calculate the mean net weight per packet from the completed table.

c The same data (see stem and leaf diagram) can be regrouped in the following class intervals:

$$24.0 \leq x < 24.5$$
$$24.5 \leq x < 25.0$$
$$25.0 \leq x < 25.5 \text{ etc.}$$

Complete a frequency table like the one in part **b** and recalculate the mean using it.

d Compare the three calculated values for the mean of these data and comment.

EXERCISE 1.6B

1 These are the weekly wages for the employees of a small manufacturing company rounded to the nearest £25:

100	125	150	175	200	225	250	275	300	350
400	500	125	150	175	200	225	125	150	175
200	150	175	150	175					

a Represent the data in a dotplot.

b Write down the mode, the median, and calculate the mean to the nearest pound.

c Repeat part **b** but this time ignore the £500 wage.

d Compare the two sets of averages. Comment on the effect of the 'extreme' value £500 on each of the different types of average.

2 The survival times in days for a group of patients suffering from a certain fatal disease are:

7	47	58	74	177	232	273	285	317	429
440	445	455	468	495	497	532	571	579	581
650	702	715	779	881	900	930	968	1077	1109
1314	1334	1367	1534	1712	1784	1877	1886	2045	2056
2260	2429	2509							

a Calculate the mean and the median survival time.

b What proportion of the patients in this group live longer than the (i) mean (ii) median?

c Which of these two averages gives a more realistic guide to the expected survival of patients who are suffering from this disease?

Boxplots

An average reduces all the collected data to a single value. However, this does not convey how variable the data are. Reducing the data to five numbers chosen from across the range of values is more informative. A **five number summary** consists of the **minimum** and **maximum** values (the **extremities**) together with the **lower quartile**, the **median** and the **upper quartile**. This numerical summary of the data can be illustrated using a **boxplot**, or **box and whisker diagram**.

Example 1 This stem and leaf diagram shows the results of the October maths test. Prepare a five number summary and draw a boxplot.

October maths test

Stem	Leaf
1	68
2	1368
3	1122335589
4	01122345689
5	0025667899
6	345699
7	0139
8	09
9	4

$n = 50$ 1 | 6 represents 16 marks

The median of the ordered data is the value in the $\frac{50+1}{2} = 25.5$th position, which is halfway between the 25th and 26th mark. From the stem and leaf diagram, the 25th mark is 46 and the 26th mark is 48. The median mark is $\frac{46+48}{2} = 47$. The median divides the ordered data into two halves. There are as many observations below the median as above it. Quartiles are values which divide ordered data into four quarters.

Warning!
Different methods for calculating the quartiles have been proposed and slightly different answers can result depending on which method is used.

A simple method for calculating quartiles:
The quartiles are taken as the medians of the lower and upper 'halves' of the data, ignoring the middle value when n is odd. This is the method used throughout this book and by some calculators.

When n is even, e.g. $n = 10$ data: 1 2 3 4 5 6 7 8 9 10

median $= \frac{1}{2}(5+6) = 5.5$

the two halves are: 1 2 3 4 5

and: 6 7 8 9 10

The lower quartile is the median of the lower half = 3

The upper quartile is the median of the upper half = 8

When n is odd, e.g. $n = 13$ data: 1 2 3 4 5 6 7 8 9 10 11 12 13

Ignore the median median = 7

the two halves are: 1 2 3 4 5 6

and: 8 9 10 11 12 13

The lower quartile is the median of the lower half = 3.5

The upper quartile is the median of the upper half = 10.5

On the stem and leaf diagram the October test data have been split into two halves as shown by the '/' between 46 and 48.

The lower quartile Q_1 = **35**
The upper quartile Q_3 = **63**

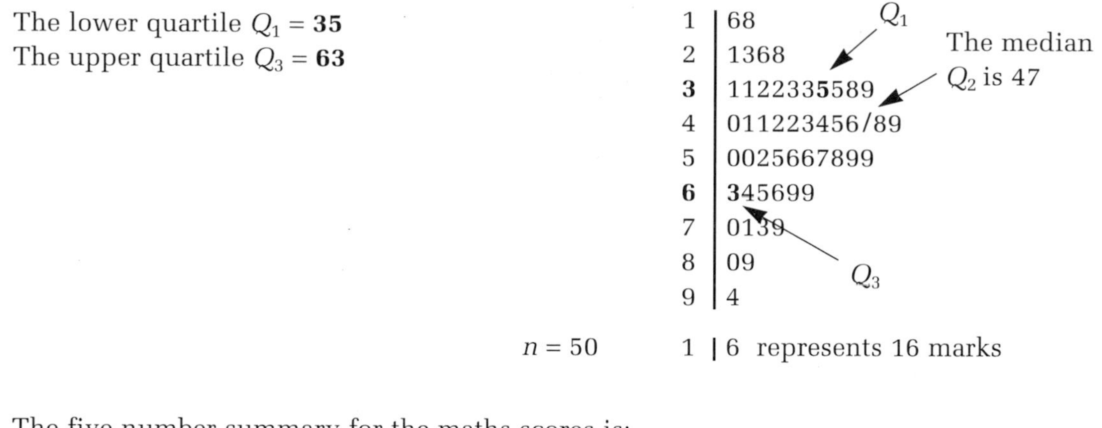

The five number summary for the maths scores is:

Minimum	Lower quartile Q_1	Median Q_2	Upper quartile Q_3	Maximum
16	35	47	63	94

The boxplot for the scores on the October test is:

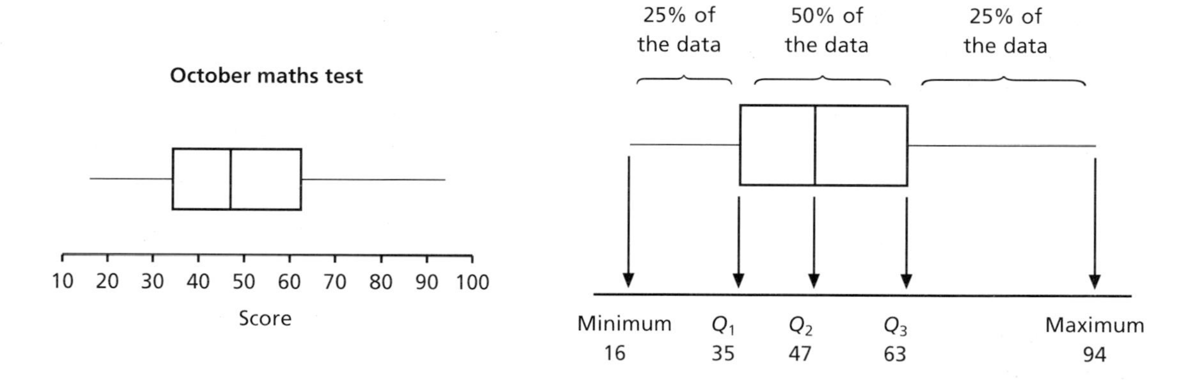

Note that:

25% of the pupils scored less than $Q_1 = 35$ (represented by the lower whisker);
50% of the pupils scored between $Q_1 = 35$ and $Q_3 = 63$ (represented by the box);
25% of the pupils scored more than $Q_3 = 63$ (represented by the upper whisker).

Simple measures of the amount of variability in the data can be calculated from the five number summary:

Range	Maximum – minimum
Interquartile range (IQR)	$Q_3 - Q_1$
Semi-interquartile range (Semi-IQR)	$\frac{1}{2}(Q_3 - Q_1)$

Example 2 During the first week at secondary school, the height of each pupil in a class was recorded to the nearest centimetre. The girls' heights were listed in order:

122 130 134 138 142 143 145 146 148 148 149 152 162

Calculate the range, interquartile range and semi-interquartile range for the girls' heights.

Range = 162 − 122 = 40 cm

$n = 13$, median = the value in the $\frac{(13+1)}{2}$ = 7th position = 145 cm

Lower half is 122 130 134 138 142 143 so $Q_1 = \frac{(134+138)}{2} = 136$ cm

Upper half is 146 148 148 149 152 162 so $Q_3 = \frac{(148+149)}{2} = 148.5$ cm

IQR = 148.5 − 136 = 12.5 cm

Semi-IQR = 12.5 ÷ 2 = 6.25 cm

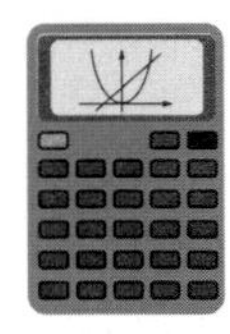

Some calculators can:

- prepare a five number summary
- draw a boxplot.

Find out what your calculator will do!

EXERCISE 1.7

1 Some letters were weighed before posting and their weights, in grams, were:

18 54 42 23 87 34 76 45 68

Calculate the median and quartiles for the data.

2 Calculate the median and quartiles for these scores on a spelling test:

16 9 12 10 18 15 11 19 10 11 17 12

3 Calculate the median and quartiles for the following artificial data sets.

Data Set 1:	1	2	3	4	5	6	7	8	9			
Data Set 2:	1	2	3	4	5	6	7	8	9	10		
Data Set 3:	1	2	3	4	5	6	7	8	9	10	11	
Data Set 4:	1	2	3	4	5	6	7	8	9	10	11	12

4 The weights in grams of a sample of eggs are shown in this stem and leaf diagram.

a Calculate a five number summary.

b Calculate the semi-interquartile range.

c Draw a boxplot to illustrate the data.

Weights of eggs

Stem	Leaf
4	023
4	6689
5	0112234
5	55789
6	044
6	67
7	2

$n = 25$ 7 | 2 represents 72 grams

5 The heights (to the nearest centimetre) of the boys in Class 1C were listed in order as follows:

127 130 135 135 136 136 137 146 148 154 155 161

a Calculate the semi-interquartile range.

b Draw a boxplot for the data.

Outliers and boxplots

Example The number of words in each of the first 20 sentences of Jonathan Swift's *Gulliver's Travels* are:

15 112 59 46 27 43 39 18 29 55 26 28 30 16 51 15 20 48 29 27

Draw a boxplot to summarise the data.

A quick way to put the data in order is to construct a stem and leaf diagram.

Number of words

Stem	Leaf
1	5568
2	0677899
3	09
4	368
5	159
6	
7	
8	
9	
10	
11	2

$n = 25$ 1 | 5 represents 15 words per sentence

From the stem and leaf diagram, calculate the five number summary:

Minimum	Lower quartile	Median	Upper quartile	Maximum
15	23	29	47	112

Notice from the stem and leaf diagram that the maximum value of 112 words is very much larger than the rest of the data. Values which are extremely small or extremely large compared with the rest of the data and so not typical are referred to as **outliers**. When drawing boxplots, possible outliers may be identified as follows.

Calculate the **lower fence** $Q_1 - 1.5 \times \text{IQR}$ and the **upper fence** $Q_3 + 1.5 \times \text{IQR}$.

Values which are beyond the fences are possible outliers:

values < the lower fence and values > the upper fence.

In this example we are looking for:

values $< 23 - 1.5(47 - 23) = -13$ and values $> 47 + 1.5(47 - 23) = 83$.

There are no sentences with less than –13 words! However, there is one value > 83, namely 112 words.

When possible outliers have been identified modify your boxplot as follows:

- plot the outliers as separate points using a * symbol;
- shorten the appropriate whisker by drawing it from the box to the data value just inside the fence.

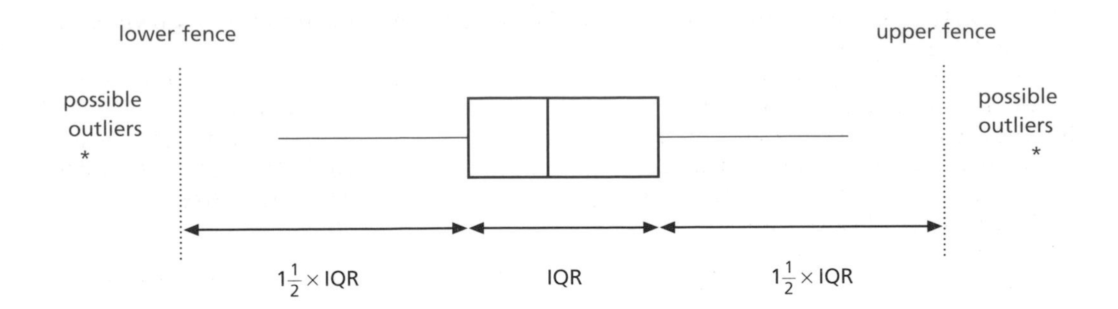

For the *Gulliver's Travels* data, a * is plotted to represent the maximum value 112, and the upper whisker is drawn from the box to 59 which is the largest value less than 83, the upper fence.

Gulliver's Travels: the first 20 sentences

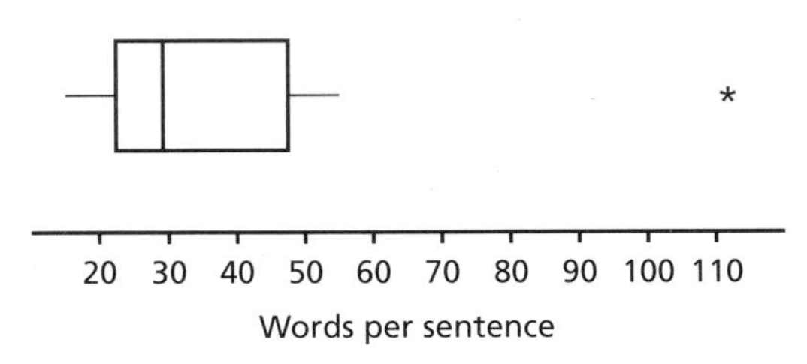

EXERCISE 1.8

1 The ages of the members of a cycling club are (in ascending order):

16 18 18 19 19 20 20 20 22 23 23 25 29 30 48 67

Draw a boxplot to illustrate the members' ages.

2 The strengths of a sample of glass fibres were measured in suitable units, and the results are displayed in this stem and leaf diagram.

a Calculate the semi-interquartile range.

b The appearance of the stem and leaf diagram suggests that there may be some outliers. Identify these values and draw a boxplot.

Strength of glass fibres

Stem	Leaf
5	5
6	
7	47
8	14
9	3
10	4
11	13
12	45789
13	069
14	28899
15	0012345589
16	0111122346667889
17	0036678
18	12449
19	
20	01
21	
22	4

$n = 63$ 22 | 4 represents 2.24 units

3 The contents of 50 packets of crisps were weighed in grams and the results are shown in the stem and leaf diagram.

a Prepare a five number summary, check for outliers and draw a boxplot.

b These data can be represented in a frequency table. Whenever data are tabulated in a grouped frequency table, information is lost because we can no longer see the individual data values. However it is possible to estimate the median and quartiles as follows.

Contents of packets of crisps (g)

Stem	Leaf
24	14578
25	02223355567788888
26	000011223333445679
27	001135678
28	5

$n = 50$ 28 | 5 represents 28.5 g

(i) Copy and complete this cumulative percentage table:

Contents	Frequency	Percentage	Cumulative percentage
$24.0 \le x < 24.5$	2	4	4
$24.5 \le x < 25.0$	3	6	10
$25.0 \le x < 25.5$	6	12	22
$25.5 \le x < 26.0$	11		
$26.0 \le x < 26.5$	14		
$26.5 \le x < 27.0$	4		
$27.0 \le x < 27.5$	5		
$27.5 \le x < 28.0$	4		
$28.0 \le x < 28.5$	0		
$28.5 \le x < 29.0$	1		
Total	50		

(ii) Carefully draw a cumulative percentage diagram on graph paper, with percentages from 0 to 100% on the vertical axis, and net weight on the horizontal axis.

(iii) Use your cumulative percentage diagram to estimate the weights corresponding to 25%, 50% and 75%, which gives estimates for the lower quartile, median and upper quartile respectively.

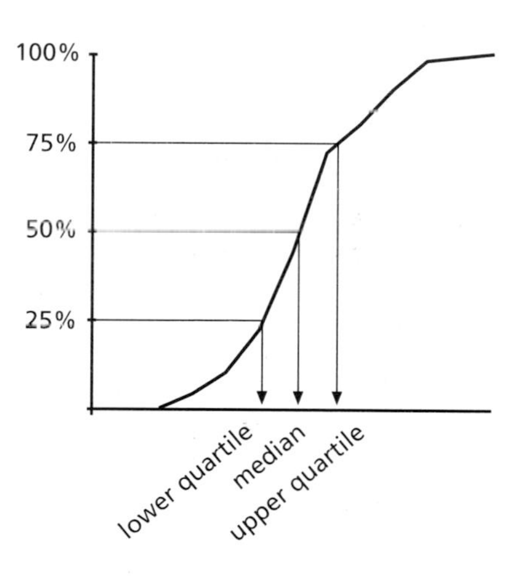

Compare your estimates in part **b** with your answer to part **a**.

Summarising data – Standard deviation

Whenever data is summarised information is lost. For example, the data sets

	9	10	11	12	13
and	1	6	11	16	21

have the same mean and median, yet these averages by themselves fail to describe that one data set is considerably more variable than the other. In addition to averages, we need numerical summaries which give a measure of this variability (spread or dispersion).

Simple measures of variability include range, interquartile range and semi-interquartile range. None of these simple measures involves all the data in their calculation. For example the range is calculated using the largest and smallest values only.

Sample standard deviation measures the variability of the data about the sample mean and all the data are involved in its calculation.

Example 1 The marks out of 10 for six children in a spelling test were:

7 5 4 5 9 6

Calculate the standard deviation of these marks.

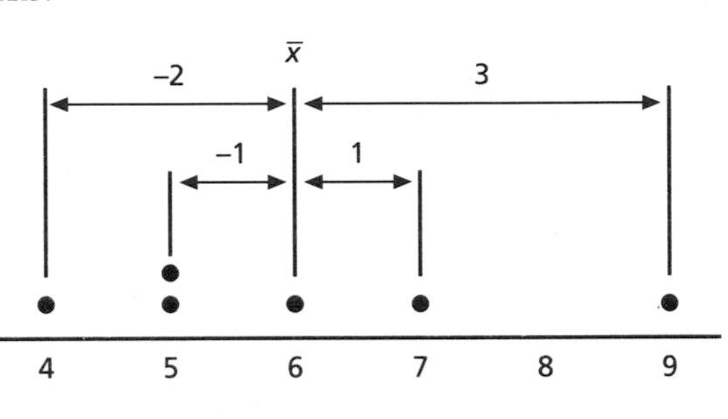

First calculate the mean $\bar{x} = \frac{\Sigma x}{n} = \frac{36}{6} = 6$ and then calculate the deviation of each observation from the mean.

Note that the sum of the deviations from the mean is always zero because the negative and positive deviations cancel. One way to overcome this effect is to square the deviations.

Score x_i	Deviation from mean $(x_i - \bar{x})$	Squared deviation $(x_i - \bar{x})^2$
7	$7 - 6 = 1$	1
5	$5 - 6 = -1$	1
4	$4 - 6 = -2$	4
5	$5 - 6 = -1$	1
9	$9 - 6 = 3$	9
6	$6 - 6 = 0$	0
Sum	0	16

Sample standard deviation:

$$s = \sqrt{\frac{\Sigma(x_i - \bar{x})^2}{n-1}} = \sqrt{\frac{16}{5}} \approx 1.8 \text{ marks}$$

The units of the standard deviation are the same as the data. In this example the units are marks.

Example 2 Calculate the sample standard deviation of these girls' heights (in centimetres).

122 130 134 138 142 143 145
146 148 148 149 152 162

$$\text{Mean} = \frac{\Sigma x_i}{n} = \frac{1859}{13} = 143$$

Sample standard deviation:

$$s = \sqrt{\frac{1258}{12}} \approx 10.2 \text{ cm}$$

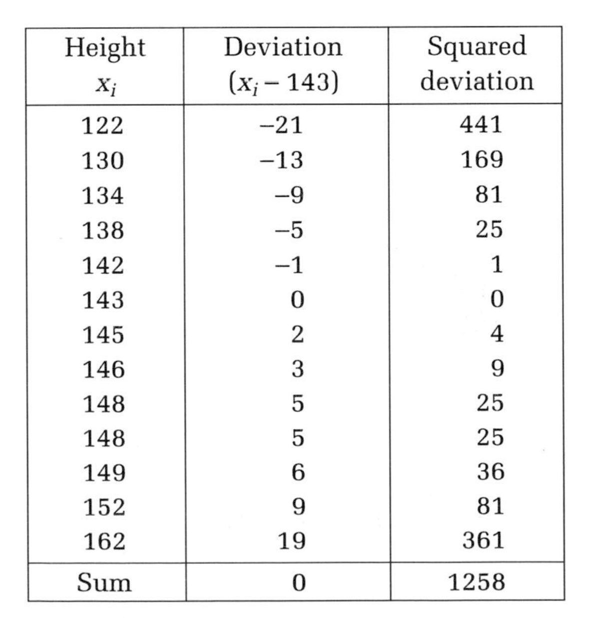

Height x_i	Deviation $(x_i - 143)$	Squared deviation
122	−21	441
130	−13	169
134	−9	81
138	−5	25
142	−1	1
143	0	0
145	2	4
146	3	9
148	5	25
148	5	25
149	6	36
152	9	81
162	19	361
Sum	0	1258

There is an alternative formula for sample standard deviation which gives the same answer and is sometimes easier to use.

Sample standard deviation:

$$s = \sqrt{\frac{\Sigma(x_i - \bar{x})^2}{n-1}}$$

or

an alternative formula:

$$s = \sqrt{\frac{\Sigma x_i^2 - (\Sigma x_i)^2/n}{n-1}}$$

$$\begin{aligned}\Sigma(x_i - \bar{x})^2 &= \Sigma(x_i^2 - 2\bar{x}x_i + \bar{x}^2)\\ &= \Sigma x_i^2 - 2\bar{x}\Sigma x_i + n\bar{x}^2\\ &= \Sigma x_i^2 - 2\frac{\Sigma x_i}{n}\Sigma x_i + n\left(\frac{\Sigma x_i}{n}\right)^2\\ &= \Sigma x_i^2 - \frac{(\Sigma x_i)^2}{n}\end{aligned}$$

so

$$s = \sqrt{\frac{\Sigma(x_i - \bar{x})^2}{n-1}} = \sqrt{\frac{\Sigma x_i^2 - (\Sigma x_i)^2/n}{n-1}}$$

Note that the quantity s^2 is known as the **sample variance**.

Example 3 Using the data for the girls' heights in Example 2 on page 26, calculate the sample standard deviation using the alternative formula.

$$s = \sqrt{\frac{\Sigma x_i^2 - (\Sigma x_i)^2/n}{n-1}}$$

$$= \sqrt{\frac{267\,095 - (1859)^2/13}{12}}$$

≈ 10.2

The alternative formula gives the same answer.

Height x_i	x_i^2
122	14 884
130	16 900
134	17 956
138	19 044
142	20 164
143	20 449
145	21 025
146	21 316
148	21 904
148	21 904
149	22 201
152	23 104
162	26 244
Sum 1859	267 095

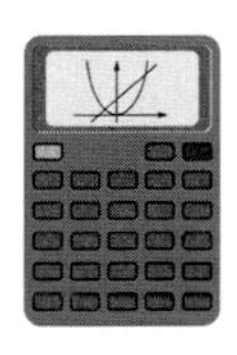

Can your calculator find the standard deviation of some data? Explore your calculator's features.

Warning!

Most calculators have two buttons to do this. Use the one labelled σ_{n-1} which will calculate the sample standard deviation s as defined above.

The $(n - 1)$ divisor is used because it gives better estimates. There is more on this in Chapter 2.

EXERCISE 1.9A

1 Five identical envelopes with second class postage stamps were mailed to various addresses in a large city. The number of days it took them to arrive at their destination was as follows:

1 2 2 3 7

Calculate the sample standard deviation for the data using:

a the sum of squared deviations method b the alternative formula.

2 Draw dotplots to illustrate these data sets:

a 9 10 11 12 13

b 1 6 11 16 21

Calculate and compare the sample mean and standard deviation of each of the data sets.

3 The heights (to the nearest centimetre) of the boys in Class 1C were as follows:

127 130 135 135 136 136 137 146 148 154 155 161

Calculate the sample standard deviation, given that $\Sigma x = 1700$ and $\Sigma x^2 = 242\,122$.

EXERCISE 1.9B

1 The contents of 50 boxes of paper clips were counted and the following table summarises the results. Copy the table and complete the last column.

Contents x	Frequency f	Number of paper clips xf	x^2f
45	1	45	2025
46	3	138	6348
47	2	94	
48	4	192	
49	5	245	
50	8	400	
51	10	510	
52	7	364	
53	6	318	
54	2	108	
55	2	110	
Total	$\Sigma f = 50$	$\Sigma xf = 2524$	$\Sigma x^2f =$

$\Sigma f = n = 50$ represents the total frequency or sample size, 50 boxes.
$\Sigma xf = 2524$ represents the total number of paper clips in all the boxes.

a Calculate Σx^2f.

b Adapt the alternative formula given on page 27 and use it to calculate the sample standard deviation.

2 The contents, in grams, of 25 g packets of supermarket brand crisps are summarised in this frequency table:

Net weight	Mid-point (x g)	Frequency f	xf	x^2f
$23.5 \le x < 24.5$	24.0	2	48.0	1152.0
$24.5 \le x < 25.5$	25.0	9	225.0	
$25.5 \le x < 26.5$	26.0	25	650.0	
$26.5 \le x < 27.5$	27.0	9	243.0	
$27.5 \le x < 28.5$	28.0	4	112.0	
$28.5 \le x < 29.5$	29.0	1	29.0	
	Total	$\Sigma f = 50$	$\Sigma xf = 1307.0$	$\Sigma x^2f =$

a Complete the table and calculate an estimate for the sample standard deviation.

b If the data were grouped differently, would your answer be the same? Explain.

Collecting data about ourselves

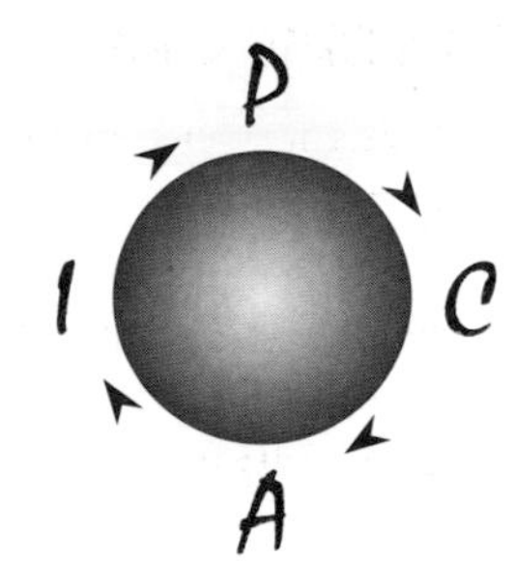

Pose a question

How do I compare with other students in the class?

Collect some data

Questionnaire-based surveys are an important method of collecting data. Each member of the class could submit possible questions in writing to the teacher ahead of time. Alternatively, your teacher may have a questionnaire which was used with previous classes and you can compare your class with others in the past. Use care and judgement when selecting and wording questions. They should not be unacceptably intrusive and should not inadvertently reinforce stereotypes. Although the questionnaire will be completed anonymously and is for educational purposes only, students should feel free to skip any question they either can't answer or feel uncomfortable answering. Avoid ambiguous questions. 'Do you smoke?' is a poor question. 'Have you smoked a cigarette in the last 24 hours?' is a question which is much easier to interpret and so is more likely to produce reliable answers. Include topics which require careful thought on how to make measurements, for example:

a Pulse rates are recorded in beats/minute. How would you measure your pulse rate?
b How would you find out the amount of sleep a person had last night?

Include questions to produce data of various types which can be used throughout the statistics unit. Your questionnaire should include at least two questions (such as 'Are you male/female?', 'Do you own a PC? Yes/No' etc.) which will produce nominal data. These data can be used to construct two-way tables as described in Chapter 2, as well as provide a basis for classifying other observations. Observations on at least two quantitative variables should be recorded with questions such as 'How much money did you spend on your last visit to the hairdresser?' (continuous) and 'How many times did you go to the cinema last month?' (discrete). Two measurements on each person such as height and hand span will be valuable data for analysis later.

Analyse the data

You will be able to practise many statistical techniques using your own data.

Interpret the results

State conclusions to any questions posed based on diagrams, summary measures, etc. Ask various additional questions:

- Is there a relationship between gender and owning a PC?
- Do girls spend more at the hairdresser than boys?
- Do PC owners visit the cinema less often than those who don't own a computer?

Further study

How do students in your class compare with those in other classes or other schools?

CHAPTER 1 REVIEW

1 The following data give the percentage protein content in ground wheat:

9.2	8.2	11.5	11.3	10.4	9.6
8.4	7.7	8.5	11.6	10.0	8.8
10.2	10.7	11.6	8.7	12.6	8.4
9.8	11.4	9.7	10.8	10.2	11.5

a Complete the stem and leaf diagram where 12 | 6 represents 12.6%.

7 |
8 |
9 |
10 |
11 |
12 |

b Calculate the median and semi-interquartile range.

2 The films showing on terrestrial TV one week were rated by a reviewer and ranged from 1-star (poor) to 5-star (outstanding). The following table shows the number of films in each category for an ordinary week and for a Bank Holiday Monday:

Star rating	1	2	3	4	5	Total
Number of films (week):	7	29	27	13	1	77
(Monday):	2	10	7	2	2	23

a Calculate the relative frequencies of each category of film for (i) the week (ii) the Monday, correct to 2 decimal places.

b Copy and complete this comparative bar chart.

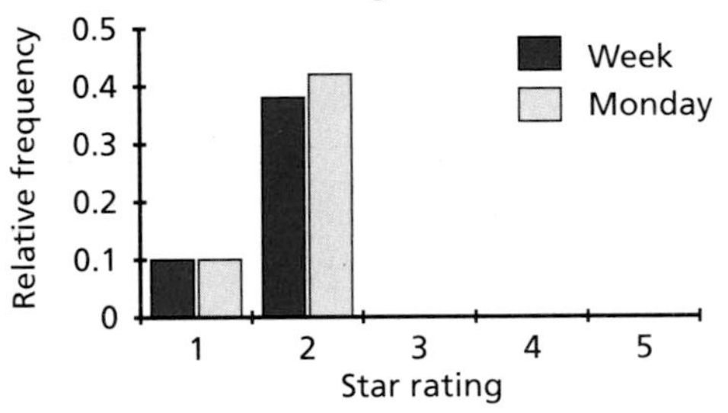

c Compare the relative frequencies of the ratings of films shown on the Bank Holiday Monday with those on the ordinary week.

3 The lengths of all films (to the nearest 5 minutes) showing on terrestrial TV one Saturday were:

85	95	100	100	105	115	95	115
120	95	105	105	95	105	100	160

Prepare a five number summary, check for possible outliers and draw a boxplot for the data.

4 A manufacturer of dishwashing liquid produces a trial size bottle containing 295 ml. A sample of 16 such bottles had the following contents:

293	301	302	299	303	293	297	291
296	291	302	299	290	288	290	301

Calculate the sample mean and standard deviation (answers to 1 decimal place).

5 A dietitian recorded the iron intake in milligrams during a 24-hour period for a sample of adult women:

15.0	12.0	18.2	17.5	12.4	13.9	19.6
13.1	18.1	13.4	15.9	7.6	6.9	13.2
22.5	11.9	11.4	15.4	16.1	9.5	10.5
14.2	12.3	14.8	9.5	23.3	12.4	16.1
14.4	8.9	14.8	20.8	16.3	17.7	19.2
18.9	14.8	14.1	11.4	9.9		

Draw a histogram with class intervals of equal width starting at $6.0 \le x < 8.0$.
On the same diagram draw the corresponding frequency polygon.
What proportion of these women had a daily intake of iron less than 14.0 mg?

6 A paint manufacturer claimed that a new formula of paint would dry in less than 2 hours. In 24 trials, the time in minutes for the paint to dry was noted. The frequency table summarises the results.

Time (minutes)	Frequency
$90 \le t < 100$	1
$100 \le t < 110$	3
$110 \le t < 120$	9
$120 \le t < 130$	6
$130 \le t < 140$	3
$140 \le t < 150$	2
Total	24

In what proportion of the trials did the paint dry in less than 2 hours?
Draw a cumulative frequency diagram and use it to estimate the median and interquartile range.

7 Describe the type of data in each of the above questions.

CHAPTER 1 SUMMARY

Statistical investigation
Pose a question.
Collect some data.
Analyse the data.
Interpret the data.

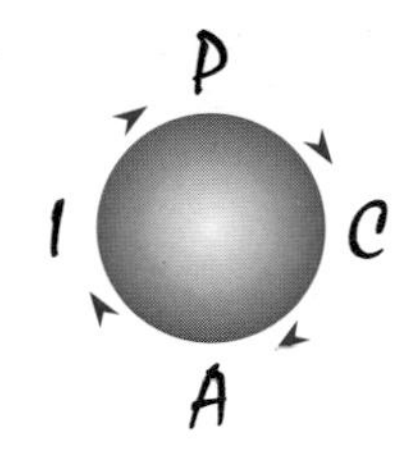

Qualitative data
Observations classify objects into categories. Numerical data is produced by counting how many observations are in each category. Includes nominal data, e.g. colour, and ordinal data, e.g. degree of burns on a body. Bar diagrams and pie charts are possible ways to display these data.

Quantitative data, discrete
Data usually produced by counting, in which case only whole number values are possible, e.g. the number of passengers in a lift. Bar diagrams and dotplots are some of the ways to display these data.

Quantitative data, continuous
Data produced by measuring; any value in an interval is possible, e.g. a person's height. Histograms and stem and leaf diagrams can be used to display these data.

Grouped data, discrete

Groups $\begin{cases} 80\text{–}84 \\ 85\text{–}89 \\ 90\text{–}94 \\ \text{etc.} \end{cases}$ consisting of whole

numbers $\begin{cases} 80, 81, 82, 83, 84 \\ 85, 86, 87, 88, 89 \\ 90, 91, 92, 93, 94 \\ \text{etc.} \end{cases}$

Grouped data, continuous

Intervals $\begin{cases} 20 \le x < 25 \\ 25 \le x < 30 \\ 30 \le x < 35 \\ \text{etc.} \end{cases}$ consisting of all possible values in each interval.

Histogram
A frequency diagram for continuous data. Similar to a bar diagram except the bars touch, emphasising the continuous nature of the data. Strictly it is the area of each bar which is proportional to the frequency. However, if the intervals are all of the same width, the height of the bar is also proportional to the frequency.

Relative frequency
Relative frequency =

$$\frac{\text{frequency of observations of interest}}{\text{total frequency}}$$

Frequency polygon
A frequency diagram for continuous data constructed by plotting the frequency against the mid-point of the interval, and joining the points with straight lines. Useful for comparing the frequencies of two sets of measurements on the same diagram.

Cumulative frequency
Gives a running total of the number of observations less the upper limit in the case of continuous data, or less than or equal to a stated value for discrete data. A cumulative frequency diagram plots cumulative frequency against the value.

Mean, median, mode

Mean: $\bar{x} = \dfrac{\Sigma x_i}{n}$

Median: the value in the $\frac{n+1}{2}$th position when the data are ranked in increasing order.

Mode: the most frequently occurring value.

Quartiles

When the data are ranked in increasing order, the quartiles are taken as the medians of the lower and upper 'halves' of the data, ignoring the middle value when n is odd.

Five number summary

Data are reduced to five numbers consisting of the minimum, lower quartile, median, upper quartile, and maximum. Simple measures of variability can be calculated from the five number summary.

Range

Maximum – minimum

Interquartile range (IQR)

$Q_3 - Q_1$

Semi-interquartile range

$\frac{1}{2}(Q_3 - Q_1)$

Boxplots

A visual display of the five number summary:

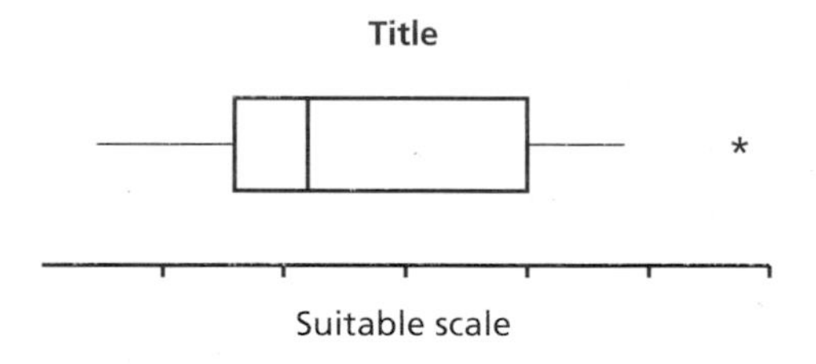

Outliers

Values that are unusually small or unusually large compared with the mass of data. Suspected outliers are:

values $< Q_1 - 1\frac{1}{2} \times \text{IQR}$;

values $> Q_3 + 1\frac{1}{2} \times \text{IQR}$.

Shown by * on a boxplot.

Sample standard deviation

A measure of variability which uses all the data in its calculation, and which measures the variability of the data about its mean value. For a sample of size n:

$$s = \sqrt{\frac{\Sigma(x_i - \bar{x})^2}{n-1}} = \sqrt{\frac{\Sigma x_i^2 - (\Sigma x_i)^2/n}{n-1}}$$

2 Exploratory Data Analysis

In general terms, Exploratory Data Analysis (EDA) is the name given to the process of looking at sample data using quick and easy methods for displaying and summarising the data, before more detailed statistical analysis is undertaken. The purpose is to make inferences about a population.

Populations, samples and inference

In a statistical investigation, the term **population** refers to the set of all objects in which we are interested. A **sample** is a selection of some objects chosen from the population. The sample should be representative of the population. Study of the sample may produce a **sample statistic** such as the sample mean $\overline{x}$ which is used to **infer** the value of the corresponding **population parameter,** namely the population mean μ. This method of using the sample statistic $\overline{x}$ to **estimate** the population parameter μ is an example of statistical **inference**. One important factor which will affect our confidence in this estimate is the method used to select the sample.

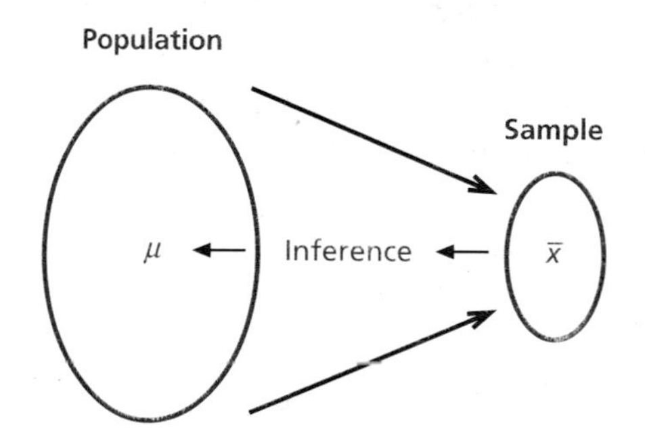

EXERCISE 2.1A

Photocopies of the Circles worksheet are required for this exercise. (See photocopiable page 129.) The worksheet shows a population of 60 circles of various sizes. The purpose of this exercise is to estimate the mean diameter of these 60 circles by measuring the diameters of a sample of five circles. Measuring the circles is easy – they have all been drawn with diameters that are some multiple of 0.5 cm. Two methods of selecting the sample of five circles will be compared.

1 Method 1: Non-random sampling

- **a** Working independently, put a check mark ✓ in each of the five circles which in your judgement are representative of this population of circles.
- **b** Measure the diameters of the five circles you have selected and calculate the sample mean.
- **c** Using a dotplot, display the sample means for the whole class, and calculate the average sample mean. (About 20 or 30 sample means should be adequate. If you are working alone, you could ask 20 or 30 people to select five circles for you and these can be measured later.)

2 Method 2: Simple random sampling
 a Number the circles from 1 to 60 in any order.
 b Produce five distinct random numbers in the range from 1 to 60.
 c Select the circles which have these random numbers, measure their diameter and calculate the sample mean.
 d Using a dotplot, display the sample means for the whole class, and calculate the average sample mean.

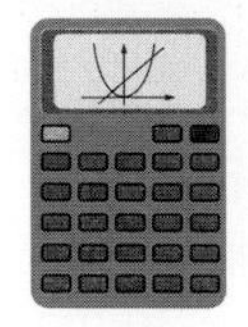

Producing random numbers on your calculator
Does your calculator have a random number function?
Try the formula Int(Rand × 60) + 1.
Rand generates random numbers $0 \leq x < 1$.
Int( ) takes the integer part of the answer.
Check what your calculator can do.

Estimation and bias

Within the population in Exercise 2.1A, the circles have different sizes. This is an example of what is referred to as **natural variation** in the sizes of circles in the population. For example, these circles might represent the different sizes of soap bubbles that occur naturally in foam. This variability means that our estimates of population parameters are surrounded by some uncertainty.
Whichever of the above methods is used to select the sample, different samples may have different circles included, and the value of the sample mean will vary depending on the sizes of the particular circles included in the sample. This is known as **sampling variation**.
The true population mean diameter of the circles is 1.0 cm. Most often, non-random sampling of these circles produces over-estimates of the population mean. Estimates which differ from the true value in some systematic way are said to be **biased**. **Random sampling** is a way of choosing a sample using random numbers which produces estimates that are centred around the true value. Although random sampling does not eliminate sampling variation, it does produce estimates which are on average **unbiased**.

Estimating the variability in a population

The sample standard deviation s is used to estimate the population standard deviation σ.

Calculator button	Formula
σ_n	Population standard deviation $\sigma = \sqrt{\dfrac{\Sigma(x_i - \mu)^2}{N}}$, N is the population size.
σ_{n-1}	Sample standard deviation $s = \sqrt{\dfrac{\Sigma(x_i - \overline{x})^2}{n-1}}$, n is the sample size.

It can be shown that dividing by $n - 1$ when calculating the sample standard deviation s produces estimates of the population standard deviation σ which are on average unbiased.

The effect of natural variation and sample size on the variability of estimates

The more variability there is in the population, the greater the uncertainty that surrounds our estimates. The larger the sample size, the more confidence we have in our estimates.

EXERCISE 2.1B

This exercise estimates the mean diameter for two populations of components with the serial numbers 1 to 20 as shown in the table.

Serial number	Population A Diameter (mm)	Population B Diameter (mm)
1	8.1	7.3
2	7.7	4.8
3	6.8	10.3
4	6.9	8.1
5	7.4	5.2
6	6.4	3.5
7	7.8	11.2
8	5.9	7.6
9	7.7	7.7
10	7.0	9.4
11	6.7	6.0
12	6.1	9.0
13	9.2	6.1
14	6.6	6.4
15	6.8	9.0
16	8.7	7.8
17	6.3	10.1
18	9.5	9.5
19	6.5	5.2
20	6.7	9.5

1 To estimate the mean μ for Population A:
 a Using four random numbers in the range 1 to 20 choose a random sample of four components from Population A.
 b Calculate the sample mean of the components' diameters.
 c Use a stem and leaf diagram to display the sample means for the whole class (about 30 results).
 d Calculate the average (mean) of the class's sample means.
 e Calculate the range of the sample means produced by the class.

2 Repeat the above procedure for Population B.

3 For each population, calculate the population mean and range.

4 Did the samples from one of the populations give less variable estimates of the population's mean? Explain.

5 **a** Estimate the mean of Population B using random samples of size $n = 9$.
 b Display and summarise the results for the whole class.
 c What effect does increased sample size have on the variability of estimates?

Univariate data

When the values taken by a single variable are observed, this is referred to as **univariate** data. For example, counting the contents of a sample of matchboxes will result in values of a discrete variable – *contents* – being determined, or measuring the height of a sample of pupils will result in values of a continuous variable – *height* – being collected. Simple plots such as dotplots, stem and leaf diagrams, bar diagrams and histograms give a visual impression of how the data are distributed which complements numerical summaries of the data such as measures of central location and dispersion.

The appearance of these plots gives important clues as to which mathematical model could be used to describe the data. For example, the outline of this histogram is a symmetrical bell shape.

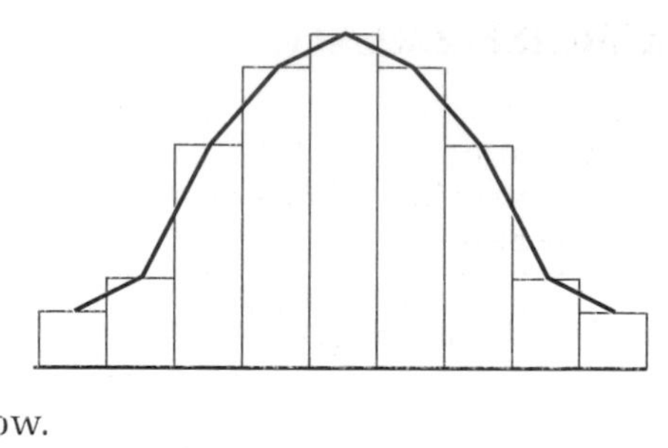

Some commonly occurring **shapes** are shown below.

Negatively skewed
Mean < Median

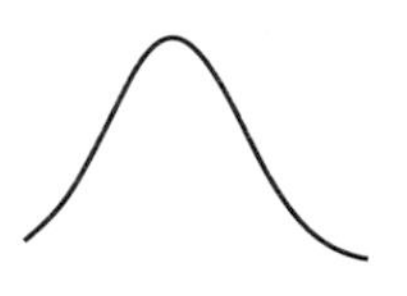

Symmetrical
Mean ≈ Median ≈ Mode approximately

Positively skewed
Mean > Median

Decreasing

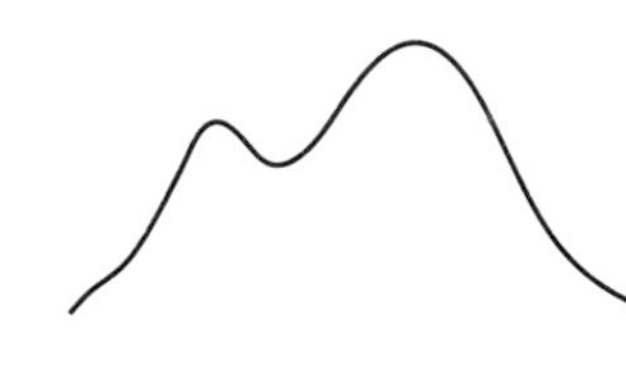

Bimodal

Uniform

For example, 1000 computer simulations of a game that involved rolling dice were made and on each simulation the number of rolls of the dice required to complete the game was recorded. The diagram shows the distribution of the data collected.

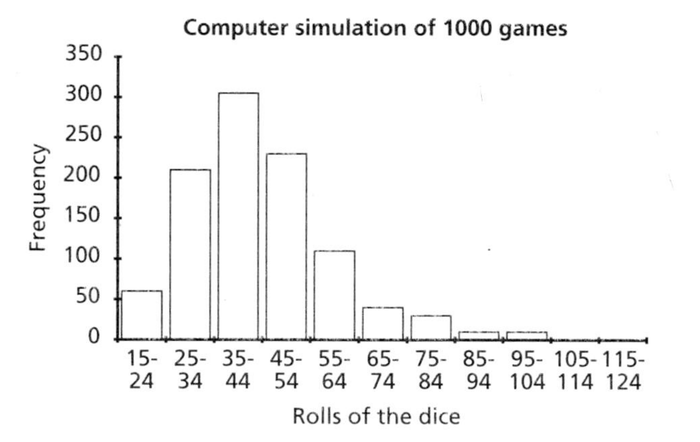

These data appear to fit the positively skewed shape where the mean is greater than the median.

Here is the numerical summary:

n	Mean	SD
1000	44.5	13.8

Notice that the mean is slightly larger than the median.

Min	Q_1	Median	Q_3	Max
16	35	43	52	118

EXERCISE 2.2A

1 The following data are very famous. They first appeared in the *Edinburgh Medical and Surgical Journal* in 1817, and have been discussed many times by statisticians over the years. The chest circumference of a large sample of 5732 Scottish soldiers was measured in inches to the nearest inch.

Chest measurement (inches)	Frequency	Chest measurement (inches)	Frequency
33	3	41	935
34	19	42	646
35	81	43	313
36	189	44	168
37	409	45	50
38	753	46	18
39	1062	47	3
40	1082	48	1

The chest measurement $x = 33$ inches should be interpreted as the interval $32.5 \le x < 33.5$ inches.

a Using such intervals, display the data using a histogram and describe the shape of the distribution.

b Calculate the sample mean and standard deviation.

c Approximately what percentage of the sample lies within $\pm$ 3 standard deviations of the mean?

2 Between 1st and 15th August 1985, there were 300 eruptions of the Old Faithful geyser in Yellowstone National Park, Wyoming, USA. These data give the time in minutes between the start of successive eruptions:

80	71	57	80	75	77	60	86	77	56	81	50
89	54	90	73	60	83	65	82	84	54	85	58
79	57	88	68	76	78	74	85	75	65	76	58
91	50	87	48	93	54	86	53	78	52	83	60
87	49	80	60	92	43	89	60	84	69	74	71
108	50	77	57	80	61	82	48	81	73	62	79
54	80	73	81	62	81	71	79	81	74	59	81
66	87	53	80	50	87	51	82	58	81	49	92
50	88	62	93	56	89	51	79	58	82	52	88
52	78	69	75	77	53	80	55	87	53	85	61
93	54	76	80	81	59	86	78	71	77	76	94
75	50	83	82	72	77	75	65	79	72	78	77
79	75	78	64	80	49	88	54	85	51	96	50
80	78	81	72	75	78	87	69	55	83	49	82
57	84	57	84	73	78	57	79	57	90	62	87
78	52	98	48	78	79	65	84	50	83	60	80
50	88	50	84	74	76	65	89	49	88	51	78
85	65	75	77	69	92	68	87	61	81	55	93
53	84	70	73	93	50	87	77	74	72	82	74
80	49	91	53	86	49	79	89	87	76	59	80
89	45	93	72	71	54	79	74	65	78	57	87
72	84	47	84	57	87	68	86	75	73	53	82
93	77	54	96	48	89	63	84	76	62	83	50
85	78	78	81	78	76	74	81	66	84	48	93
47	87	51	78	54	87	52	85	58	88	79	

Using the intervals $40 \le t < 45$, $45 \le t < 50$, etc., draw a histogram for the data. Can you suggest an explanation for the appearance of this histogram?

3 In 1910, Rutherford and Geiger published the results of an experiment to study the radioactive decay of a quantity of the element polonium. They counted the number of alpha particles detected in consecutive intervals of 72 seconds. Altogether they detected 10 097 particles during 2608 intervals.

Count	0	1	2	3	4	5	6	7	8	9	10	11	12	13	14
Frequency	57	203	383	525	532	408	273	139	45	27	10	4	0	1	1

Display the data and comment on the shape of the distribution.
Calculate the sample mean and standard deviation for the number of particles detected per time interval.

EXERCISE 2.2B

1 Sometimes data are collected over a period of time and our interest is focused on the patterns over time in the data. The following data recording the number of casualties in Great Britain due to road accidents on Fridays in 1986, for each hour of the day, illustrate this.

Time of day	Casualties	Time of day	Casualties
0000-0100	938	1200-1300	3015
0100-0200	621	1300-1400	2966
0200-0300	455	1400-1500	2912
0300-0400	207	1500-1600	4305
0400-0500	138	1600-1700	4923
0500-0600	215	1700-1800	4427
0600-0700	526	1800-1900	3164
0700-0800	1933	1900-2000	2950
0800-0900	3377	2000-2100	2601
0900-1000	2045	2100-2200	2420
1000-1100	2078	2200-2300	2557
1100-1200	2351	2300-0000	4319

Display the data using a line graph with 'Time of day' on the horizontal axis. One way to do this is to plot the points (1, 938), (2, 621), ... (24, 4319), and join the points with straight line segments. Can you explain the appearance of the line graph? Think about what people may be doing on a Friday.

2 The following data show the number of births each month in a large hospital in Basel, Switzerland. Display the data using a line graph. Do you think the births are spread evenly throughout the year?

Month	J	F	M	A	M	J	J	A	S	O	N	D
No. of births	66	63	64	48	64	74	70	59	54	51	45	42

Independent samples

Sometimes a statistical investigation involves comparing the univariate data in two or more samples. For example, the heights of a random sample of first year boys are measured and compared with the heights of a random sample of first year girls. These are an example of **independent samples** because there is no reason for relating the height of one of the boys with the height of one of the girls. The question posed may be 'Is there a difference in the heights of first year boys and girls?'

Suppose, however, that the heights of the same group of boys are measured six months later. In such a case the two sets of measurements on the same boys are related and unlike the previous example can no longer be considered independent. The purpose of a study such as this may be to answer the question 'By how much do first year boys grow over a six month period?'

In this section we will concentrate on comparing independent samples.

Example 1 Three mixed ability classes took a French vocabulary test out of 20 marks. The following dotplots and numerical summaries show the results for each class. Compare the performance of the three classes.

Class 2B

5 6 7 8 9 10 11 12 13 14 15 16 17 18 19 20

Class 2C

5 6 7 8 9 10 11 12 13 14 15 16 17 18 19 20

Class 2R

5 6 7 8 9 10 11 12 13 14 15 16 17 18 19 20

A numerical summary shows:

Class	n	Mean	SD	Min	Q_1	Median	Q_3	Max
2B	30	12.0	3.0	6	10	12	14	18
2C	30	16.2	2.7	9	15	17	18	19
2R	30	12.3	2.4	8	11	12	13	20

Note that in Class 2R there is one mark that is very much different from the others. This high score of 20 marks has a considerable influence on the value of the sample mean and standard deviation. The median and interquartile range, however, are measures of central location and dispersion (spread) which are less likely to be influenced by extreme data values.

The marks for Class 2B and Class 2R have a symmetrical distribution. Both classes have a mean and median of 12 marks although there is more variability in the marks for Class 2B.

The distribution of marks for Class 2C has a very different appearance. The marks are negatively skewed and the mean is less than the median. By comparing means and medians it seems that on average the pupils in Class 2C scored considerably better than the pupils in the other two classes.

To explain the similarities and differences in the marks for these classes, more details about the context are needed. For example, it would be helpful to know whether:

- 'mixed ability' classes may be assumed to have the same language ability
- the same teaching methods were used
- the same exam conditions were followed when the test was taken, and so on.

Discuss with your class some of the other factors which could have influenced these results. The interpretation of data is helped by an understanding of the context in which the data were collected.

When comparing two or more samples, a multiple boxplot diagram is helpful. The multiple boxplot shown here was drawn using a computer package, and displays the marks for a French vocabulary test.

The three boxplots, one for each class, are drawn above the same scale, enabling comparisons to be made quickly by eye:

- Classes 2B and 2R have similar medians, but the interquartile range (length of the box) is greater for Class 2B
- the median mark for Class 2C is noticeably greater than those of the other classes
- possible outliers are clearly visible.

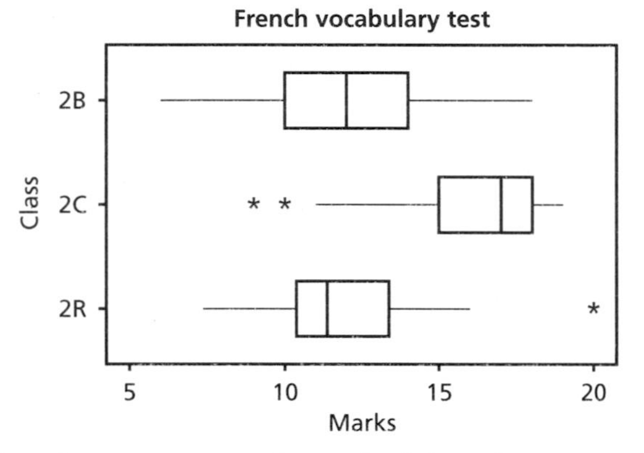

Example 2 Compare the heights (measured to the nearest centimetre) of these boys and girls in Class 1B.

Girls	122	130	134	138	142	143	145	146	148	148	149	152	162
Boys	127	130	135	135	136	136	137	146	148	154	155	161	

Girls $n = 13$		Boys $n = 12$
2	12	
	12	7
40	13	0
8	13	55667
32	14	
98865	14	68
2	15	4
	15	5
2	16	1

16 | 1 represents 161 cm

These heights can be displayed using a **back-to-back** stem and leaf diagram.

From this display we can see that in Class 1B the range of boys' and girls' heights is about the same and that the most likely height for boys (135 cm to 139 cm) is less than the most frequently occurring height for girls (145 cm to 149 cm).

Warning!

These samples of boys' and girls' heights contain only a few measurements. When small data sets are displayed they may have a very jagged appearance. The shape, mode and other characteristics are seen more clearly when larger samples are studied.

EXERCISE 2.3A

1 The marks achieved by pupils in Classes 1B, 1C and 1R on a maths test are compared in this computer drawn multiple boxplot.
A numerical summary for these marks is shown below.

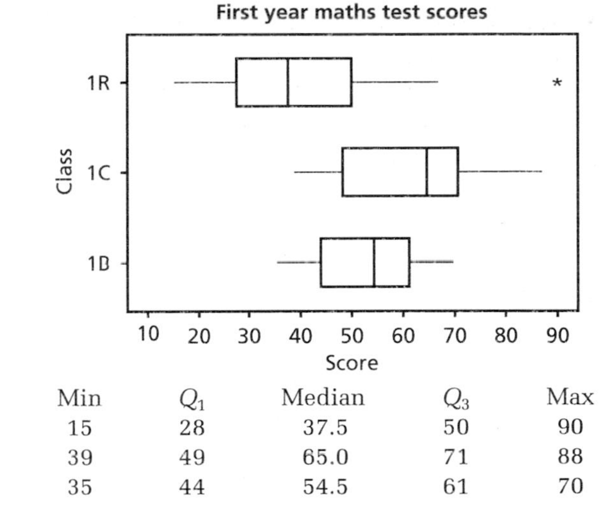

Class	n	Mean	SD	Min	Q_1	Median	Q_3	Max
1R	30	40.4	17.1	15	28	37.5	50	90
1C	30	61.8	13.3	39	49	65.0	71	88
1B	30	52.8	9.0	35	44	54.5	61	70

a Write a short report on how these classes performed on the maths test.
b What other information would it be useful to know when interpreting these data?

2 The grip strength of a group of senior school pupils was measured in suitable units and the following data show the results for males and females separately:

Males

56	48	46	53	49
48	55	44	55	47
37	32	45	53	36
39	51	44	34	44
38	41	50	44	45

Females

33	25	34	35	22
29	30	28	26	25
26	29	33	37	23
29	31	36	28	17
36	28	37	20	24

a (i) Draw a back-to-back stem and leaf diagram to display these data.
(ii) Prepare separate five number summaries for males and females.
(iii) Draw a multiple boxplot to illustrate the data.
(iv) Calculate semi-interquartile ranges for males and females.
(v) Calculate the sample means and standard deviations for males and females.
(vi) Describe the shape of the data for males and for females.

b Using your answers to part **a**, compare and contrast the grip strength of these males and females.

3 In 1960-61 a large study was carried out in California on 3154 middle-aged men to investigate the relationship between behaviour and the risk of heart disease. In one part of the study the 40 heaviest men (each weighed at least 225 pounds) had their cholesterol measured (milligrams per 100 ml) and their behaviour type noted. Type A behaviour is characterised by urgency, aggression and ambition. Type B behaviour is relaxed, non-competitive and less hurried. Here are their cholesterol levels:

Type A	233	291	312	250	246	197	268	224	239	239
	254	276	234	181	248	252	202	218	212	325
Type B	344	185	263	246	224	212	188	250	148	169
	226	175	242	252	153	183	137	202	194	213

Do you think that for heavy middle-aged men, cholesterol level is related to behaviour type? Use appropriate statistical diagrams and summaries to justify your answer.

4 Libraries often collect a variety of data describing how their collection of books is borrowed. One variable of interest is a count of the number n_k of books borrowed k times in a one-year period.

Here are the data for two large university libraries:

Hillman Library, University of Pittsburgh	k	1	2	3	4	5	6	7	8
	n_k	63 526	25 653	11 855	6055	3264	1727	931	497
	k	9	10	11	12	13	14	15	16
	n_k	275	124	68	28	13	6	9	4
Long-loan collection, Sussex University	k	1	2	3	4	5	6	7	8
	n_k	9674	4351	2275	1250	663	355	154	72
	k	9	10	11	12	13	14		
	n_k	37	14	6	2	0	1		

Calculate relative frequencies and use a suitable diagram to compare these two independent samples.

EXERCISE 2.3B

In this exercise support your conclusions with appropriate diagrams and summary statistics.

1 Caffeine is a stimulant drug that is in tea, coffee and other sources. Thirty male college students were trained in finger tapping, a task used by psychologists to measure manual skill. They were then divided at random into three groups of ten students, and each group received a different dose of caffeine. Two hours after the dose of caffeine was given, each student was asked to do the finger tapping exercise and the number of taps per minute was recorded:

Dose	Finger tapping rate									
0 mg	242	245	244	248	247	248	242	244	246	242
100 mg	248	246	245	247	248	250	247	246	243	244
200 mg	246	248	250	252	248	250	246	248	245	250

a Does caffeine affect performance on this task? If so, can you describe the effect?

Note A good feature of this study is that it was conducted as a **double-blind** experiment, meaning that neither the student nor the experimenter knew the dose administered to each student. Only the statistician knows which student received which dose. This is important because it is believed that when people know the details of an experiment or treatment, this knowledge changes their behaviour. What the researcher really wants to know is how the drug changes behaviour.

It is possible that different people have different abilities to perform manual tasks and a possible weakness of this experiment is that these differences between the students are more variable than the differences caused by the drug.

b Can you think of ways to improve the experiment to take account of the differences between people?

2 These data give the average butterfat percentages in cows' milk for random samples of ten two-year-old and ten mature cows from each of five breeds:

Jersey		Holstein-Friesian		Guernsey		Canadian		Ayrshire	
2-yr	Mature	2-yr	Mature	2-yr	Mature	2-yr	Mature	2-yr	Mature
5.75	4.80	3.79	3.40	5.30	4.54	4.29	3.92	4.44	3.74
5.14	6.45	3.66	3.55	4.50	5.18	5.24	4.95	4.37	4.01
5.25	5.18	3.58	3.83	4.59	5.75	4.43	4.47	4.25	3.77
4.76	4.49	3.38	3.95	5.04	5.04	4.00	4.28	3.71	3.78
5.18	5.24	3.71	4.43	4.83	4.64	4.62	4.07	4.08	4.10
4.22	5.70	3.94	3.70	4.55	4.79	4.29	4.10	3.90	4.06
5.98	5.41	3.59	3.30	4.97	4.72	4.85	4.38	4.41	4.27
4.85	4.77	3.55	3.93	5.38	3.88	4.66	3.98	4.11	3.94
6.55	5.18	3.55	3.58	5.39	5.28	4.40	4.46	4.37	4.11
5.72	5.23	3.43	3.54	5.97	4.66	4.33	5.05	3.53	4.25

Mature cows are five or more years old.

Does either age or breed have an effect on the percentage of butterfat in cows' milk?

Paired data

Repeated measurement of the same variable on the same people or objects leads to data that are related and so are not independent. Matching similar people or objects in a planned way can improve investigations and this also leads to data that are not independent. Two measurements of the same variable made in these situations result in what are referred to as **paired data**. The following examples illustrate these ideas.

Example 1 Class 1R sat an arithmetic test on decimal numbers and their teacher was not satisfied with their progress. Over the next month the class practised decimal arithmetic further and then sat the same test again. Do these results suggest there has been an improvement?

First attempt	18	4	20	4	17	13	7	27	10	4	21
Second attempt	14	8	29	10	16	18	8	25	15	18	25
Difference	–4	4	9	6	–1	5	1	–2	5	14	4
First attempt	5	30	6	6	23	27	19	23	13	24	3
Second attempt	10	32	8	6	*	29	19	27	21	25	6
Difference	5	2	2	0	*	2	0	4	8	1	3
First attempt	12	7	8	23	14	6	17	19	21	15	23
Second attempt	17	8	13	28	25	13	26	27	23	23	29
Difference	5	1	5	5	11	7	9	8	2	8	6

The mark '*' means that this pupil was absent on the second occasion when the test was sat by the class. A common practice when handling paired data is to calculate the differences and to study these differences as if they were one sample. The differences were calculated as

second mark – first mark

so that positive differences represent an improvement, and negative differences indicate that the pupil did less well on the second occasion (three pupils are in this category).

This dotplot displays the differences in the scores. Almost all the pupils showed an improved performance.
In one instance an improvement of 14 marks was recorded. However, on average the improvement was approximately 4 marks.

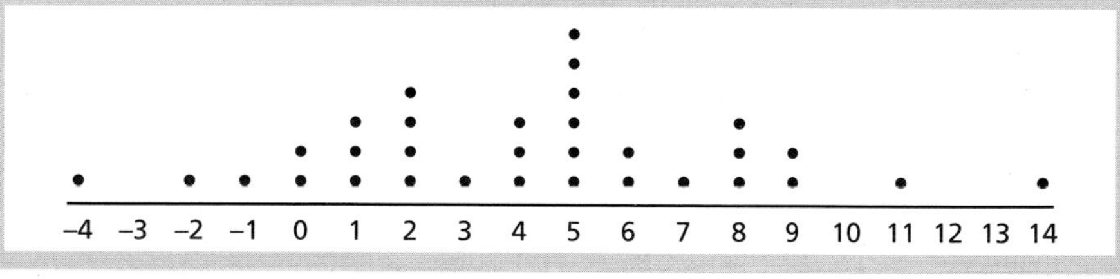

A numerical summary of the above data is:

(Note: n^* shows how many results are missing.)

	n	n^*	Mean	SD
First	33		14.8	8.0
Second	32	1	18.8	8.1
Difference	32	1	4.2	3.9

A **scatter plot** with a **line of equality** drawn is a good way to illustrate the results of the two tests. Each point plotted represents one pupil and has the co-ordinates (first score, second score).
The line of equality joins (0, 0) to (35, 35), and represents no change between tests. Points above the line represent pupils who improved their score. The further above the line the point is, the greater the improvement. Notice that three points are below the line – these pupils scored less on the second test.

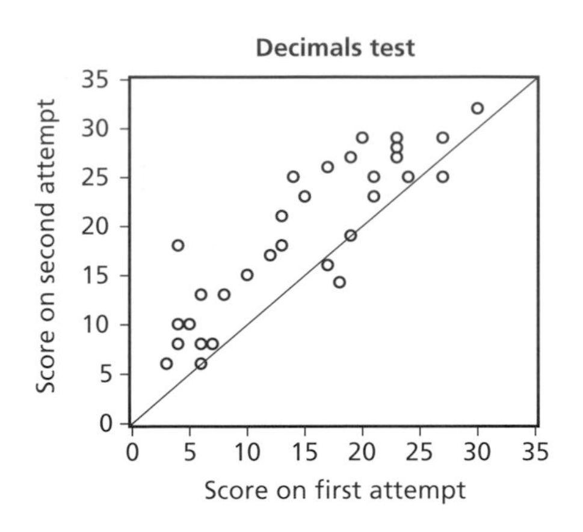

Example 2 A shoe manufacturer wishes to test a new material for the soles of boys' shoes. Some boys are more active than others and as a result are tougher on their shoes. Small improvements in the performance of the new material may be hidden by the large variability in the way boys behave. The manufacturer makes special pairs of boys' shoes where the sole of one shoe is made of the original material and the sole of the other shoe is made from the new material. The new material has the same appearance as the original and is allocated at random to make left and right shoes. Each of 15 boys wears a pair of these special shoes for a few months so that each boy tests both materials. This is an experimental design which leads to paired data in a planned way. At the end of the trial period measurements (in suitable units) of the amount of wear were made. Examine these results and say if you think the new material wares better.

Boy	New material	Original material	Difference new – original
1	6.7	7.5	−0.8
2	10.9	11.3	−0.4
3	9.5	10.8	−1.3
4	11.1	11.4	−0.3
5	13.9	14.4	−0.5
6	6.5	7.4	−0.9
7	11.7	11.6	0.1
8	15.5	15.3	0.2
9	12.1	12.6	−0.5
10	8.3	9.2	−0.9
11	7.1	7.9	−0.8
12	7.5	7.5	0.0
13	8.0	8.7	−0.7
14	7.6	7.9	−0.3
15	12.0	12.4	−0.4
Mean	9.89	10.39	−0.50
SD	2.79	2.60	0.41

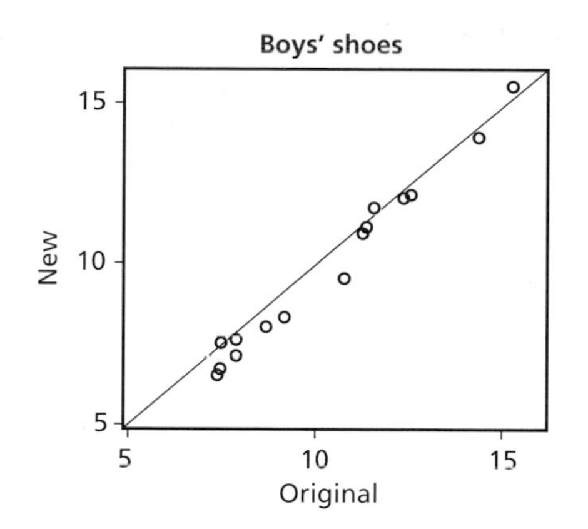

This diagram shows that the new material is slightly harder wearing, and this seems to be a fairly consistent effect, as the new material performed better in 12 out of the 15 pairs of shoes.
Points below the line of equality show that the wear measured less on shoes made from the new material.

EXERCISE 2.4A

1 'Slim-Jim's Diet Plan' advertises a 10 lb weight loss in the first month. The following data show the initial weight of ten new recruits together with their weight after one month on the diet.

Person	1	2	3	4	5	6	7	8	9	10
Initial weight	132	156	142	137	138	184	166	168	153	151
Final weight	124	141	125	126	122	164	156	151	145	138

a Draw a scatter plot with a line of line of equality and discuss the effectiveness of this diet plan.
b Calculate the differences: initial weight – final weight.
c Calculate the mean and standard deviation of the weight differences for this sample of recruits.
d Is the advertising claim fair?

2 A new computer intensive learning program claims to be more effective than the traditional method of teaching statistics. To test this claim, a teacher chooses pairs of similar students matched according to their previous performance in maths. A student from each pair is chosen at random to be taught using the computer program while the other student receives instruction by the traditional method. At the end of the course each student is tested. Here are their marks:

Pair	1	2	3	4	5	6	7	8	9	10
Computer	82	68	82	74	98	77	88	92	80	91
Traditional	79	71	91	68	92	75	84	82	85	90

a Display the data using a scatter diagram with a line of equality.
b Calculate the differences: computer – traditional mark.
c Calculate the mean and standard deviation of the differences in the marks for these students.
d The computer program is expensive. Would you recommend that the teacher use it?

3 Class 1B collected these data on themselves:

	Height (cm) June 96	Height (cm) Dec 96	Weight (kg) June 96	Weight (kg) Dec 96
Boy	157	162	43	44
Boy	145	154	35	41
Boy	159	160	40	43
Boy	143	145	35	34
Boy	142	146	37	40
Boy	152	153	42	40
Boy	147	157	50	48
Boy	135	136	28	29
Boy	141	143	33	38
Boy	155	161	38	43
Boy	150	157	41	43
Boy	145	146	38	38
Girl	152	152	42	43
Girl	166	166	45	45
Girl	154	158	36	36
Girl	136	140	26	28
Girl	145	148	40	41
Girl	154	156	49	52
Girl	160	162	39	41
Girl	177	179	41	50
Girl	158	162	50	53
Girl	155	162	36	44
Girl	157	159	45	47
Girl	152	164	42	49
Girl	147	151	39	44
Girl	159	160	48	46
Girl	142	147	30	31

a State whether the following are independent samples or paired data:
(i) the heights of girls in June and December
(ii) the weights of boys and girls in December.

b With the aid of a multiple boxplot, compare the independent samples identified in part **a**.

c With the aid of a dotplot and summary statistics, describe the differences for the paired data identified in part **a**.

4 Two virus preparations were soaked into cloth and each was rubbed onto different halves of a tobacco leaf. The numbers of lesions which appeared as small, dark rings on each half leaf were counted for the eight leaves studied.

a Are these independent samples or paired data?

b Do the two preparations produce different effects?

Leaf	Prep 1	Prep 2
1	31	18
2	20	17
3	18	14
4	17	11
5	9	10
6	8	7
7	10	5
8	7	6

EXERCISE 2.4B

1 Blood samples were taken from 11 normal (fit) runners before and after a Tyneside Great North Run and measurements of the plasma beta endorphin concentrations were recorded. Blood samples were also taken from another 11 runners after they had collapsed from exhaustion near the end of the race. The first two columns in the table are paired data and

the last column gives the results from a different group of runners (those who collapsed).

a How do the plasma beta concentrations change during the race in normal runners?

b How do the plasma beta concentrations in collapsed runners compare with those of normal runners?

Illustrate your answers with appropriate diagrams and numerical summaries.

Beware of outliers!

Normal runner before race	Same runner after race	Collapsed runner after race
4.3	29.6	66
4.6	25.1	72
5.2	15.5	79
5.2	29.6	84
6.6	24.1	102
7.2	37.8	110
8.4	20.2	123
9.0	21.9	144
10.4	14.2	162
14.0	34.6	169
17.8	46.2	414

2 Three groups of patients were suffering from a condition that caused them to be under weight. Each group received a different treatment over a fixed period of time. The following data give each patient's weight (in pounds) before and after treatment.

Treatment A		Treatment B		Treatment C	
Before	After	Before	After	Before	After
80.5	82.2	80.7	80.2	83.8	95.2
84.9	85.6	89.4	80.1	83.3	94.3
81.5	81.4	91.8	86.4	86.0	91.5
82.6	81.9	74.0	86.3	82.5	91.9
79.9	76.4	78.1	76.1	86.7	100.3
88.7	103.6	88.3	78.1	79.6	76.7
94.9	98.4	87.3	75.1	76.9	76.8
76.3	93.4	75.1	86.7	94.2	101.6
81.0	73.4	80.6	73.5	73.4	94.9
80.5	82.1	78.4	84.6	80.5	75.2
85.0	96.7	77.6	77.4	81.6	77.8
89.2	95.3	88.7	79.5	82.1	95.5
81.3	82.4	81.3	89.6	77.6	90.7
76.5	72.5	78.1	81.4	83.5	92.5
70.0	90.9	70.5	81.8	89.9	93.8
80.4	71.3	77.3	77.3	86.0	91.7
83.3	85.4	85.2	84.2	87.3	98.0
83.0	81.6	86.0	75.4		
87.7	89.1	84.1	79.5		
84.2	83.9	79.7	73.0		
86.4	82.7	85.5	88.3		
76.5	75.7	84.4	84.7		
80.2	82.6	79.6	81.4		
87.8	100.4	77.5	81.2		
83.3	85.2	72.3	88.2		
79.7	83.6	89.0	78.8		
84.5	84.6				
80.8	96.2				
87.4	86.7				

Using suitable diagrams and numerical summaries, compare the different treatments. Do you think it is possible to generalise your conclusions about these patients and come to a decision on the effectiveness of these treatments for all who suffer from this condition?

Bivariate data - Quantitative variables

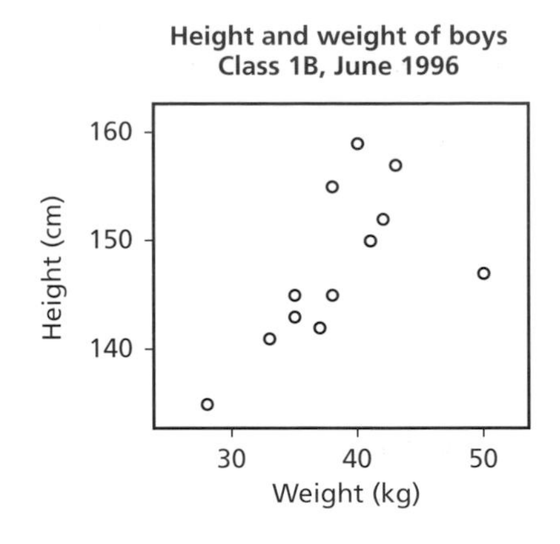

Data consisting of pairs of values can occur in another way, for example when the values of **two variables** are determined on the same person or object. For example in the last exercise, the height (cm) and weight (kg) measurements collected by Class 1B would be classed as **continuous bivariate data**, and the pairs of measurements (weight, height) for each pupil can be displayed in a scatter diagram as shown.

The points on the scatter diagram (with the exception of one point) seem to lie roughly along a straight line. This indicates that there is a relationship between height and weight – on average, taller people weigh more. One point seems to lie far away from the line. This pupil weighs considerably more than other pupils of the same height, so this point may be considered an outlier.

Warning!

When scatter diagrams are drawn the scales on the axes may not start at zero. Always read the scales on the axes carefully.

Some commonly occurring patterns in scatter diagrams are shown below.

Strong positive relationship

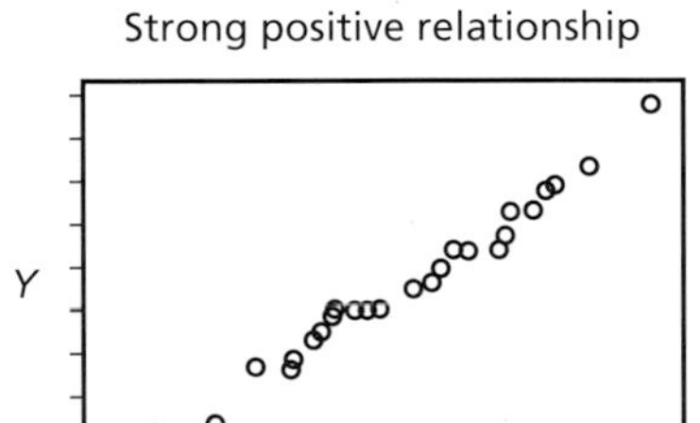

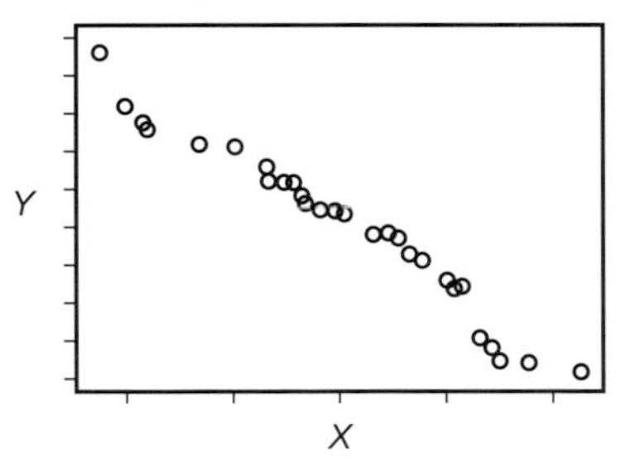

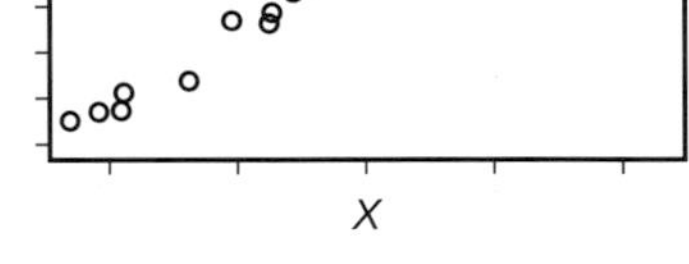

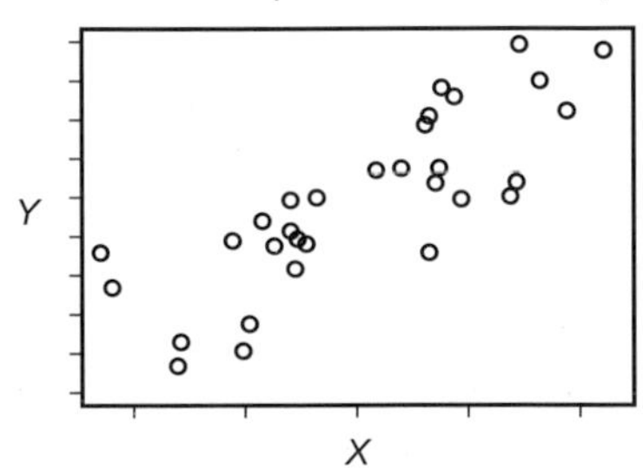

Moderate negative relationship

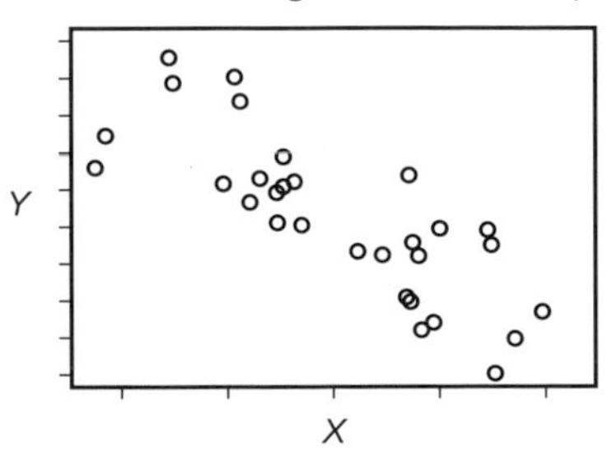

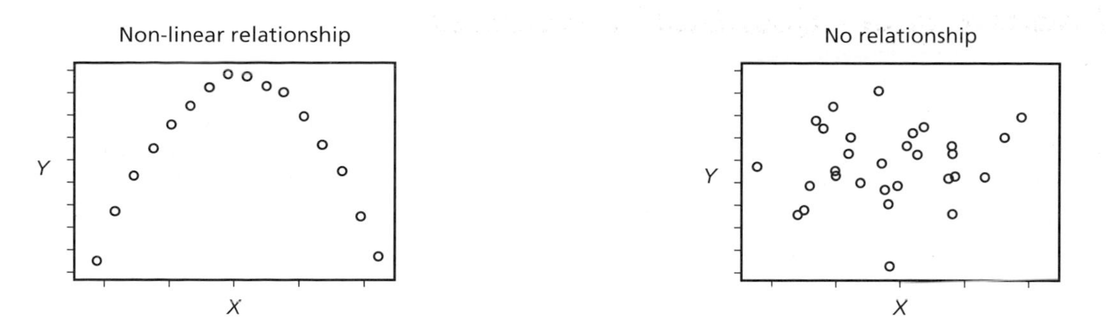

Methods for describing linear relationships will be discussed in more detail in Chapter 5.

EXERCISE 2.5A

1 In December 1996 the heights and weights of the boys in Class 1B were:

Boy	1	2	3	4	5	6	7	8	9	10	11	12
Height (cm)	162	154	160	145	146	153	157	136	143	161	157	146
Weight (kg)	44	41	43	34	40	40	48	29	38	43	43	38

Draw a scatter diagram for the data and comment on the pattern.

2 A toy car was released from different starting positions, x cm, up a ramp. For each starting position on the ramp (x = 10, 20, 30, ... cm) the distance travelled, y cm, was measured. This was repeated a few times for each starting point.

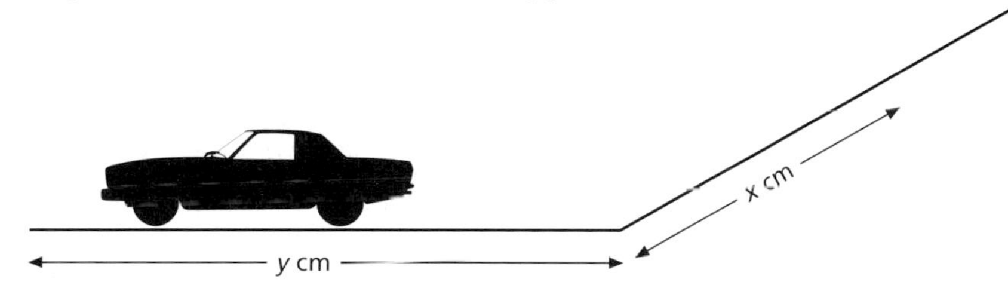

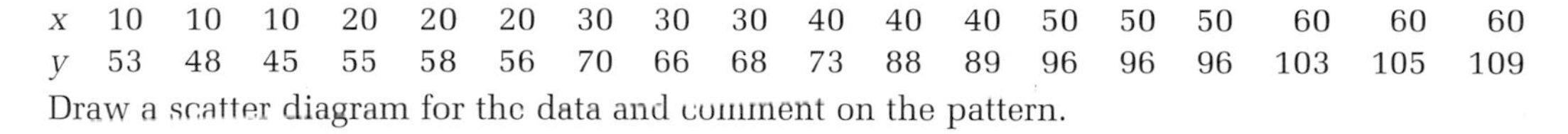

x	10	10	10	20	20	20	30	30	30	40	40	40	50	50	50	60	60	60
y	53	48	45	55	58	56	70	66	68	73	88	89	96	96	96	103	105	109

Draw a scatter diagram for the data and comment on the pattern.

3

Y	X	Y	X
10.7	9.5	11.7	9.8
6.5	5.0	25.6	19.0
29.4	23.0	16.3	14.6
17.2	15.2	9.5	8.3
18.4	11.4	28.8	21.6
19.7	11.8	31.2	26.5
16.6	12.1	6.5	4.8
29.0	22.0	25.7	21.7
40.5	28.2	26.5	18.0
14.2	12.1	33.1	28.0

These data give the distance by road Y km and the straight line distance X km (as the crow flies) between 20 different pairs of locations in Sheffield.

a Draw a scatter diagram for the data.

b What is the relationship between the two variables?

c How well can the road distance be predicted from the linear distance?

4 Counting the number of finger ridges of each twin in 12 pairs of identical twins produced the data in this table.
Numbers of finger ridges are obviously similar within the pairs, but vastly different between different sets of twins.
Draw a scatter diagram for the data and comment.

Pair	Twin A	Twin B
1	71	71
2	79	82
3	105	99
4	115	114
5	76	70
6	83	82
7	114	113
8	57	44
9	114	113
10	94	91
11	75	83
12	76	72

EXERCISE 2.5B

1 The table shows the well known Forbes' data on the boiling point of water.
James Forbes was a Scottish physicist who was interested in finding a way to estimate altitude from measurements of the boiling temperature of water. He collected the data given here during his researches and they consist of 17 observations on boiling point (°F) and barometric pressure (inches of mercury).
Draw a scatter diagram and comment.

Boiling point	Pressure
194.5	20.79
194.3	20.79
197.9	22.40
198.4	22.67
199.4	23.15
199.9	23.35
200.9	23.89
201.1	23.99
201.4	24.02
201.3	24.01
203.6	25.14
204.6	26.57
209.5	28.49
208.6	27.76
210.7	29.04
211.9	29.88
212.2	30.06

2 These data show the percentage male unemployment rate in 1987 in the 11 main regions of the UK, and the average percentage of household weekly expenditure on motoring and travel fares.

Region	Unemployment rate 1987 (%)	Average percentage spent on motoring and fares (1986-87)
England		
North	14.0	12.8
Yorkshire and Humberside	11.3	14.5
East Midlands	9.0	15.4
East Anglia	6.8	15.0
South East	7.1	15.0
South West	8.2	15.3
West Midlands	11.1	14.6
North West	12.7	14.2
Wales	12.5	14.4
Scotland	13.0	14.1
Northern Ireland	17.6	15.5

Draw a scatter diagram and comment. Identify the possible outlier.

Bivariate data - Qualitative variables

Scatter diagrams are helpful when searching for relationships between two continuous variables measured on the same units (people or objects). With qualitative bivariate data, as might be produced by the responses to a survey for example, cross-tabulating the results in a **two-way table** can reveal relationships between two qualitative variables.

Example A sample of 62 pupils at a certain school was asked how often they used the new milk bar at lunch times. The questionnaires recorded the replies listed below. Did boys use the milk bar as much as girls?

Sex	Use	Sex	Use	Sex	Use	Sex	Use
Girl	never	Boy	some	Boy	never	Girl	never
Girl	some	Girl	never	Boy	never	Boy	some
Boy	some	Girl	some	Girl	some	Boy	never
Boy	never	Girl	never	Boy	some	Girl	some
Girl	never	Boy	most	Girl	most	Boy	never
Girl	never	Girl	never	Girl	never	Boy	some
Boy	some	Boy	some	Girl	some	Girl	some
Girl	some	Girl	never	Girl	some	Boy	never
Boy	never	Boy	never	Boy	never	Girl	some
Boy	never	Boy	never	Boy	some	Boy	never
Boy	never	Girl	some	Boy	some	Girl	some
Boy	never	Girl	some	Girl	some	Boy	never
Girl	most	Girl	never	Boy	never	Boy	some
Girl	some	Boy	some	Girl	never	Boy	never
Girl	never	Girl	some	Boy	never		
Boy	some	Boy	never	Girl	some		

The two variables of interest are *sex* (boy, girl) and *use of milk bar* (most days, some days, never).

Tally chart:

	Boy	Girl
most	/	//
some	~~////~~ ~~////~~ //	~~////~~ ~~////~~ ~~////~~ /
never	~~////~~ ~~////~~ ~~////~~ ////	~~////~~ ~~////~~ //

Two-way tables:

		Count			Percentage		
		Boy	Girl	Total	Boy	Girl	Total
Use of milk bar	most days	1	2	3	3.1	6.7	4.8
	some days	12	16	28	37.5	53.3	45.2
	never	19	12	31	59.4	40.0	50.0
	Total	32	30	62	100.0	100.0	100.0

The basic two-way table shows the count in each category. For example, 16 girls said they used the milk bar 'some days'. It is often easier to interpret the table if these counts are converted to proportions or percentages. The question posed requires a comparison of boys' and girls' use of the milk bar. The percentage table shows the counts converted to percentages of the column totals. It would appear that, on the evidence in this sample of pupils, the percentage of girls who use the milk bar 'most days' and 'some days' is considerably greater than the corresponding percentage of boys, while the percentage of girls who never use the milk bar is substantially lower than for boys. Put simply, a greater proportion of girls use the milk bar.

EXERCISE 2.6B

1 This table shows the numbers of male and female sandflies caught in light traps set 3 ft and 35 ft above the ground at a site in eastern Panama.

Does the proportion of males vary with height?

	Height above ground	
	3ft	35ft
Males	173	125
Females	150	73
Total	323	198

2 Separate health and lifestyle surveys were conducted in each of five regions. Each person questioned was asked to tell the interviewer if they considered themselves to have good, fairly good, or not good health.

Do the regions differ with respect to how people feel about their health?

Region	Good	Fairly good	Not good
Southampton	954	444	78
Swindon	985	504	87
Jersey	459	175	43
Guernsey	377	176	35
West Dorset	926	503	109

3 A random sample of 50 pupils at a certain school were observed. It was noted whether they were male or female and whether they were wearing a school blazer (Y) or not (N).

Sex	Wear	Sex	Wear	Sex	Wear	Sex	Wear	Sex	Wear
F	N	F	N	F	Y	M	Y	M	N
F	N	M	N	M	N	M	N	M	Y
F	Y	M	Y	F	N	F	Y	M	N
M	N	F	N	M	Y	F	N	F	Y
M	Y	M	N	F	N	F	Y	F	N
F	N	M	N	F	N	F	Y	M	N
M	N	F	N	F	N	M	N	F	Y
M	N	F	Y	M	N	F	N	M	N
F	Y	M	N	M	N	M	N	M	N
F	N	M	N	F	N	M	N	F	Y

Cross-tabulate these data in a two-way table.
Is there a difference in the proportions of boys and girls wearing a school blazer?

How long is a piece of string?

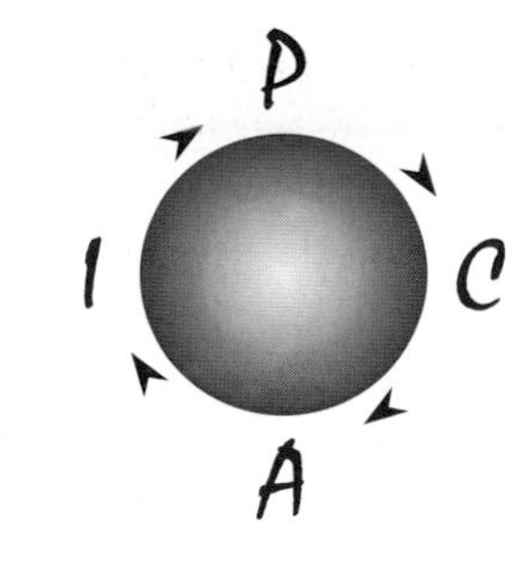

Pose a question

How well can we estimate length by eye without using measuring instruments?

Collect some data

Work with a partner. You will need a ball of string and a pair of scissors. Make sure all measuring instruments are well hidden. Unwind some string and hold it for your partner to cut off a piece which he or she judges to be 200 mm long. Set this aside out of view. Make sure there is no cheating by lining up the string beside parts of the body or familiar objects. After your partner has completed five or six different estimates reverse roles. Only when all the estimating is complete should the measuring begin. You should then measure each other's estimates to the nearest millimetre.

Analyse the data

Summarise each other's performance by calculating the sample mean and standard deviation of your estimates. Compare each other's mean with the target length. The results for one group of students are shown on the right. For each student, the dot shows the mean estimate, and the vertical line indicates the range of their estimates.

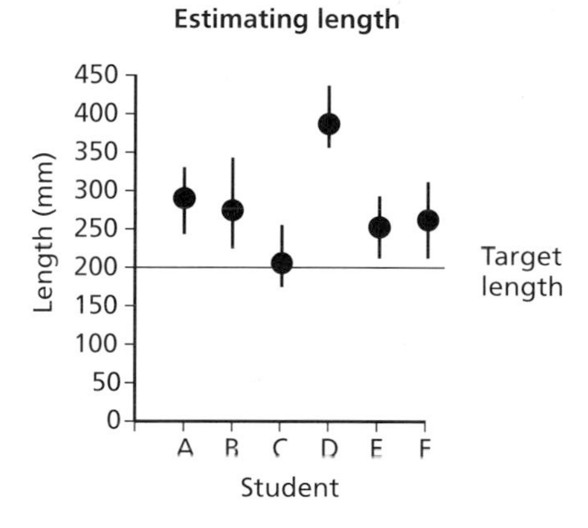

Interpret the results

Most of the students in the example above overestimated the target length. Write a brief report which describes how well your class can estimate length.

Further study

Is there a difference between the estimating abilities of 12-year-olds and 17-year-olds?
Do students' performances improve if between each estimate they are told how 'well' they are doing?
In each case, give very careful thought to how the data collection should be organised.

Visual analogue scores

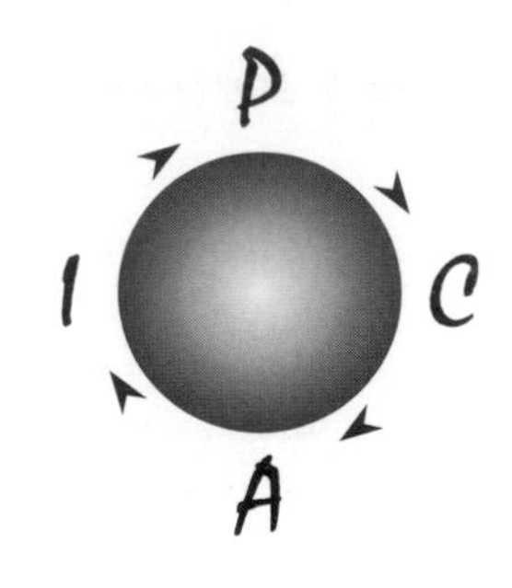

Pose a question

Do the students in your class enjoy studying mathematics?

Collect some data

How can we measure people's opinions? One way to measure this is to ask each member of the class to place a mark on a 100 mm line to indicate how much they enjoy the subject.

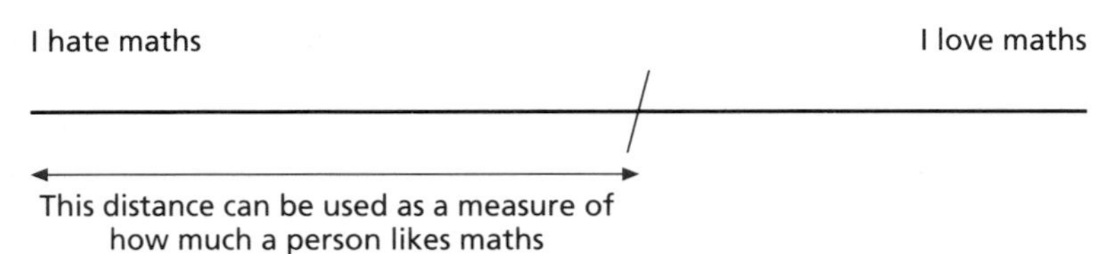

If you measure the position of the mark to the nearest millimetre this can be used as a measure of the student's feelings about mathematics. These measurements are often referred to as **visual analogue scores**.

Analyse the data

Use a stem and leaf diagram or a boxplot to display the results for the class. Calculate the sample mean and standard deviation for the results. Sometimes a stem and leaf diagram shows a bimodal shape which may mean there are two distinct views – one group of students enjoys maths more than the other!

Interpret the results

Write a brief report describing the opinions in your class.

Further study

Extend this idea by measuring the class's feelings about other subjects, or investigating the opinions of other classes. You can also use this method to gauge agreement or disagreement with controversial statements such as 'I think statistics is more useful than trigonometry!', where the left-hand end on the scale indicates complete disagreement.
Use this technique to collect measurements from *independent samples* such as males and females, or perhaps gather data from different year groups to see if age makes a difference.
You could also use this technique to produce *paired data* by taking measurements on the same people on two occasions to see if their opinions have changed. You may suspect that people's opinions on two topics are related and use this method to collect *bivariate data* which could be displayed in a scatter plot.

CHAPTER 2 REVIEW

1 A manufacturer conducts a survey to determine its customers' satisfaction with the products and services it provides. Customers' opinions were measured using visual analogue scores, where a measurement of 0 indicates complete dissatisfaction. The following boxplots summarise the results for large and small customers. Write a brief report on the company's performance.

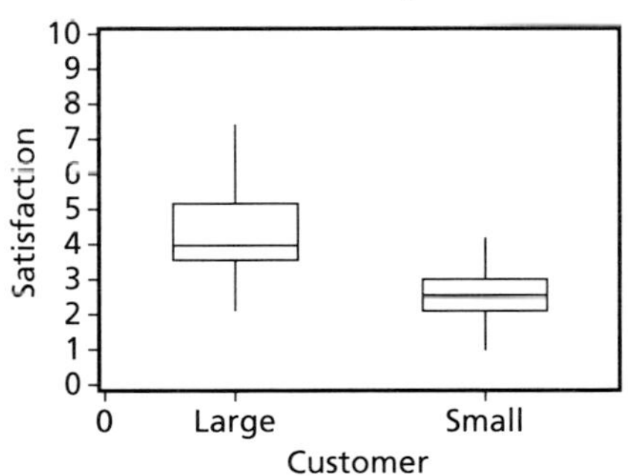

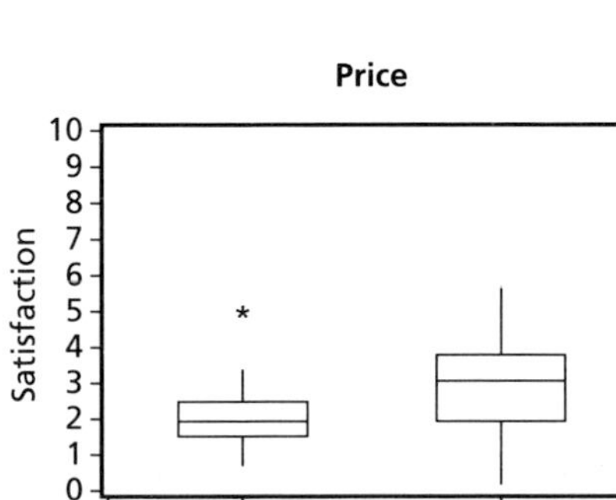

2 To verify that a water company is checking its discharges reliably, a study was conducted where 11 samples of effluent were thoroughly mixed, divided and sent to two laboratories for testing. One half of each sample was sent to the water company's lab and the other half sent to a commercial lab. Each lab was asked to make measurements of two variables for each of the sample splits. The results are shown in the following scatter plots on which a line of equality has been drawn.

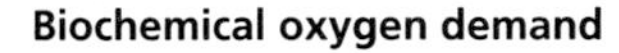

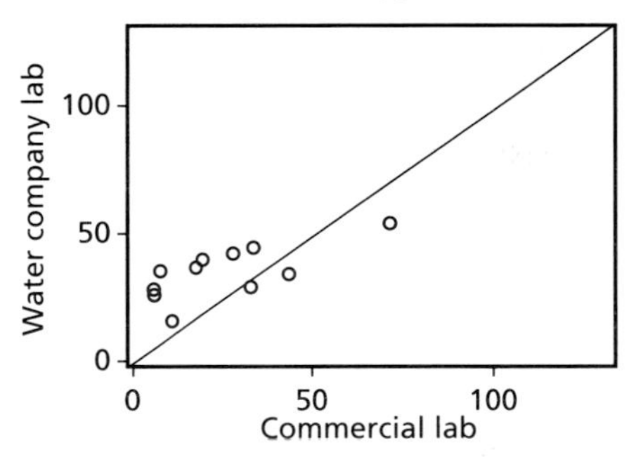

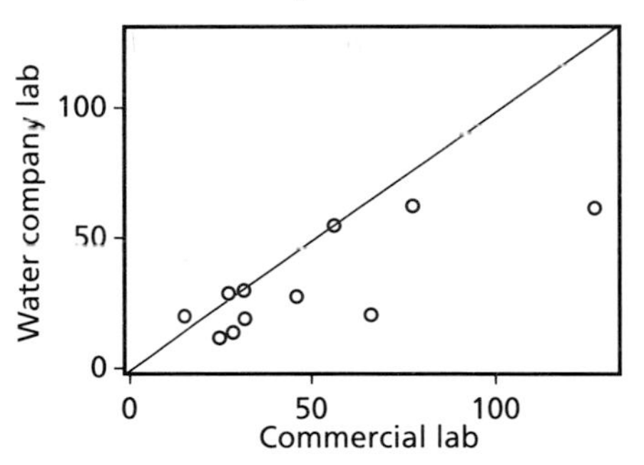

Do the two laboratories' chemical analyses agree? If differences exist, describe their nature.

CHAPTER 2 SUMMARY

EDA (Exploratory Data Analysis)
Looking at sample data using quick plots and numerical summaries. Searching for patterns in the data, trying to find answers to questions, or posing new questions for further investigation. The methods used depend on the nature of the investigation and the type of data.

Statistical inference
From a population consisting of all the items of interest a representative sample is selected. Sample statistics such as the mean $\overline{x}$ and standard deviation s may be used to infer the values of μ and σ, the corresponding population parameters.

Univariate data
Data consisting of the values recorded for one variable. The contents of a box of paper clips are counted: *contents* is a discrete variable. The weights of students are recorded: *weight* is a continuous variable. Simple plots show the shape of the data display which together with measures of central location and variability give clues to the type of mathematical model which would best describe the population.

Independent samples
If the values in one sample are not related to the values in another, then the samples are said to be independent. Back-to-back stem and leaf diagrams and multiple boxplots are suitable ways to compare independent samples.

Paired data
The values in one sample are linked with values in another. This may happen because two measurements on the same units (people or objects) are made on two occasions, or sometimes investigations are planned in such a way that two measurements of the same variable are related because different people or objects have been matched beforehand. This matching is done on the basis of a characteristic which shows the two units in each pair are very similar in some way. The usual practice with paired data is to calculate the difference between the pairs and to analyse these differences as though they were one sample. A scatter plot with a line of equality superimposed is an effective way to illustrate paired data.

Bivariate data
The values of two variables are determined on each unit (person or object of interest). These pairs of values may be examined to see if there is a relationship between the two variables. Quantitative variables are usually displayed in a scatter diagram. Qualitative variables may be cross-tabulated in a two-way table.

Note The results of interpreting data using EDA are subjective, which means two people may look at the same data and yet arrive at different conclusions. This uncertainty results from the variability in the data being examined. What is required is an agreed set of rules which enable decisions to be made in the face of such uncertainty. To be able to use these rules we first need an understanding of how uncertainty is measured and how to model uncertainty mathematically. These ideas are introduced in more detail in the next two chapters.

3 Probability

How sure are you?

We cannot say for certain how many sweets there are in an unopened jar. Although if data had been collected about the number of sweets in similar jars it would be possible to give an estimate of a 'likely' value. But what does 'likely' mean? Words such as likely, probably, good chance, fifty-fifty, certain, impossible are all descriptions of the **probability** of an event occurring.
In many everyday situations uncertainty is often measured **subjectively** using such words. For example you may give an opinion on the likelihood of Scotland winning the Grand Slam based on past performance, team players, nationality, and so on. If you want to be more precise or unambiguous about measuring uncertainty, it is possible to estimate probability using numbers. Gamblers do this when they bet using odds.
An estimate of probability is often made **experimentally** by conducting a **random experiment** – an experiment whose result cannot be predicted with certainty. For example, throwing a die:

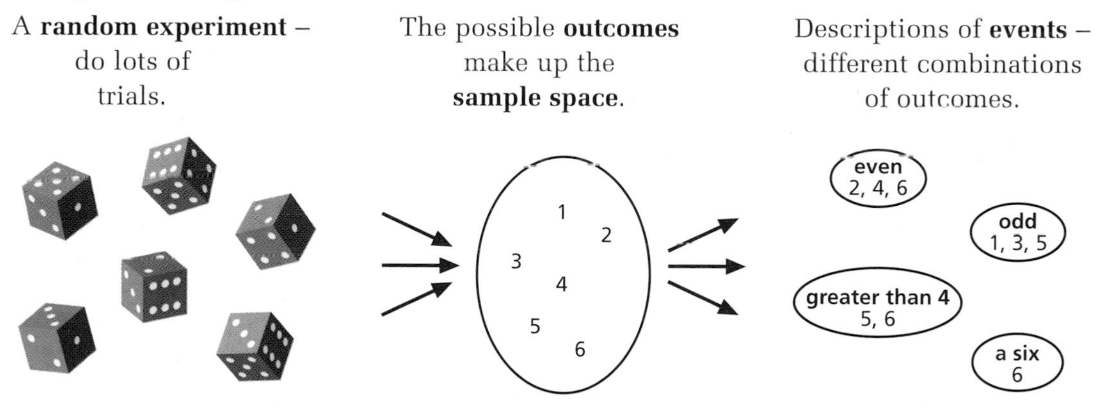

The probability of an event is a number between 0 and 1 that indicates how likely that event is to occur when the random experiment is carried out. More specifically, it is the proportion of times that the event occurs in the long run when the random experiment is carried out many times. An event that occurs only rarely has a probability close to 0, while an event that occurs very often has a probability close to 1.

Another type of random experiment is to ask a question in a survey. Each time we ask the question we are performing a **trial**. The result of a trial is known as an **outcome**. The question may be 'How do you normally travel to school?'. The outcomes may be {walk, bike, bus, car, taxi, other} and this list of all possible outcomes is the **sample space**. The school council may be concerned about traffic congestion outside the school and so be interested in the event {bus, car, taxi}. Notice an **event** is either a simple outcome or several outcomes from within the sample space, as in this example. The probability of the event {bus, car, taxi} just means the proportion of all journeys to school that make use of these vehicles. This probability may be estimated from the sample survey by determining the proportion of all pupils surveyed who say they normally travel to school by bus, car or taxi.

Example In a school of 900 we find that 36 out of a sample of 300 are left-handed. Estimate the probability of a randomly selected pupil in that school being left-handed.

The required probability is just the proportion of pupils who are left-handed,

i.e. $\frac{36}{300} = 0.12$.

If the sample is representative of the whole population of pupils in the school, then the estimate of the probability of a pupil being left-handed is 0.12.

The estimate is in fact simply the **relative frequency** of the event and the estimate would be expected to improve if more pupils were sampled. Since relative frequency is a proportion, the measure of probability will always be between 0 and 1 (or 0%–100%).

EXERCISE 3.1

1 Match the words to the letters on the number line:
quite likely, as likely as not, unlikely, fifty-fifty, almost certain, practically impossible.

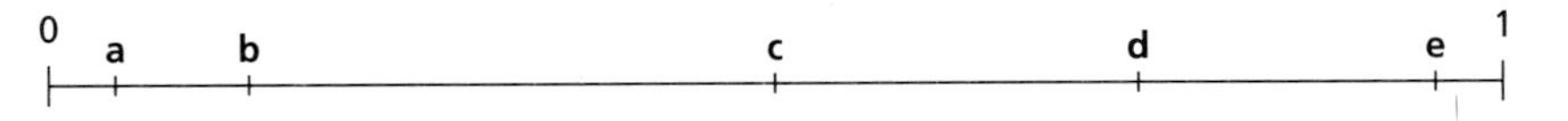

2 Suggest a value p, $0 \leq p < 1$, which you think describes the following words and hence place them on a number line like the one shown below:
impossible, good chance, evens, fair chance, certain, improbable.

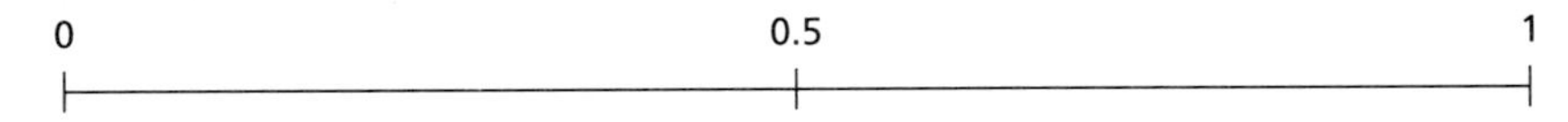

3 Copy and complete the following for each random experiment.

Random experiment	Sample space	Are all outcomes equally likely to happen? (yes or no)
a rolling a die		
b measuring the height of a class of 15-year-olds (cm)	{160 < height < 190}	
c tossing a coin		
d survey of customers' answers to the question 'do you prefer low fat spread to butter?'	{yes, no, don't know}	
e number of car sales made by a salesperson from 5 customers		

4 Using your general knowledge, state which is the better estimate of the probability.
  a Winning any prize in the National Lottery. 0.1 or 0.8
  b The average maximum daytime temperature in Glasgow in July being above 15 °C. 0.4 or 0.8
  c A head when an ordinary coin is tossed, given that it landed heads on each of the last three occasions. 0.4 or 0.5

5 For several successive years, sports day at Seaview High School had been postponed because of rain. So each day in June for the last two years the PE department in the school recorded whether or not it rained for more than one hour during afternoon school. The results are shown below.

	Rainy afternoons	Dry afternoons	Total
Frequency Relative frequency	6	34	40

Calculate the relative frequencies and estimate the probability of a rainy afternoon in June. Was the PE department unlucky?

6 It is suspected that a die is biased against a six being thrown. Using the die, the number of sixes scored after several throws was recorded as follows:

	20 throws	50 throws	100 throws	200 throws	500 throws
No. of sixes	2	11	17	35	70

By calculating relative frequencies, give estimates of the probability of throwing a six at each stage in the experiment. Plot the values of your estimates on the vertical axis against the number of throws on the horizontal axis and comment on the results.

Calculating probability

Consider the results of a random experiment which involves tossing a coin a hundred times.
The results start: T, H, T, T, T, T, T, H, H, T, H, H, H, H, T, H, ...
The proportion of heads as the experiment proceeds changes as follows:

$\frac{0}{1}, \frac{1}{2}, \frac{1}{3}, \frac{1}{4}, \frac{1}{5}, \frac{1}{6}, \frac{1}{7}, \frac{2}{8}, \frac{3}{9}, \frac{3}{10}, \frac{4}{11}, \frac{5}{12}, \frac{6}{13}, \frac{7}{14}, \frac{7}{15}, \frac{8}{16}, \ldots$

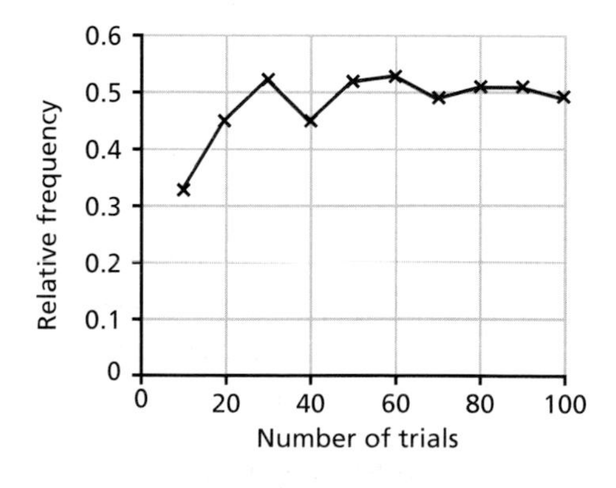

The table shows the proportion of heads (or relative frequencies) at various stages.

Number of trials	10	20	30	40	50	60	70	80	90	100
Relative frequency	0.33	0.45	0.53	0.45	0.52	0.53	0.49	0.51	0.51	0.49

The plot shows that, as the number of trials increases, the relative frequency settles down to a particular value, the probability of a head, and in general:

as the number of trials increases, relative frequency $\xrightarrow[\text{closer to}]{\text{gets}}$ probability.

But in some situations it is possible to calculate the exact value of a probability by considering what is expected to happen. When a coin is tossed, each result is **equally likely to occur on the grounds of symmetry**, so the probability of a head would be 1 in 2 or $\frac{1}{2}$,

i.e. $\dfrac{\text{number of different possible outcomes giving 'head'}}{\text{total number of different possible outcomes}}$

And in general we can say:

if E is the desired event, which may be one or several outcomes of a trial,
and S is the set of all possible outcomes (the sample space),
then provided each outcome is **equally likely,**

$$\text{the probability of } E = \mathrm{P}(E) = \frac{\text{number of different possible outcomes in } E}{\text{total number of different possible outcomes in } S}$$

Example 1 If a letter is chosen at random from the word 'lottery', find the probability of getting a vowel.

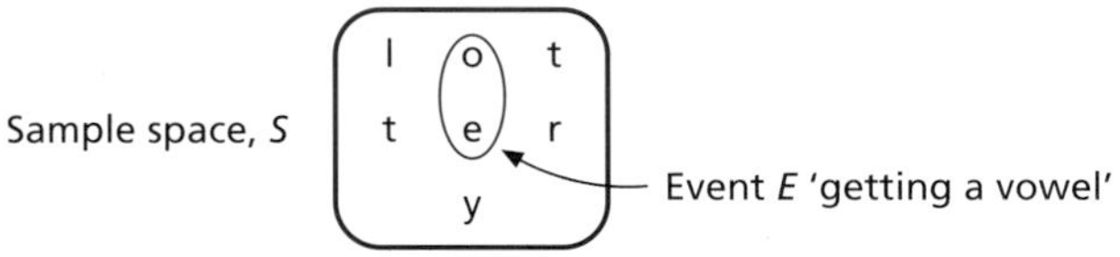

Sample space, S — l, o, t, t, e, r, y — Event E 'getting a vowel' (o, e)

Now if E = getting a vowel = {o, e}, there are 2 outcomes in E;
and S = {l, o, t, t, e, r, y}, so there are 7 outcomes in S.
As they are chosen 'at random' each letter is equally likely to be chosen.

$$\mathrm{P}(E) = \frac{\text{2 vowel outcomes}}{\text{7 total outcomes}} = \frac{2}{7}$$

An important part of calculating probabilities is listing the members of E and S in order to count them. When listing try to be systematic. Sometimes a table or a tree diagram can be useful in the listing process.

Example 2 Find P(a total of 8 when two dice are thrown).
The outcomes in both E and S can clearly be seen in the table.

Number of outcomes in $E = 5$.
Number of outcomes in $S = 36$.

$\mathrm{P}(E) = \frac{5}{36} \approx 0.139$ to 3 dp.

1st \ 2nd	1	2	3	4	5	6
1	(1,1)	(1,2)	(1,3)	(1,4)	(1,5)	(1,6)
2	(2,1)	(2,2)	(2,3)	(2,4)	(2,5)	(2,6)
3	(3,1)	(3,2)	(3,3)	(3,4)	(3,5)	(3,6)
4	(4,1)	(4,2)	(4,3)	(4,4)	(4,5)	(4,6)
5	(5,1)	(5,2)	(5,3)	(5,4)	(5,5)	(5,6)
6	(6,1)	(6,2)	(6,3)	(6,4)	(6,5)	(6,6)

required event

Example 3 A teacher has five textbooks, three in good condition and two falling to bits. She gives the books out at random. Find the probability that the first two pupils given books receive **a** no good books **b** one bad and one good book **c** two good books. Label the books A, B, C, D, E, and draw a 'tree diagram'.

Total number of outcomes = 20

a P(0 good) = $\frac{2}{20}$ or 0.1

b P(1 good, 1 bad) = $\frac{12}{20}$ or 0.6

c P(2 good) = $\frac{6}{20}$ or 0.3

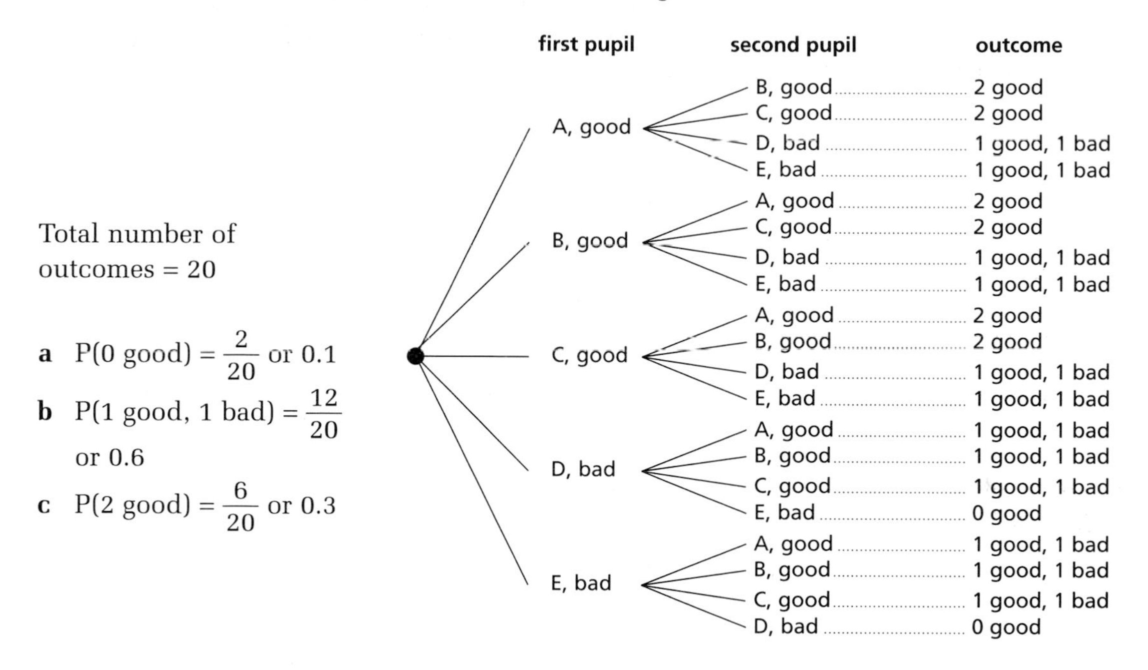

This is an example of selection without replacement, i.e. once the first pupil receives book A, it is not available to be given to the second pupil. Always consider carefully whether selection is *with* or *without replacement*. The following example is with replacement.

Example 4 A binary number is one which is composed of 0s and 1s. Find the probability that in a four-digit binary number there are two 0s and two 1s.

Whether the digit 1 was chosen for the first place or not, it is available to be chosen in any other place. As each outcome is equally likely,
P(two 0s and two 1s)
$= \frac{6}{16} = \frac{3}{8}$.

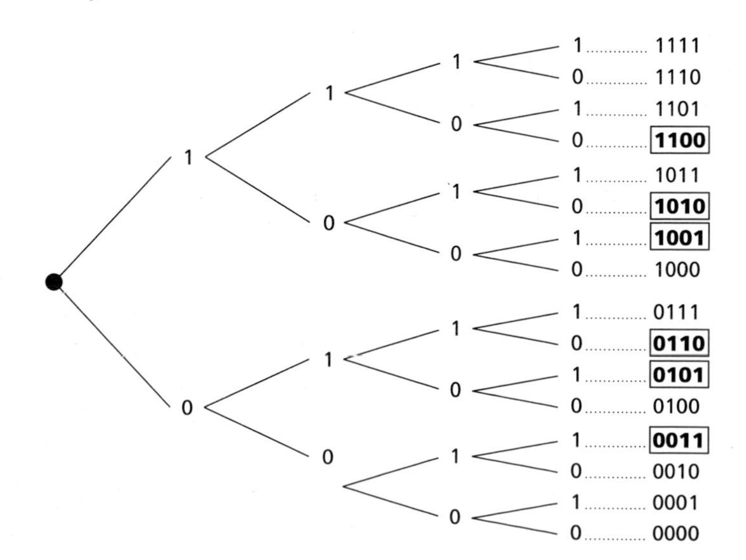

EXERCISE 3.2

1 A pack of cards is cut. Calculate:
a P(king of hearts) **b** P(red king) **c** P(heart or a king).

2 In a raffle there is one prize of £100 and five prizes of £10. Eight hundred tickets are sold. Find:
a P(winning £100) **b** P(winning something) **c** P(not winning anything).
d Find a relationship between your answers to **b** and **c**.

3 **a** Complete the list of possible outcomes when two coins are tossed: HH, . . .
Hence find P(one head when two coins are tossed).
b Complete the list of possible outcomes when three coins are tossed: HHH, HHT, HTH, . . .
Hence find P(one head when three coins are tossed).

4 When both a coin is tossed and a die is thrown, find:
a P(tail with a 6) **b** P(head with an even number) **c** P(tail with a number less than 3).

5 The dotplot illustrates the height of 30 pupils in a class to the nearest centimetre. Find the probability that a pupil chosen at random from this class will be less than 165 cm tall.

160 165 170 175 180

6 A pupil's lateness record shows 44 late arrivals in 200 possible attendances. Based on past experience, estimate the probability that the next day the pupil will arrive at school:
a late **b** on time.

7 In a display of 30 photos recalling a school trip, 15 showed Funny Faces, 20 showed Spectacular Scenes and 6 showed Tremendous Teachers.
a Copy and complete the diagram to show the numbers in each part of the display.
b A photo is chosen at random to be published in the school magazine. Find:
(i) P(photo shows an FF and a TT)
(ii) P(photo shows an FF or a TT) (iii) P(photo shows neither an FF nor a TT).

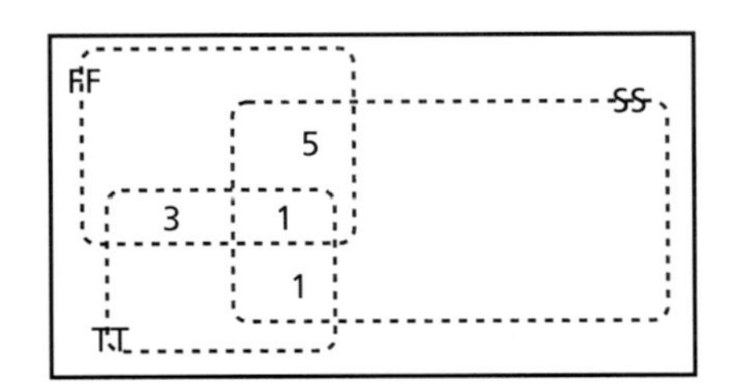

8 The table shows the number of brown eggs occurring in a sample of 1000 boxes which each contain six eggs.

Number of brown eggs	0	1	2	3	4	5	6
Frequency	1	12	15	27	162	430	353

Find an estimate of the probability that a particular egg is: **a** brown **b** not brown.

9 From a list of five poets, three are to be chosen at random as names of streets in a new housing scheme. What is the probability that the first one on the list is chosen?

10 In an election for captain and vice-captain of a debating club, six candidates, of whom two are female, are equally likely to be chosen for either position. Find the probability that one male and one female are chosen.

Reminder

The basic ideas of probability you have used so far can be summarised as follows:

P(*E*) = *p* implies **0 ≤ *p* ≤ 1**
P(*E*) = 0 if ***E* is impossible**
P(*E*) = 1 if ***E* is certain**
P(*E*) = *p* implies **P(not *E*) = 1 − *p***

Counting methods – Permutations

Counting outcomes by listing can be tedious. Imagine trying to count outcomes by listing all the possible choices of six balls from the 49 in the lottery! Some simple techniques using *multiplication* may help. For example, travelling from Glasgow to Edinburgh, I have a choice of three methods of transport, and continuing from Edinburgh to Inverness, I can choose from five methods.

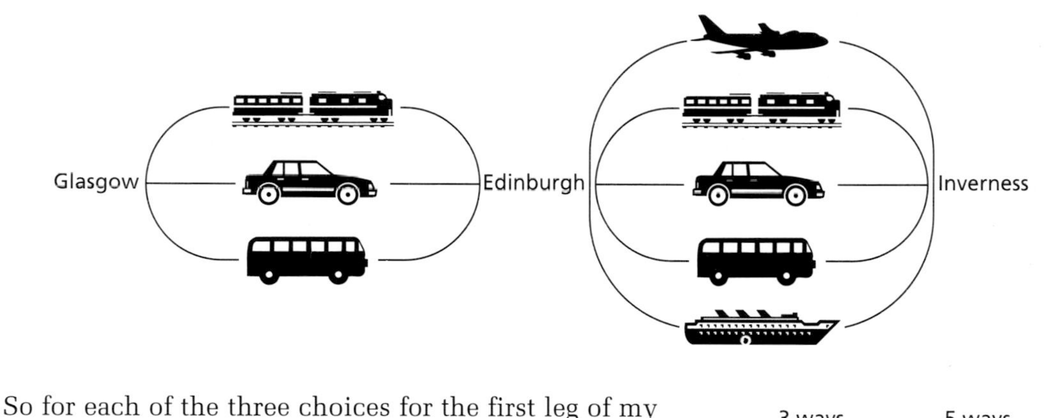

So for each of the three choices for the first leg of my journey, I have a further five choices for the second leg. This gives $3 \times 5 = 15$ different choices in total for the whole journey.

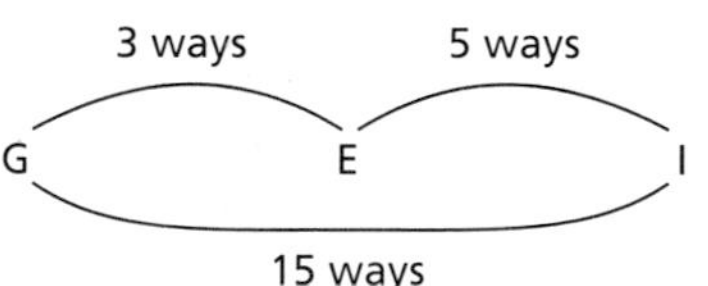

Method 1: In a two-stage experiment where the first stage can occur in n ways and the second can occur in m ways, the experiment consisting of stage 1 followed by stage 2 has $n \times m$ possible outcomes. This idea can easily be extended when there are more than two stages.

The same idea can be used to find the number of ways of arranging, say, five objects *in order*. There are *five* ways of choosing the first object, then *four* ways of choosing the second object, *three* ways of choosing the third object, but only *two* ways of choosing the fourth object and *no* choice in the last object. So altogether there must be $5 \times 4 \times 3 \times 2 \times 1$ or 120 ways of arranging these objects in order.
The product $5 \times 4 \times 3 \times 2 \times 1$ can be written 5! This is read '5 factorial'.
Method 2: There are $n \times (n - 1) \times (n - 2) \times \ldots \times 3 \times 2 \times 1$ or $n!$ ways of arranging n different objects in order, where $n!$ is read as 'n factorial'.

Suppose, however, that only two of these five objects were arranged, the first could be chosen in five ways and the second in four ways, giving only $5 \times 4 = 20$ arrangements.
Notice:

$$5 \times 4 = \frac{5 \times 4 \times 3 \times 2 \times 1}{3 \times 2 \times 1} = \frac{5!}{3!} = \frac{5!}{(5-2)!}$$

Method 3: There are $\frac{n!}{(n-r)!}$ ways of *arranging* r objects from n different objects, often called the number of **permutations** of r from n, where $\frac{n!}{(n-r)!}$ is written as $^{n}\boldsymbol{P}_{r}$ and read 'perm r from n'.

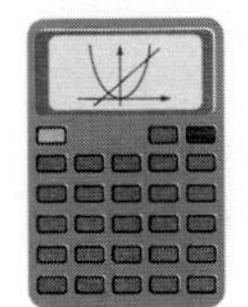

Locate the factorial function (!) on your calculator. Find if your calculator has the $^{n}P_{r}$ function and how to use it. It may be on a menu.

EXERCISE 3.3

1 **a** Calculate:
(i) $6 \times 5 \times 4 \times 3 \times 2 \times 1$ (ii) $6!$ (iii) 6^2 (iv) 6^6 (v) 2^6
b Now compare the size of n^2, n^n, $n!$, 2^n when $n = 2, 3, 4, 5, 10$. Can you make any general conclusions?

2 Calculate $^{n}P_{r}$ using $\frac{n!}{(n-r)!}$ by cancelling,

e.g. $^{7}P_{3} = \frac{7!}{4!} = \frac{7 \times 6 \times 5 \times \cancel{4} \times \cancel{3} \times \cancel{2} \times \cancel{1}}{\cancel{4} \times \cancel{3} \times \cancel{2} \times \cancel{1}} = 7 \times 6 \times 5 = 210$

a $^{5}P_{2}$ **b** $^{10}P_{6}$ **c** $^{4}P_{1}$ **d** $^{35}P_{2}$

3 Six athletes run in a race. How many different results are possible? (Assume there are no ties.)

4 How many ways can a captain and vice-captain be chosen from a football team of 11?

5 Two volumes of *Encyclopaedia Europa* are missing from the set of ten. In how many ways can the remaining volumes be arranged on a shelf?

Counting methods – Combinations

In an arrangement the order of the objects is important, i.e. the arrangement ABCD is different from DCBA. When the order is not important, then clearly there is only one combination of four objects, i.e. the choice ABCD is identical to the choice DCBA and every other choice which combines A, B, C, D. Such a choice, when *order is unimportant*, is called a **combination**.
Now consider combinations in more detail. Consider choosing various combinations of the four letters A, B, C and D.

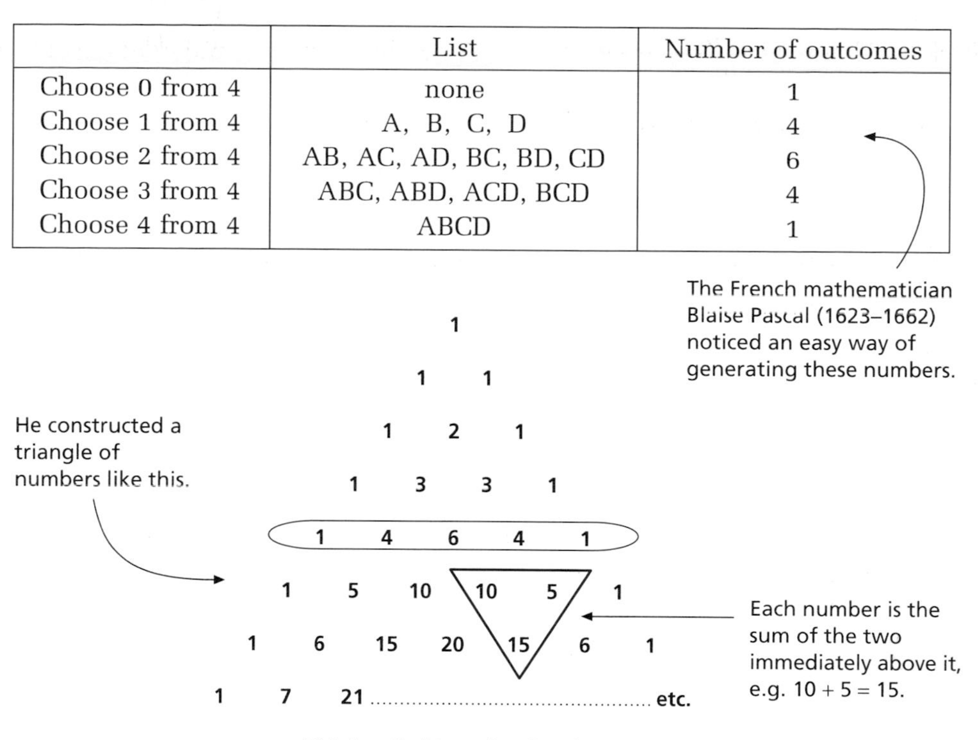

	List	Number of outcomes
Choose 0 from 4	none	1
Choose 1 from 4	A, B, C, D	4
Choose 2 from 4	AB, AC, AD, BC, BD, CD	6
Choose 3 from 4	ABC, ABD, ACD, BCD	4
Choose 4 from 4	ABCD	1

This is called **Pascal's triangle.**

Notice the fifth row, 1 4 6 4 1. It gives the number of outcomes when choosing 0 from 4, 1 from 4, 2 from 4, etc., from the table. A short way of writing 'the number of ways of choosing 2 from 4' is ${}^4C_2$ or $\binom{4}{2}$, so the fifth row shows $\binom{4}{0}\binom{4}{1}\binom{4}{2}\binom{4}{3}\binom{4}{4}$.

In general, the number of ways of choosing r from n different objects

or the number of combinations of r from n is ${}^nC_r$ or $\binom{n}{r}$.

From Pascal's triangle it can be seen that, for example,

$\binom{3}{2} = {}^3C_2 = 3$ (fourth (3 + 1) row, third (2 + 1) entry)

$\binom{5}{3} = {}^5C_3 = 10$ (sixth row, fourth entry)

EXERCISE 3.4

1 Complete the first 11 rows of Pascal's triangle. (Each number is the sum of the two immediately above it.) Use it to compute:

a ${}^2C_1$ **b** ${}^5C_1$ **c** ${}^7C_2$ **d** ${}^7C_5$ **e** ${}^{10}C_4$ **f** ${}^6C_6$ **g** ${}^{10}C_0$

2 How many ways can:

a three examination questions be chosen from seven?
b two CDs be selected from eight?
c eight books be chosen from ten on a reading list?
d four candidates be chosen from a list of nine?
e five photos be chosen from six?

Using counting methods

Although Pascal's triangle is a useful aid to computation, finding $^{15}C_5$ say, using it becomes unwieldly. Many scientific or graphic calculators will work it out directly using the ^nC_r function. However, if this function is not available, the alternative formula $^nC_r = \frac{n!}{(n-r)!r!}$ may be used, e.g. $^{15}C_5$ becomes $\frac{15!}{10!\ 5!}$

Notice the number of combinations of r from n different objects is the number of permutations of r from n divided by $r!$ (the $r!$ ways we can arrange r different objects are all equivalent to one combination), i.e. $^nC_r = \frac{^nP_r}{r!}$.

Example Donald deals the first four cards from a shuffled pack of cards.
Find: **a** P(no kings) **b** P(at least one king).

a The number of combinations or selections of four cards which are not kings = $^{48}C_4$

or $\frac{48!}{44!\ 4!}$ or $\frac{(48 \times 47 \times 46 \times 45 \times \cancel{44} \times \cancel{43} \times \cancel{42} \times \cancel{41} \times \ldots)}{(\cancel{44} \times \cancel{43} \times \cancel{42} \times \cancel{41} \times \ldots) \times (4 \times 3 \times 2 \times 1)}$

The number of combinations or selections of any four cards = $^{52}C_4$

or $\frac{52!}{48!\ 4!}$ or $\frac{(52 \times 51 \times 50 \times 49 \times \cancel{48} \times \cancel{47} \times \cancel{46} \times \cancel{45} \times \ldots)}{(\cancel{48} \times \cancel{47} \times \cancel{46} \times \cancel{45} \times \ldots) \times (4 \times 3 \times 2 \times 1)}$

$$\text{P(no kings)} = \frac{\text{number of selections with no kings}}{\text{number of selections of any four cards}} = \frac{^{48}C_4}{^{52}C_4} = 0.719$$

b P(at least one king) = 1 – 0.719 = 0.281

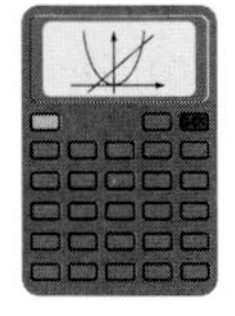

Find if your calculator has the ^nC_r function and how to use it. It may be on a menu.

EXERCISE 3.5

1 Use the ^nC_r and ^nP_r functions on your calculator (or use alternative formulas) to calculate:

a $^5C_4$ **b** $^8C_3$ **c** $^7P_2$ **d** $^7P_5$

e $^{20}C_4$ **f** $^4P_4$ **g** $^{11}P_0$

2 Three tracks are chosen from 11 on a CD. How many selections (combinations) are possible?

3 Three tracks are chosen from 11 on a CD. How many permutations (arrangements) are possible?

Reminder

Order unimportant: selection or combination

Order matters: arrangement or permutation

4 How many different totals can be made with exactly three coins from this selection?

5 Find the number of different hands when seven cards are dealt from an ordinary pack of 52 cards.

6 Find the number of different hands which contain four spades when seven cards are dealt from an ordinary pack of 52 cards. (Hint: hand must also contain three cards which are not spades.)

7 **a** How many ways can (i) four (ii) three different objects be arranged?
b If three of four objects are identical, how many arrangements of these four can be made?

Note Question 7 illustrates the fact that, generally, the number of arrangements of n objects, of which r are identical, is $\dfrac{n!}{r!}$

8 How many different totals can be made with exactly three coins from this selection?

9 Tamsin cannot decide which three courses to choose to complete her university applications. Her choice is from five Science and two Business Studies courses. She wants two Science and one Business Studies. How many ways can she choose: **a** the two Science courses **b** the Business Studies course **c** the two Science courses and one Business Studies course?

10 An investor chose to buy three shares at random from a list of 20. Find:
a P(his three share selections were the top three performers on the list)
b P(his three share selections were all in the top ten on the list).

11 Twelve fruit trees were planted in a field as shown in the diagram. Three trees were hit at random by a mystery virus. Find the probability that the three affected trees are:
a all in the same row
b all in the same column.

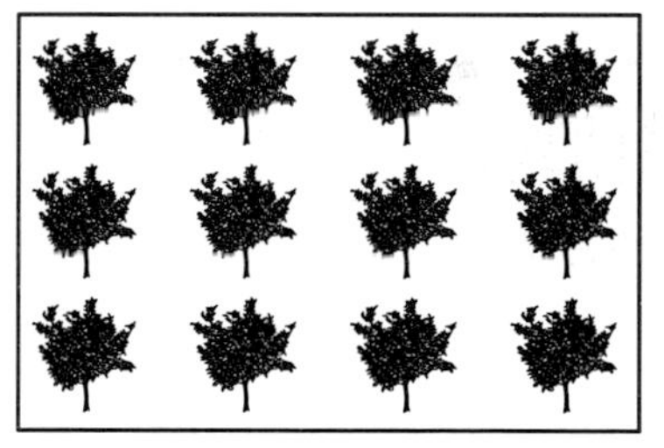

12 A customs officer searches at random 10% of the vehicles disembarking from a cross-Channel ferry. It is known that three vehicles on the ferry are carrying drugs. Two hundred vehicles are disembarking altogether. Find:
a P(customs officer doesn't search any of the offending vehicles)
b P(customs officer searches at least one of the offending vehicles).

Combining events

In many statistical investigations the probability of two or more combined events is required. It is often easier to visualise a problem using a **Venn diagram** which is helpful in seeing how the events relate to each other. The sample space is represented as a rectangle and the events are represented as shapes inside. For example, consider various events which may be of interest when a die is thrown.

A = {even numbers} = {2, 4, 6}
B = {odd numbers} = {1, 3, 5}
C = {prime numbers} = {2, 3, 5}

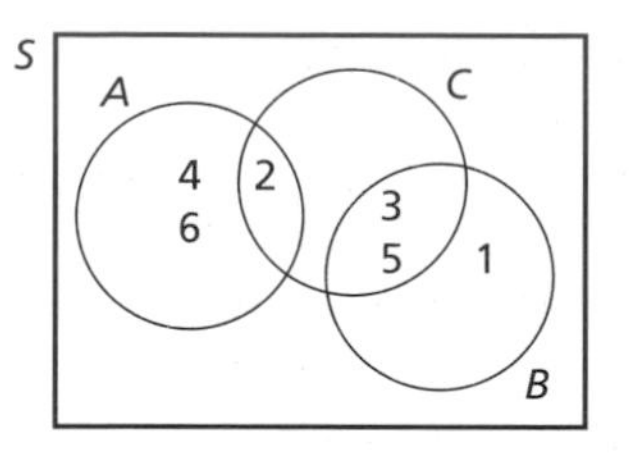

If two or more events can never happen together then they are called **mutually exclusive** events. These events have no outcomes in common.

The Venn diagram shows A and B are mutually exclusive, since if the outcome is even it cannot be odd.

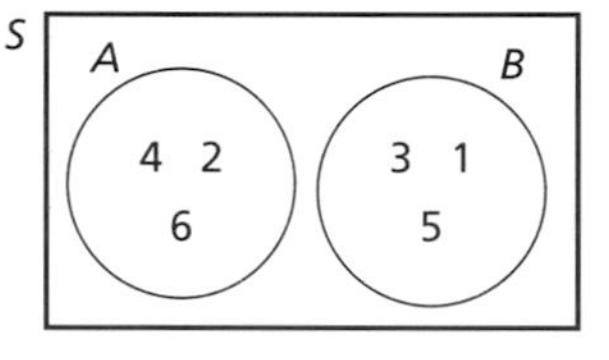

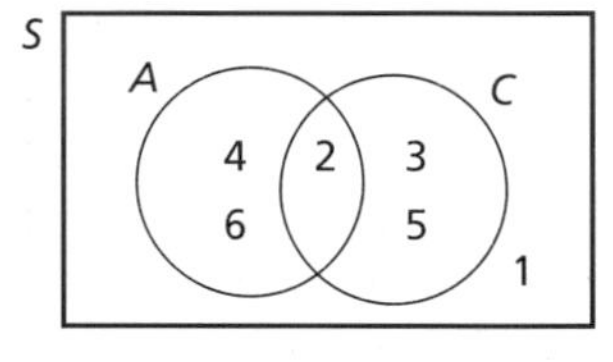

A and C are not mutually exclusive, since the outcome {2} is in both events.

If one event contains certain outcomes in a sample space, then the event which contains all the other outcomes in the sample space and no others is called the **complementary** event. The complement of event E is the event $\overline{E}$, or E', and is read 'not E'.

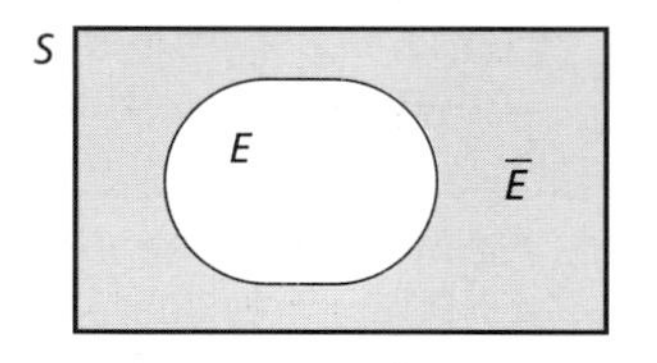

For the above events,

- A and B are complementary, since outcomes not in A are all in B.
- A and C are not complementary, since the outcome {1} is in neither event and, as well as this, the outcome {2} is in both.

If two or more events combine to form the complete sample space then they are called **exhaustive** events. In the Venn diagram X and Y are exhaustive, but X and Z are not. Exhaustive events are not necessarily mutually exclusive. For the above events, A and B are exhaustive, A and C are not, but A, B, C are.

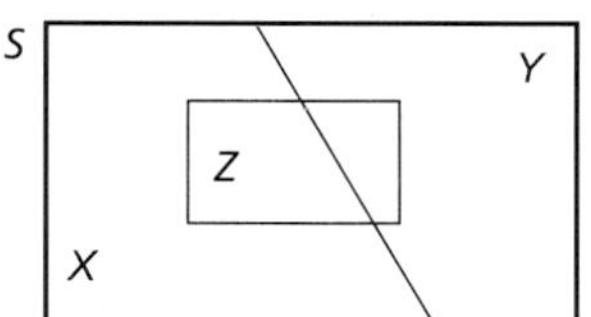

EXERCISE 3.6

1 **a** A die is rolled. Are the events 'square' and 'prime':
(i) mutually exclusive (ii) exhaustive
(iii) complementary?

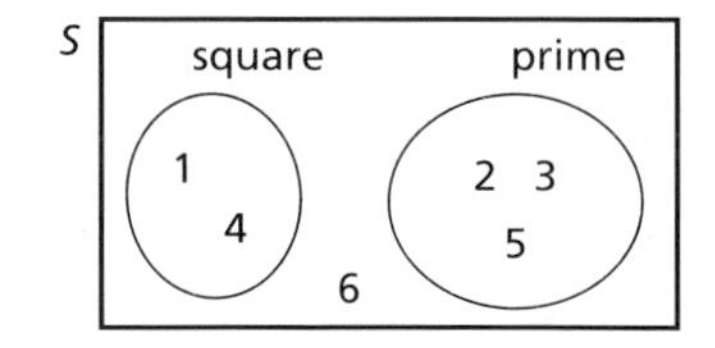

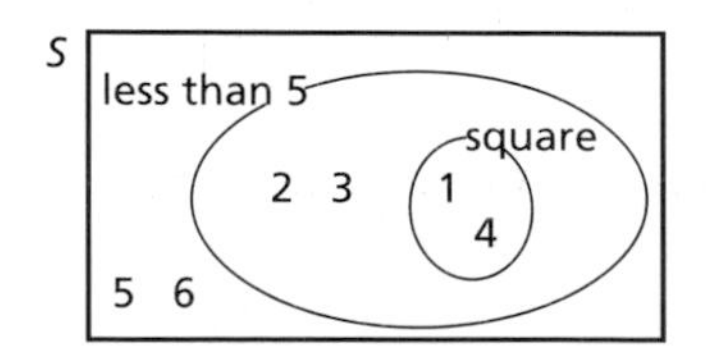

b Repeat **a** for the following events: 'square' and 'less than 5'.

2 If the sample space = {52 cards of a normal pack}, consider the events:
A = {a king}, B = {an ace}, C = {a red card}, D = {a black card}.

a Which of the following are mutually exclusive?
(i) A, B (ii) A, D (iii) C, D (iv) A, B, C

b Which of the following are complementary?
(i) A, B (ii) A, D (iii) C, D (iv) B, C

c Which of the following are exhaustive?
(i) A, B (ii) A, D (iii) C, D (iv) B, C

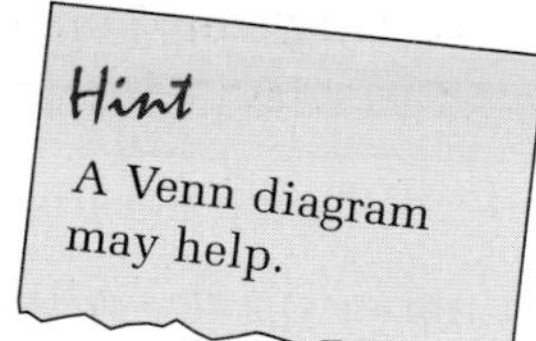

3 A survey was conducted in a school to find the number of cars per family. The responses ranged from 0 to 4 cars. The following events are of interest:

A = the family runs at least 2 cars B = the family runs 0 cars
C = the family runs less than 3 cars D = the family runs 1 car

a Describe in words the event (i) not A (ii) $\overline{C}$.
b Draw a Venn diagram to represent the events A, B, C and D.
c List pairs of events which are mutually exclusive.
d Select (i) any two (ii) any three events which are exhaustive.

4 The diagram represents three events A, B, C within a sample space S. Which of these events are: **a** mutually exclusive **b** not mutually exclusive?

5 Draw a Venn diagram which shows three mutually exclusive events within a sample space. How would the diagram be changed if the events were both mutually exclusive and exhaustive?

6 The diagram represents three events A, B, C within a sample space S. Which of the events $\overline{A}$, $\overline{B}$, $\overline{C}$ are:
a mutually exclusive
b not mutually exclusive
c exhaustive?

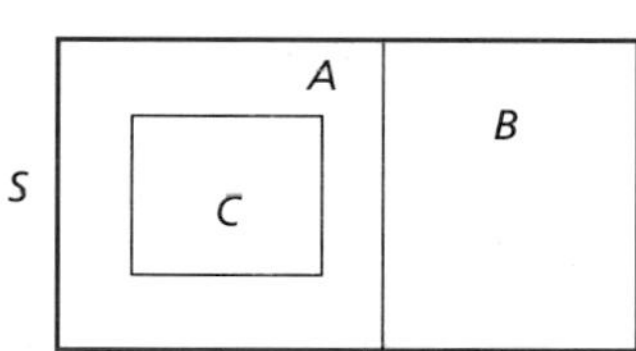

7 An integer n is chosen at random. Find:
a P(n is even) **b** P(n is odd) **c** P(n is divisible by 4)
d P(n is divisible by 5) **e** P(n is not divisible by 4) **f** P(n is not divisible by 5)

The Addition Law

Consider the following example. An engineering manufacturer produces washers in batches of 100. As part of a quality assurance programme, 250 of these batches are inspected for defective items with the following results:

Number of defectives	0	1	2	3	4	5	6	
Number of batches	112	118	12	5	2	0	1	Total = 250

A batch is selected at random. By definition,

P(batch has 0 defectives) $= \dfrac{112}{250}$ or 0.448, P(batch has 1 defective) $= \dfrac{118}{250}$ or 0.472.

Now the batch is considered satisfactory if there is at most one defective,
i.e. satisfactory $\Rightarrow$ 0 defectives *or* 1 defective

and so P(batch is satisfactory) $= \dfrac{112 + 118}{250} = \dfrac{230}{250}$ or 0.92

but notice $0.448 + 0.472 = 0.92$
i.e. P(batch is satisfactory) = P(batch has 0 defectives) + P(batch has 1 defective).

So the probabilities of the individual events can be added to find the probability of the **combined event** '0 defectives or 1 defective'. Notice however that the event '0 defectives' and the event '1 defective' are mutually exclusive.
This example illustrates

the Addition Law for mutually exclusive events: $\mathrm{P}(A \text{ or } B) = \mathrm{P}(A) + \mathrm{P}(B)$.

However, now consider the following. A survey recorded the reading habits of 100 young people. Some results are shown in the table.

Reading preferences	Frequency
comics	54
newspapers	15
fighting fantasy	23
romance novels	46
classical novels	32
science fiction	52
none of these	21

Notice the total of the frequencies is greater than 100. Some young people obviously like to read more than one type of literature. After further enquiry it was found that 28 young people had recorded a liking for both romance and classical novels and so had been included in both counts. The event 'liking romance novels' and the event 'liking classical novels' are **not mutually exclusive**.

$$\text{P(likes romance novels)} = \frac{46}{100} = 0.46$$

$$\text{P(likes classical novels)} = \frac{32}{100} = 0.32$$

but $\text{P(likes romance or classical novels or both)} = \dfrac{46 + 32 - 28}{100} = \dfrac{50}{100} = 0.5 \neq 0.46 + 0.32$

so P(likes romance or classical novels or both)
$\neq$ P(likes romance novels) + P(likes classical novels).

The Addition Law fails because the events are not mutually exclusive! So when calculating probabilities using the Addition Law, first of all decide whether the events are mutually exclusive.

Note (i) $\mathrm{P}(A \text{ or } B) \geq$ the larger of $\mathrm{P}(A)$, $\mathrm{P}(B)$
(ii) when events are not mutually exclusive '**or**' means '**one or the other, or both**'.

EXERCISE 3.7A

1 Each star represents an equally likely outcome in S. A and B are events. Find $\mathrm{P}(A)$, $\mathrm{P}(B)$, and $\mathrm{P}(A \text{ or } B)$ using the Addition Law.

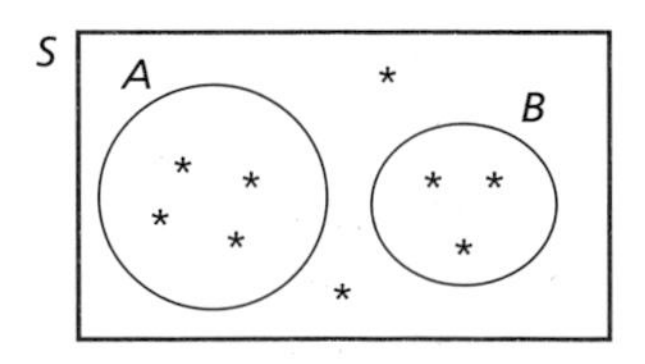

2 School leavers from a certain school went to particular destinations with the following probabilities:

P(going to higher education) = 0.35 P(going to further education) = 0.3

P(going to employment) = 0.15

Draw a Venn diagram to represent these events. Find:

a P(going into either higher or further education)

b P(not going to any of the above destinations).

3 A chef knows from long experience that when desserts are chosen, fruit salad, cheesecake, ice-cream or chocolate cake are chosen with the following probabilities:

P(fruit salad) = 0.25 P(cheesecake) = 0.18

P(ice-cream) = 0.37 P(chocolate cake) = 0.14

What is the probability that a person orders: **a** one of these **b** some other dessert?

4 In a marathon road race P(Nick wins) = 0.3, P(Greg wins) = 0.2, P(Chris wins) = 0.1. Find:

a P(either Nick or Greg wins) **b** P(neither Nick nor Greg nor Chris wins).

5 The probability that a football club will win is 0.5 and a draw or a defeat are equally likely. The team needs to win or draw to be top of the league. Find the probability that the team goes top.

6 Are X and Y mutually exclusive if:

a $P(X) = \frac{1}{6}$, $P(Y) = \frac{1}{5}$, $P(X \text{ or } Y) = \frac{11}{30}$ **b** $P(X) = 0.35$, $P(Y) = 0.55$, $P(X \text{ or } Y) = 0.8$

c $P(\overline{X} \text{ or } \overline{Y}) = 1$?

7 A sample space consists of four events A, B, C and D, one and only one of which can occur.

$P(A) = \frac{3}{8}$, $P(\text{not } B) = \frac{5}{6}$, and C and D are equally likely to happen.

Find: **a** $P(C)$ **b** $P(\text{not } D)$.

8 Each star represents an equally likely outcome in S. A and B are events.

a Find $P(A)$, $P(B)$, $P(A) + P(B)$.

b Now find $P(A \text{ or } B)$ and $P(A \text{ and } B)$ using

$$p = \frac{\text{number of outcomes in event}}{\text{total outcomes in } S}$$

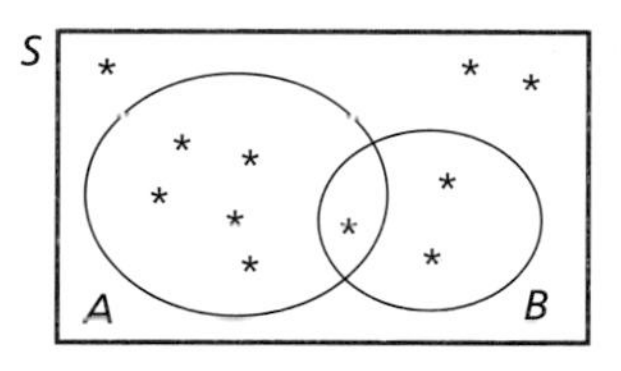

EXERCISE 3.7B

1 Twenty customers in a supermarket were asked if they preferred butter or butter substitute and the results are shown in the table below. Copy and complete the table.

	Butter	Butter substitute	Totals
Men	3	5	
Women	8	4	
Totals			20

One of the 20 customers is chosen at random. By considering the number of people in these events find:

a P(person is a man)

b P(person prefers butter)

c P(person is either a man or prefers butter).

d Why is answer **a** + answer **b** ≠ answer **c**?

e Now find P(person is both a man and prefers butter) and show that answer **a** + answer **b** – answer **e** = answer **c**.

Note Question 1 illustrates the **General Addition Law** that for *any* two events A, B:

$$P(A \text{ or } B) = P(A) + P(B) - P(A \text{ and } B).$$

Make use of the General Addition Law in the following questions. A Venn diagram may help.

2 A group of students, some doing degrees in Maths and others doing degrees in English, were asked about their hobbies. Of the 44 Maths students 13 gave music as a hobby, whereas of the 61 English students 34 gave music as a hobby. What is the probability that a student chosen at random from the group:
a did not give music as a hobby
b is an English student or gave music as a hobby?

3 At a particular time of year a doctor finds that she diagnoses stress on average once in every five patients but both flu and stress on average once in every 20 patients. On average three patients in every five are diagnosed with neither of these ailments. Find the probability of being diagnosed with: **a** either flu or stress **b** flu **c** stress but not flu.

The Multiplication Law

A person is chosen at random from the delegates at an international statistics conference. What is the probability that the person chosen is *both* female *and* British? This time the events female and British must both occur. There are many situations where the probability that both of two events happen is of interest. Can this sort of probability be found easily?

First, consider the following problem. I have two bags of sweets, both containing two pear and six orange flavoured sweets. On a hike I dip my hand into the first bag for a sweet, then some time later I take a sweet from the second bag. If I didn't look as I was choosing, what is the probability that I selected two pear sweets?

As before, a table could be drawn to display the 64 possible outcomes, four of which give two pear sweets. So P(pear from both bags)
$= \frac{4}{64}$ or $\frac{1}{16}$
but P(pear from first bag)
$= \frac{2}{8}$ or $\frac{1}{4}$
and P(pear from second bag)
$= \frac{2}{8}$ or $\frac{1}{4}$
and notice $\frac{1}{4} \times \frac{1}{4} = \frac{1}{16}$

2nd bag / 1st bag								
	✘	✘	✘	✘	✘	✘	✘	✘
	✘	✘	✘	✘	✘	✘	✘	✘
	✘	✘	✘	✘	✘	✘	✘	✘
	✘	✘	✘	✘	✘	✘	✘	✘
	✘	✘	✘	✘	✘	✘	✘	✘
	✘	✘	✘	✘	✘	✘	✘	✘
	✘	✘	✘	✘	✘	✘	✔	✔
	✘	✘	✘	✘	✘	✘	✔	✔

This suggests that a quick way of finding the probability of choosing a pear sweet from both bags is to multiply the probability of choosing a pear sweet from the first bag by

the probability of choosing a pear sweet from the second bag. This is an illustration of the use of the **Multiplication Law**.
An alternative way of looking at this problem is to draw a **tree diagram** as follows:

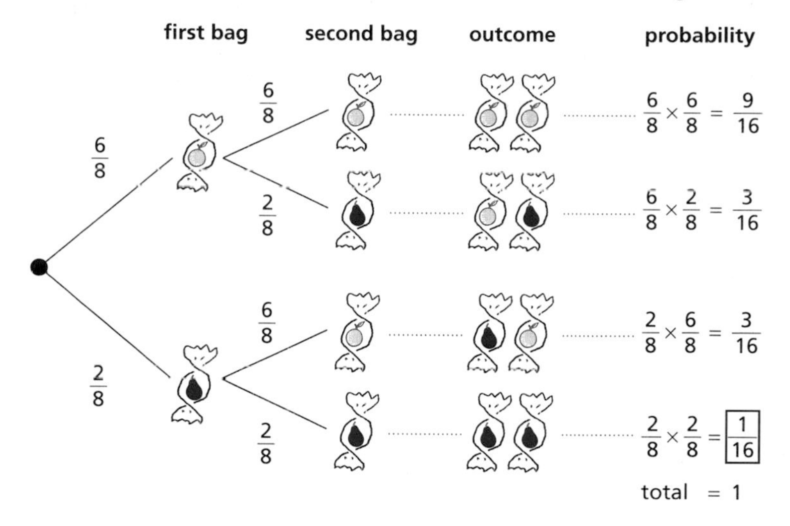

Notice the probability of each event is now displayed along a branch. The probability of each outcome is found by multiplying the probabilities along the branches. When the probabilities of all the possible outcomes are evaluated, their total is always 1.
However, consider a similar situation where I have only one bag of sweets. Is the probability of choosing two pear sweets still $\frac{1}{16}$?
Now, whereas when I have two bags the outcome of the first choice had no effect on the outcome of the second, when I only have one bag, the probability that the second sweet is a pear sweet clearly depends on my first choice. I only have seven sweets for my second choice and I may have one or two pear sweets left! Think carefully about the probabilities for my second choice. A tree diagram is again helpful in dealing with this problem.

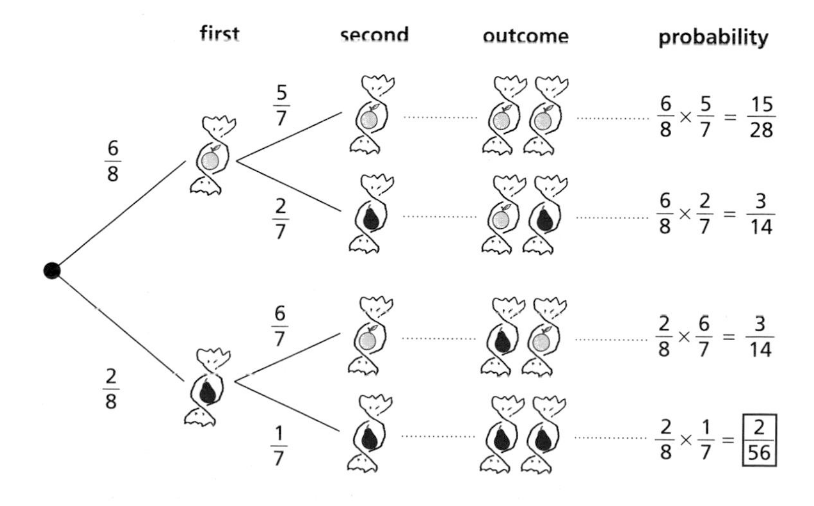

So the probability of choosing two pear sweets is now $\frac{2}{56}$.

In this second case the two events choosing a pear sweet are **not independent**, i.e. **the occurrence of the first event affects the occurrence of the second event**. In summary, we should take care when using the Multiplication Law.
If the **independence of *A* from *B*** can be assumed, i.e. the occurrence of A does not affect the occurrence of B, then

the Multiplication Law for independent events $P(A \text{ and } B) = P(A) \times P(B)$

can be used.
If the outcome of event A does affect the probability of the possible outcomes of event B then the Multiplication Law would have to be modified using a different argument.

Example 1 A roulette wheel has 38 numbers of which 18 are red, 18 are black and 2 are green. A gambler bets red on three successive plays of the wheel. What is the probability that the gambler wins on each of the three plays?
Let A = event that ball lands on red on the first play.
Let B = event that ball lands on red on the second play.
Let C = event that ball lands on red on the third play.
Since we can assume the events are independent (the roulette wheel cannot 'remember' the result of a previous play), $P(A) = P(B) = P(C) = \frac{18}{38}$ or 0.474
so $P(A \text{ and } B \text{ and } C) = P(A) \times P(B) \times P(C) = \frac{18}{38} \times \frac{18}{38} \times \frac{18}{38} = 0.106$

Example 2 Jamie draws a card from a pack, replaces it and shuffles the pack. He continues the process until he draws an ace. What is the chance he has to make exactly four draws?

Now on each and every draw, $P(\text{ace}) = \frac{4}{52}$ or $\frac{1}{13}$ so $P(\text{no ace}) = \frac{12}{13}$

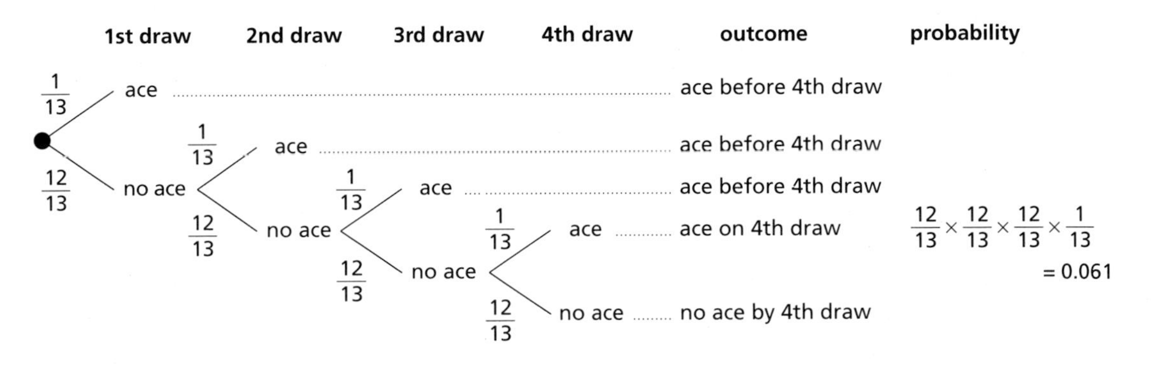

P(makes exactly four draws to get an ace) = 0.061
Note (i) $P(A \text{ and } B) \leq$ the smaller of $P(A)$, $P(B)$
(ii) 'with replacement' leaves probabilities unchanged in successive trials; 'without replacement' changes probabilities in successive trials.

EXERCISE 3.8A

1 Usman tosses a coin five times. What is the probability that:
a he gets five heads **b** he does not get five heads?

2 If the probability that a person is right-handed is $\frac{6}{7}$ and has blond hair is $\frac{1}{5}$, and assuming independence, find the probability that someone chosen at random:
   a is right-handed and has blond hair
   b is right-handed but does not have blond hair.

3 G is the event 'the flight from Geneva is late' and E is the event 'the flight from Edinburgh is late'. P(G) = 0.05 and P(E) = 0.04 and G and E are independent events. Find P(G and E). Why might G and E not be independent?

4 A die is thrown twice. Find the probability that neither throw gives a six.

5 One year the odds for snow on Christmas Day were quoted as 20 to 1 against. This means P(snow on Christmas Day) = $\frac{1}{21}$. Similarly the odds for high winds are 5 to 1 against.
   a Would it be reasonable to assume these are mutually exclusive events? Why?
   b Would it be reasonable to assume independence for these events? Why?
   c Calculate: (i) P(no snow on Christmas Day) (ii) P(no high winds on Christmas Day).

6 In a large batch of silicon chips, 8% are known to be defective.
   a Find P(chip chosen at random is not defective).
   b A sample of ten chips is taken at random and tested. Find P(all the chips are good).

7 P(Andrea gets an offer of a university place to study Law) = 0.8.
   P(Charlotte gets an offer of a university place to study Medicine) = 0.6.
   Assuming independence, find:
   a P(both Andrea and Charlotte receive these offers)
   b P(neither Andrea nor Charlotte receives these offers).

EXERCISE 3.8B

1 The relative frequencies with which different types of vehicle pass along a certain stretch of motorway during a one-hour period are shown in the table.

Type of vehicle	Relative frequency
car	0.33
lorry	0.31
coach	0.17
van	0.14
motorbike	0.05

   a Assuming independence of events, find:
      (i) P(three consecutive vehicles are lorries)
      (ii) P(in four consecutive vehicles, none are cars)
      (iii) P(two consecutive vehicles are either vans or motorbikes).
   b Why might the events not be independent?

2 David, an avid stamp collector, has made a database of successful bids at previous postal stamp auctions. He can estimate, from the database, the probability of being successful in bidding for a stamp at the reserve price. For a Ugandan stamp, he estimates the probability of success is $\frac{2}{3}$, but for a Kenyan stamp, he estimates the probability of success is $\frac{2}{5}$. At the next auction, David places bids for both a Kenyan and a Ugandan stamp and will try at a second auction if he is unsuccessful with either bid. Find:
   a P(David is successful with both bids in the first auction)
   b P(David is successful with the bid for the Ugandan stamp, but unsuccessful with the Kenyan stamp in the first auction)
   c P(David has successfully bid for both stamps by the end of the second auction).

3 Use a tree diagram to find the probability of dealing a 'pontoon' (an ace with a king, queen, jack or ten) when a hand of two cards is dealt.

More practice on calculating probabilities

We have seen that a probability may be found using a variety of techniques. Some problems are best solved using combinations of these techniques, e.g. tree diagrams, the Addition Rule, the Multiplication Rule.

Example The probabilities that Paul, Jenny and John pass a particular exam are respectively 0.95, 0.85, 0.75. Assuming independence, find the probability that:

a exactly two out of the three pass the exam

b at least one of them passes the exam.

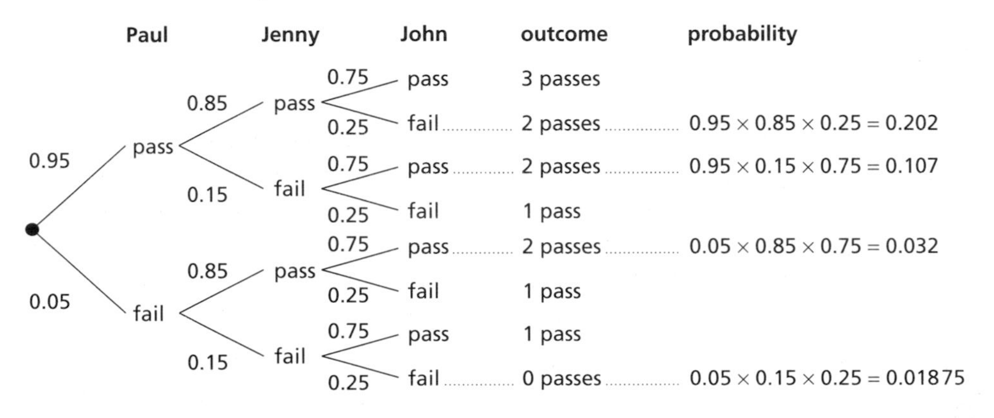

a P(two out of three pass the exam) $= 0.202 + 0.107 + 0.032 = 0.341$

b It can often be easier to calculate $P(\overline{E})$ in order to calculate $P(E)$.

P(at least one of them passes) $= 1 - $ P(none of them passes)

$= 1 - 0.018\,75 = 0.981\,25$

EXERCISE 3.9B

1 In a certain maternity unit, for a birth chosen at random P(girl) = 0.49.

a Find P(boy).

b For two consecutive births, find (i) P(2 girls) (ii) P(boy and girl, in either order).

2 In a two-car family, the chance that the big car breaks down is 0.05 while for the small car it is 0.25. At any one time, what are the chances that exactly one car has broken down?

3 In a raffle draw, pink tickets are in one bag and blue tickets are in another identical bag. One hundred tickets of each colour were sold, numbered 1 to 100. The celebrity guest first chooses a bag, then chooses a ticket. Find the probability that he chooses a single-digit, blue ticket.

4 On his business trips, an engineer takes the plane with probability 0.3, the train with probability 0.1 and a car with probability 0.6. During May, the engineer makes two business trips. Assuming events are independent, find the probability that:

a both his trips are by plane

b neither are by car

c at least one trip is by train.

5 Two friends, Jane and Louise, go to hire ski boots. They both wear the same size boot. Four pairs of boots of the appropriate size are available. One pair is soaking wet inside from the previous day. Find the probability that:

a neither of them is given the wet pair **b** one of them is given the wet pair.

6 Simon draws a card from a pack, replaces it and shuffles the pack. He continues the process until he draws an ace. What is the chance he has to make:

a at most three draws **b** at least three draws?

Simon now decides to deal face up until he deals an ace. What is the chance he deals:

c at most three draws **d** at least three draws?

7 In a show jumping competition, the chances that each of three riders completes a clear round are $\frac{1}{2}, \frac{2}{3}, \frac{3}{4}$ respectively. Find the probability that:

a only one of them completes a clear round

b there is at least one clear round.

Simulation

Various ways of calculating probabilities have been considered, but some problems are not easily solved using these methods – diagrams get too complicated, the laws don't seem to apply. An alternative method is to *simulate* the outcomes of a random experiment using a sequence of *random numbers.* These can be produced in various mechanical ways: rolling dice, tossing coins, using a ten-sided spinner, shaking and drawing numbered discs from a hat, using a lottery machine, and so on.

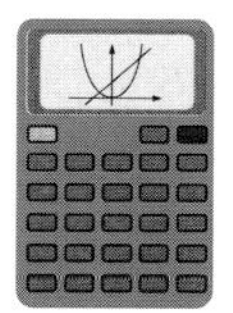

Most scientific calculators can produce 'random numbers'. Look for something like ' rand #', or 'random' which may be on a menu. (If your calculator doesn't have this facility you can use tables of random digits.) Thus we could produce a sequence of decimal numbers between 0 and 1 similar to these:

0.976 0.829 0.018 0.679 0.660 0.599 0.353 0.545 0.104 0.363 ...

(With tables there may be no decimal points.)

Example 1 Simulate rolling two dice and noting the total score.

Ignoring any 0 or number greater than 6, the above list gives the sequence:

	62	16	66	53	53	54	51	43	63	...
So the total scores for two dice are:	8	7	12	8	8	9	6	7	9	...

Notice that lots of digits are thrown away using this method.

A graphics calculator can be more efficient than this.

6 rand # EXE .... gives random numbers between 0 and 6

6 rand # +1 EXE .... gives random numbers between 1 and 7

Int (6 rand # +1) EXE ... gives the whole number part of random numbers between 1 and 7, i.e. the numbers 1, 2, 3, 4, 5 or 6.

Example 2 Simulate the results of an experiment where two coins are tossed 20 times.

A calculator produced the following 20 pairs of random numbers.

0.150, 0.160	0.838, 0.109	0.103, 0.619	0.096, 0.362	0.340, 0.402
0.802, 0.866	0.558, 0.288	0.594, 0.479	0.084, 0.907	0.823, 0.396
0.597, 0.982	0.993, 0.086	0.076, 0.497	0.720, 0.418	0.596, 0.216
0.647, 0.315	0.445, 0.320	0.942, 0.541	0.353, 0.706	0.257, 0.815

$0 \le n < 0.5$ represents the outcome {head}, $0.5 \le n < 1$ represents the outcome {tail} giving:

2H	H&T	H&T	2H	2H	2T	H&T	H&T	H&T	H&T
2T	H&T	2H	H&T	H&T	H&T	2H	2T	H&T	H&T

Summary: 5 2Hs, 3 2Ts, 12 H&Ts.

The results of this simulation are not in exact agreement with the proportions predicted by the theoretical probabilities (the same number of double heads as tails might have been expected).

Example 3 Estimate the probability that in a sequence of six digits, there are consecutive digits which are the same.

Sixty groups of six digits are generated, where the digits are 0 to 9.

636680 √	574051	243762	476312	191073	353302 √
614103	952326	241895	232975	262726	517448 √
446740 √	637003 √	317142	399476 √	637218	375253
568486	428012	330641 √	950155 √	724765	494053
203117 √	640511 √	685911 √	362546	815764	889011 √
870981	359729	066234 √	280618	749177 √	867387
756747	726940	559004 √	651117 √	360544 √	730576
320122	√629245	474031	921599 √	891653	667966 √
994235 √	898711 √	893761	529764	389337 √	200171 √
664017 √	970541	621338 √	984302	416551 √	604333 √

$$\text{Estimate of P(consecutive digits the same)} = \frac{\text{number of ticks}}{\text{number of groups}} = \frac{27}{60} = 0.45.$$

(This set of results was generated by a spreadsheet package with a random number command, but could also have been generated with a calculator.) Some variation in the results of simulations should always be expected, but as the size of a simulation increases results become more reliable.

EXERCISE 3.10

1 Simulate 20 tosses of a coin using random numbers.

2 In a psychology experiment, a rat is equally likely to choose one of three exits to a box. Simulate the rat's behaviour in a series of ten trials.

3 A transport engineer observed the traffic flow at a set of four toll booths and wanted to simulate various conjectures. Simulate the choices made by the drivers of 20 vehicles arriving separately if:
   a each of the toll booths is equally likely to be chosen
   b the two centre booths are each twice as likely to be chosen as the outside ones.

4 In a bacterial population it has been observed that in a one-hour period each bacterium either dies or produces two offspring then dies. The probability of producing offspring in a one-hour period is 0.9. Simulate the growth of ten bacteria over a two-hour period, giving the size of your population after two hours.

5 Simulate 20 trials where five integers are chosen from the list 0, 1, 2, 3, 4 at random. Hence estimate the probability that the product of the five numbers is even. (Assume 0 is neither odd nor even.) If possible, compare your results with others in your class. Pool your results to get a better estimate. Can you *calculate* the probability that the product of the five numbers is even?

Simulating a game

A popular game involves rolling a die and collecting the parts of a beetle as indicated by the score on the die. The winner is the person who can draw a complete beetle in as few throws of the die as possible. The rules are:
The body must be drawn before any other part can be added.
The head must be drawn before the eyes or the feelers.

6 →	Body
5 →	Head
4 →	Tail
3 →	Feelers (two)
2 →	Legs (six)
1 →	Eyes (two)

Pose a question

On average, how many throws of the die will it take to complete the beetle?

Collect some data

Using a calculator, or otherwise, generate random whole numbers from 1 to 6 inclusive, representing scores when rolling a die. Note that hundreds of such numbers can be generated very quickly using a spreadsheet and these could be printed ahead of time. Play the beetle game using these random numbers and note how many random numbers you used to complete your beetle. Each member of the class should simulate the game a few times, noting the number of rolls of the die (random numbers used) to complete the beetle each time. Gather the results from each member of the class to make a larger set of results (the more the better, but about 50 should be enough).

Analyse the data

Analyse the results by drawing a dotplot, calculating an average and a measure of spread.

Interpret the results

Write a conclusion which answers the question posed and which includes an indication of the variability in your results.

Further study

Write a computer program which will simulate the beetle game many times and save the results in a file.
Investigate other simple games which use a die.

CHAPTER 3 REVIEW

1 A student notices that for 17 out of 20 dinner times she is tenth or later in her dinner queue. What is the probability that on one particular day she is among the first nine?

2 A coin is tossed and a die is thrown. Find:
  a P(either a head or a six)
  b P(both a head and a six).

3 The probability that Bruce goes to Edinburgh University is $\frac{3}{4}$ and to Newcastle University $\frac{1}{9}$. The probability that Angela goes to Edinburgh University is $\frac{3}{5}$.
  a Calculate the probabilities that:
    (i) Bruce and Angela both go to Edinburgh University
    (ii) Bruce will not go to either Edinburgh or Newcastle Universities.
  b What assumptions have you made?

4 A group of 5 is to be chosen from 6 fifth-year pupils and 8 sixth-year pupils to represent a school at a particular conference. Assuming each pupil is equally likely to be chosen, find the probability that the group is composed of 2 fifth-year and 3 sixth-year pupils.

5

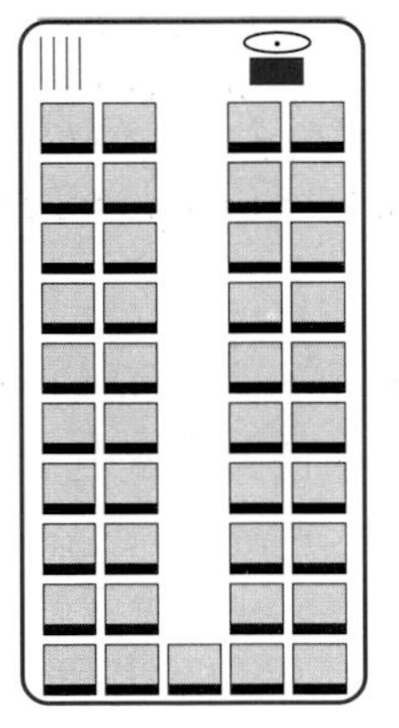

On a school trip, three passengers became travel sick on the coach. There were 41 passengers. If the sick passengers were seated at random on the coach, find the probability that they were all sitting in the back row.

6 In a particular department store, payment can be made by cash, cheque, debit card or storecard with probabilities 0.56, 0.23, 0.09 and 0.12 respectively. Find the probability that of the four people in front of you in the queue:
  a all pay by storecard
  b at least one person pays by cheque.

7 A statistics student who had a holiday job as a waiter recorded the orders of his first 100 customers. The information is displayed in the diagram.

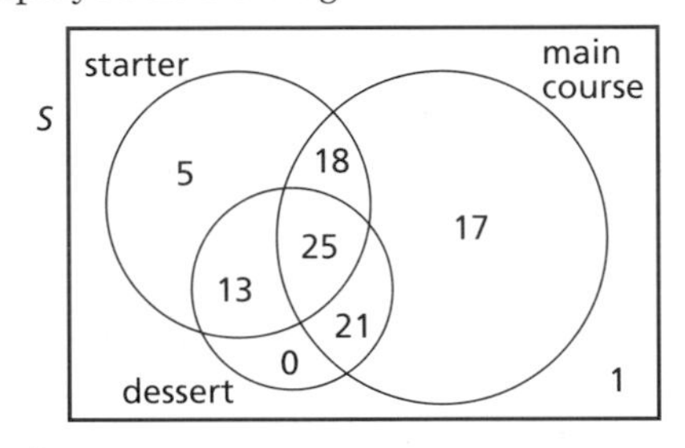

Find:
  a P(a starter was ordered)
  b P(a main course was ordered)
  c P(a dessert was ordered)
  d P(only a starter and a main course were ordered)
  e P(either a starter or a main course was ordered)
  f P(all three courses were ordered).

8 Simulate 20 trials where four integers are chosen from the list –2, –1, 0, 1, 2 at random. Hence estimate the probability that the product of the four numbers is positive. If possible, compare your results with others in your class. Pool your results to get a better estimate. Can you *calculate* the probability that the product of the four numbers is positive?

CHAPTER 3 SUMMARY

Random experiment
An experiment whose result cannot be predicted with certainty.

Sample space, S
List of all possible outcomes of a random experiment.

Event, E
One or more outcomes from S.

Complement of E, $\overline{E}$
The event containing all outcomes in S not in E (not E).

Probability of an event E, P(E)
The relative frequency of an event as the number of trials increases indefinitely,

or $P(E) = \dfrac{\text{number of outcomes in } E}{\text{number of outcomes in } S}$

provided each outcome is equally likely.

Basic properties of P(E)
$0 \le P(E) \le 1$
$P(E) = 0$ if E is impossible
$P(E) = 1$ if E is certain
$P(\overline{E}) = 1 - P(E)$

Counting methods
Number of combinations of r objects from n objects

$$\binom{n}{r} = {}^nC_r = \frac{n!}{(n-r)!r!}$$

Number of permutations of r objects from n objects

$${}^nP_r = \frac{n!}{(n-r)!}$$

Mutually exclusive events
Events that have no outcomes in common.

Addition Law
For mutually exclusive events, A, B:
$P(A \text{ or } B) = P(A) + P(B)$

Multiplication Law
For independent events, A, B:
$P(A \text{ and } B) = P(A) \times P(B)$
where independent events occur as a result of independent situations or experiments, or as a result of independent repetitions of the same experiment with the same conditions.

Simulation
Using random numbers to imitate the results of a random experiment.

4 Random Variables

What is a random variable?

When gathering information about a population, it is likely that the results of random experiments are recorded by counting or measuring some feature of a sample. For example, a quality control engineer is interested in controlling the production of a high precision bolt. He might take random samples of five and count how many were defective. The number of defectives would vary randomly (or unpredictably) from sample to sample and is therefore called a 'random variable'. Since he is counting, this random variable can only take 'discrete' values, i.e. 0, 1, 2, … 5.
However, if he had chosen a bolt at random and measured its length then because of the variation inherent in any production process the length of the bolt would also be a random variable, taking any value within a certain 'continuous' range.
So a **random variable** is defined to be **a quantity whose value depends on the outcome of a random experiment** and may be either **discrete** or **continuous**.
Random variables can be used, together with a knowledge of probability, to provide a 'model' for many kinds of data. If a satisfactory mathematical model can be found, it can often be used to make predictions. It is usual to name a random variable using capital letters and denote particular values of the random variable by the corresponding small letter. It is usually possible to define all the possible values of a random variable from its description.

Example 1 Name and give values for a random variable which counts the number of sixes when a die is thrown three times in a random experiment.

S = number of sixes in three throws of a die.
$s = 0, 1, 2$ or 3.

Example 2 Name and give values for a random variable which counts the number of driving tests taken until a pass is achieved for a learner driver chosen at random.

T = number of tests taken until a pass is achieved.
$t = 1, 2, 3, \ldots$ and is potentially infinite!

Example 3 Name and give possible values for a random variable which measures the weight of live newborn babies chosen at random from hospital records.

W = weight of babies in kilograms to the nearest gram.
w takes any value in the interval $0.500 \le w \le 6.000$.
(Live birth weights are not observed outside this interval.)

Notice a discrete random variable is usually a count, whereas a continuous random variable is likely to be a measurement.

EXERCISE 4.1

1 Name and give possible values for a random variable representing:

a the total score when two dice are thrown

b the number of sixes when n dice are thrown

c the number of sales made by a car salesman with five different customers chosen at random who visited a garage in a week

d the time taken in minutes for movement between school classes at period changeover of a randomly chosen pupil

e the height of 16-year-olds in metres to the nearest centimetre.

2 Say whether the following random variables are discrete with a finite number of values, discrete with an infinite number of values, or continuous.

a R = the number of cracked eggs in a box of half-a-dozen

b T = the time between successive trains at a particular junction

c L = the number of lottery tickets bought until a person wins the jackpot (in theory!)

d F = the percentage of fat in samples of yoghurt

e S = the score out of 10 given to a wine chosen at random by a taster at a wine tasting.

Discrete random variables

To make use of a random variable it is necessary to know not only the values that the random variable can take, but in some way to allocate probabilities to these values. As different techniques are used when the random variable is discrete to that when it is continuous, it will now be necessary to consider each type separately.
Associated with each value of a discrete random variable is its probability of occurrence. For example, if T = the number of tails when a coin is tossed twice, then $t = 0$, 1 or 2 and we could calculate the probability associated with any of these values, e.g.

$P(T = 0)$ = probability that there are no tails (or P(0) for short) $= \frac{1}{2} \times \frac{1}{2} = \frac{1}{4}$

The probabilities of occurrence of each and every value of the random variable form its **probability distribution** and may be written in a table. Thus the probability distribution for T is given by:

t	0	1	2
$P(T = t)$	$\frac{1}{4}$	$\frac{1}{2}$	$\frac{1}{4}$

(Can you see why $P(T = 1)$ is $\frac{1}{2}$ and $P(T = 2)$ is $\frac{1}{4}$?)

Notice that: (i) each probability value is between 0 and 1
(ii) the sum of the probabilities in a probability distribution must always be 1 since the random variable must take one of its values.
So for a discrete random variable D whose probability distribution is given by

d	d_1	d_2	d_3	...	d_n	total
$P(D = d)$	p_1	p_2	p_3	...	p_n	1

$$0 \le p_i \le 1, \quad \Sigma p_i = p_1 + p_2 + \ldots + p_n = 1$$

The probability distribution of a random variable may be derived from:

- basic probability rules
- considering relative frequencies of experimental data
- a formula, as long as the conditions, $0 \leq p_i \leq 1$, $\Sigma p_i = p_1 + p_2 + \ldots + p_n = 1$, hold.

Example 1 Find the probability distribution for the random variable X which represents the number of girls in a three-child family chosen at random when P(girl) = 0.49.

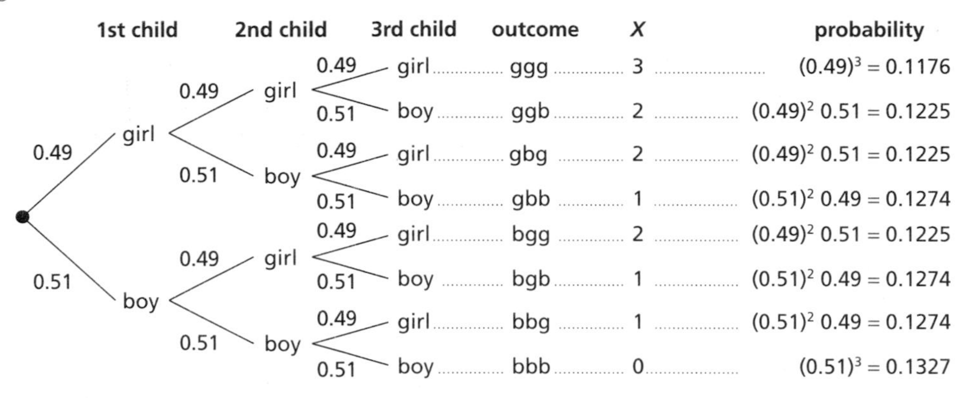

So the probability distribution (given to 3 decimal places) is:

x	0	1	2	3	
$P(X = x)$	0.133	3(0.1274) = 0.382	3(0.1225) = 0.367	0.118	check total = 1

Example 2 Records of delivery times in days of 2000 first class letters in Statland are shown in the frequency table.

No. of days	1	2	3	4	5	6
Frequency	1800	100	40	30	20	10

Assuming that this *sample* is representative of the *population* of first class letters, find:

a the probability distribution of the random variable D, number of days taken for a first class letter to be delivered in Statland

b P(a first class letter does not arrive on the first day after posting)

c P(a first class letter takes no longer than three days)

d P(a first class letter takes longer than six days).

a Assume the relative frequencies become the probabilities:

d	1	2	3	4	5	6	
$P(D = d)$	$\frac{1800}{2000}$	$\frac{100}{2000}$	$\frac{40}{2000}$	$\frac{30}{2000}$	$\frac{20}{2000}$	$\frac{10}{2000}$	check total
or	0.9	0.05	0.02	0.015	0.01	0.005	= 1

b $P(D > 1) = 1 - P(1) = 1 - 0.9 = 0.1$

c $P(D \leq 3) = P(1) + P(2) + P(3) = 0.9 + 0.05 + 0.02 = 0.97$

d $P(D > 6) = 0$ (since $0.9 + 0.05 + 0.02 + 0.015 + 0.01 + 0.005 = 1$)

Example 3 The probability distribution of a discrete random variable D is given by the following formula:

$$P(D = d) = \begin{cases} 0.5 & \text{if } d = 1 \\ kd & \text{if } d = 2, 3 \\ 0 & \text{otherwise} \end{cases}$$

a Find the value of k.
b Find $P(D > 2)$.
c Illustrate the probability distribution using a bar diagram.

Now the probability distribution is

d	1	2	3
$P(D = d)$	0.5	$2k$	$3k$

So

a $0.5 + 2k + 3k = 1$

$5k = 0.5$

$k = 0.1$

b $P(D > 2) = P(3) = 3k = 0.3$

c

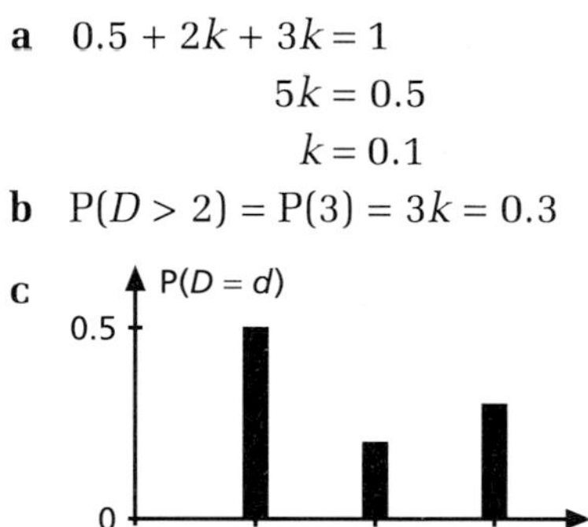

This diagram emphasises the discrete nature of the distribution.

EXERCISE 4.2A

1 Which of these tables could possibly describe the probability distribution of a random variable?

a

x	1	2	3
$P(X = x)$	0.1	0.4	0.2

b

y	1	2	5
$P(Y = y)$	0.3	0.5	0.2

c

i	0	1
$P(I = i)$	0.5	0.5

d

r	0	10	20
$P(R = r)$	0.1	1.1	0.2

2 Two dice are rolled. If T = total score in this random experiment, find the probability distribution of T and show it in a bar diagram.

3 A random variable D has a probability distribution given by:

d	0	1	2	3	4	5	6	7	8	9
$P(D = d)$	0.05	0.05	0.1	0.1	0.15	0.15	0.2	0.1	0.05	0.05

Find: **a** $P(D < 2)$ **b** $P(3 \leq D \leq 7)$ **c** $P(D \geq 6)$ **d** $P(D \geq 2)$.

4 A random variable R has a probability distribution given by:
Find: **a** k **b** $P(R \leq 3)$.

r	1	2	3	4
$P(R = r)$	k	$4k$	$9k$	$16k$

5 A turn in a game consists of rolling a die. If a six appears, the die is rolled once more. Find the probability distribution of S = total score of a turn taken at random.

EXERCISE 4.2B

1 In a particular school, records show that the number of Standard Grades achieved by each pupil in fourth year at Credit level has the following frequency distribution:

Number of Standard Grades	0	1	2	3	4	5	6	7	8
Frequency	12	15	19	24	30	25	23	20	12

a Assuming that records are representative of the school population, find the probability distribution of S, the number of Standard Grades achieved by a pupil chosen at random from fourth year at this particular school.

b Calculate $P(2 < S < 4)$ and $P(2 \le S \le 4)$.

2 A soap powder manufacturer conducts experiments to see how many washes are required until a garment is clean. Let W = number of washes until a heavily soiled garment is clean, and

$$P(W = w) = \begin{cases} k(5 - w) & \text{for } w = 1, 2, 3, 4 \\ 0.01 & \text{for } w = 5 \\ 0 & \text{for } w > 5 \end{cases}$$

Find k and tabulate the actual values of the probability distribution of W.

3 A spectator who has no knowledge of the three horses (A, B and C) in a race tries to place them in winning order before a race. Find the probability distribution of D, the number of horses correctly placed on the list after the race.

4 In families where neither mother nor father are colour blind, but the mother is a carrier of colour blindness, the probability that a son is colour blind is 0.5. In families of four sons, find the probability distribution of S, the number of sons who are colour blind, and illustrate the probability distribution in a bar diagram.

The mean or expected value of a discrete random variable

Consider again the sample of 2000 letters delivered in Statland.

No. of days	1	2	3	4	5	6
Frequency	1800	100	40	30	20	10

To find a representative value of the distribution of delivery times of first class letters, the mean of the *sample*, $\bar{x}$, can be calculated:

$$\bar{x} = \frac{\Sigma fx}{\Sigma f} = \frac{(1800 \times 1) + (100 \times 2) + (40 \times 3) + (30 \times 4) + (20 \times 5) + (10 \times 6)}{2000} = \frac{2400}{2000} = 1.2 \text{ days}$$

Now consider how to find the mean of the random variable D, the number of days taken for a first class letter to arrive, whose distribution is:

d	1	2	3	4	5	6
$P(D = d)$	0.9	0.05	0.02	0.015	0.01	0.005

Take each value of D and 'weight' it according to its chance of occurrence thus:

$$(0.9 \times 1) + (0.05 \times 2) + (0.02 \times 3) + (0.015 \times 4) + (0.01 \times 5) + (0.005 \times 6) = 1.2$$

$$\left(\text{or } \frac{1800}{2000} \times 1 + \frac{100}{2000} \times 2 + \frac{40}{2000} \times 3 + \frac{30}{2000} \times 4 + \frac{20}{2000} \times 5 + \frac{10}{2000} \times 6\right)$$

Now in this case the result is identical to the sample mean, which is to be expected since the probabilities were assumed to be precisely the relative frequencies which were used in the sample mean calculation. However, this result is actually the **distribution mean**, also called the **population mean.**

So to find the mean of a random variable, the same process is used as finding the mean of a sample of observations except that each relative frequency is replaced by a probability.

In general the mean or expected value of a discrete random variable D is denoted by $E(D)$ or μ. When the probability distribution of D is

d	d_1	d_2	$d_3 \ldots$	d_n
$P(D = d)$	p_1	p_2	$p_3 \ldots$	p_n

the mean is given by $E(D) = \Sigma d_i p_i = d_1 p_1 + d_2 p_2 + \ldots + d_n p_n = \mu$

Notice that $\overline{x}$ is a *sample statistic,* whereas $E(D)$ is μ, the *distribution* or *population* mean. (When a sample is chosen from a population $\overline{x}$ may not be exactly equal to μ, due to sampling variation.)

Example 1 A random variable takes the values 1, 2, 3, ... 10 with equal probabilities. Find the probability distribution of R, $E(R)$, and illustrate in a bar diagram.

Now each value of R must take a probability of $\frac{1}{10}$, so

r	1	2	3	4	5	6	7	8	9	10
$P(R = r)$	0.1	0.1	0.1	0.1	0.1	0.1	0.1	0.1	0.1	0.1

$$E(R) = 1 \times 0.1 + 2 \times 0.1 + 3 \times 0.1 + \ldots + 10 \times 0.1$$
$$= 0.1(1 + 2 + 3 + \ldots + 10)$$
$$= 5.5$$

(Notice $E(R)$ is a theoretical value and R can never take the value 5.5.)

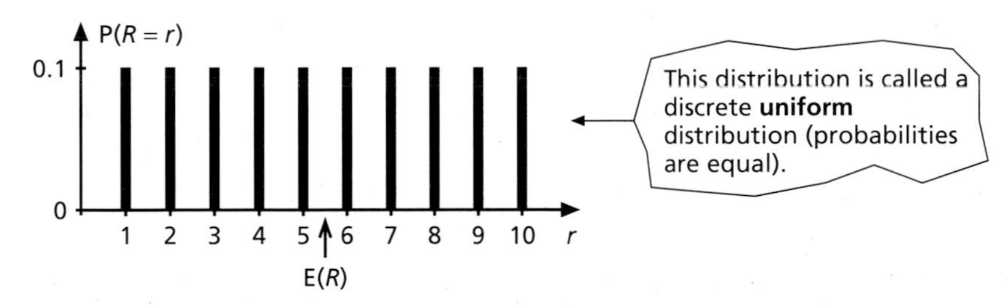

Example 2 A lottery which issues 5000 tickets awards 20 prizes: a first prize of £100, four second prizes of £50 and 15 third prizes of £10. What can a person expect to win on average if he or she buys one ticket? What would be a fair price for the ticket?

Let W = amount won on one ticket, then

w	100	50	10	0
$P(W = w)$	$\frac{1}{5000}$	$\frac{4}{5000}$	$\frac{15}{5000}$	$\frac{4980}{5000}$

$$E(W) = 100 \times \frac{1}{5000} + 50 \times \frac{4}{5000} + 10 \times \frac{15}{5000} + 0 \times \frac{4980}{5000} = 0.09$$

Notice a person can never expect to win 9p but the average of a person's winnings if he or she bought lots of tickets would be 9p. A mathematical interpretation of a 'fair' price would be that the cost of the ticket is the same as the expected winnings, so a fair price would be 9p. But this would mean the organiser 'expects' no profit.

EXERCISE 4.3A

1 Calculate $\mu = \text{E}(X)$ for the random variable X with the following probability distribution and illustrate in a bar diagram.

x	1	2	3	4
$\text{P}(X = x)$	$\frac{1}{2}$	$\frac{1}{4}$	$\frac{1}{6}$	$\frac{1}{12}$

2 Calculate $\mu = \text{E}(Z)$ for the random variable Z with the following probability distribution and illustrate in a bar diagram.

z	−2	−1	0	1	2
$\text{P}(Z = z)$	0.05	0.15	0.2	0.5	0.1

3 Calculate $\mu = \text{E}(Y)$ for the random variable Y with the following probability distribution and illustrate in a bar diagram.

y	−2	0	2	4	6
$\text{P}(Y = y)$	0.1	0.2	0.4	0.2	0.1

What do you notice about $\text{E}(Y)$ in this case?

Note When the distribution is *symmetrical,* $\text{E}(X)$ is at the *centre* of the distribution.

4 From past records, T, the number of practical tests sat before a driving test is passed, is known to have the following probability distribution:

t	1	2	3	4	5	≥ 6
$\text{P}(T = t)$	0.641	0.235	0.079	0.040	0.005	0

Find $\text{E}(T)$, the expected number of tests before passing.

5 A 'uniformly' distributed random variable R has a probability distribution given by the following function:

$$\text{P}(R = r) = \begin{cases} \frac{1}{n} & \text{for } r = 1, 2, 3, \ldots\ n \\ 0 & \text{otherwise} \end{cases}$$

Find the expectation of R, $\text{E}(R)$, when $n = 7$.

6 At a charity fund-raising event, tickets can be bought for the 'Raffle Race' on which you write the names of the three horses you think will win in order. From 20 horses 'running', three winners will be picked out of a hat. Any ticket which has the three winners in the order they were picked out will win £100. Find the expected winnings for a ticket.

EXERCISE 4.3B

1 Two dice are thrown. By drawing a table of results, find the probability distribution of S, the lower of the two scores on the dice, or on a double, the score on either die. Find $\text{E}(S)$.

2 A saleswoman receives £250 commission for every conservatory she sells. From past experience her company knows that the probability distribution of the random variable C, the number of conservatories that a typical salesperson sells per month, is given by

c	0	1	2	3	4	5	6	7	8
$P(C = c)$	0.02	0.09	0.25	0.3	0.18	0.08	0.05	0.02	0.01

a Find E(C), the expected number of conservatories sold by a typical salesperson per month.

b If A = the amount of commission received per month in £ for a typical salesperson, construct the probability distribution for the random variable A. Hence find E(A), the expected amount of commission.

c Express A in terms of C. Using your answers to **a** and **b** complete:
E(A) = E(. . . . . .) = ... × E(. . . . . .)

3 A random variable X has a probability distribution:

x	0	1	2	3
$P(X = x)$	0.2	0.3	0.4	0.1

and a random variable Y has a probability distribution:

y	10	11	12	13
$P(Y = y)$	0.2	0.3	0.4	0.1

a Find E(X), E(Y).

b If $Y = X + 10$, use these results to complete: E(Y) = E(......) = E(...) + ...

4 A random variable R has a probability distribution:

r	0	1	2	3
$P(R = r)$	0.1	0.5	0.3	0.1

and a random variable S has a probability distribution:

s	3	5	7	9
$P(S = s)$	0.1	0.5	0.3	0.1

a Find E(R), E(S).

b If $S = 2R + 3$ use these results to complete: E(S) = E(......) = ... E(...) + ...

Note Questions 2 to 4 illustrate the general result:
for any random variable R, if a and b are constants then $E(aR + b) = aE(R) + b$.

Make use of this general result in the next question.

5 If E(R) = 1.5, find: **a** E($5R$) **b** E($R + 3$) **c** E($4R + 2$).

6 In a certain game, the score on a particular go is given by the square of the value shown on a roll of a die, e.g. if the die shows a 5, the score is 25.

a If V = value shown on a roll of the die, find the probability distribution of V and hence find E(V). Now find $(E(V))^2$.

b If S = score from a roll of the die, then $S = V^2$. Find the probability distribution of S and hence find $E(S) = E(V^2)$. What do you notice?

Note For any random variable R (as long as R is not a constant), $E(R^2) \neq (E(R))^2$.
So $E(R^2)$ cannot be found from E(R), but must be worked out from the probability distribution using:
$E(R^2) = \sum_{\text{all } i} (r_i)^2 p_i$ (an averaging or 'weighting' process for R^2).
This is an illustration of the general result $E(g(R)) = \sum_{\text{all } i} g(r_i)p_i$
where $g(R)$ is any function of R.

Make use of this general result in the next question.

7 If X is the random variable given by:

x	−2	−1	0	1	2
$P(X = x)$	0.1	0.1	0.4	0.2	0.2

a Find $\mu = E(X)$.

b By considering the probability distribution of X^2, find $\mathrm{E}(X^2)$.

x^2	4	1	0	1	4
$\mathrm{P}(X = x)$	0.1	0.1	0.4	0.2	0.2

$\Rightarrow$

x^2	0	1	4
$\mathrm{P}(X^2 = x^2)$	0.4	0.3	0.3

c Find the possible values of the random variable $(X + 1)^2$ and hence find the probability distribution of $(X + 1)^2$ and $\mathrm{E}((X + 1)^2)$.

Variance of a discrete random variable

When summarising a data set, both a representative value (measure of location, mean, $\overline{x}$) and a measure of variation about the mean (variance, s^2, or standard deviation, s) can be calculated. In a similar way the **variance** of a random variable measures the theoretical spread in the population of possible values about its mean μ and is denoted by σ^2.

$$\mathrm{Var}(R) = \mathrm{E}((R - \mu)^2) = \sigma^2$$

$$\text{where } \mathrm{E}((R - \mu)^2) = \sum_{\text{all } i} (r_i - \mu)^2 p_i$$

(This is a special case of the general result on page 89).

$$\begin{aligned} \text{Now consider } \mathrm{E}((R - \mu)^2) &= \mathrm{E}((R^2 - 2\mu R + \mu^2)) \\ &= \mathrm{E}(R^2) - 2\mu\mathrm{E}(R) + \mu^2 \\ &= \mathrm{E}(R^2) - 2\mu \times \mu + \mu^2 \text{ since } \mathrm{E}(R) = \mu \\ &= \mathrm{E}(R^2) - \mu^2 \\ &= \mathrm{E}(R^2) - (\mathrm{E}(R))^2. \end{aligned}$$

So we also have the alternative formula $\mathrm{Var}(R) = \mathrm{E}(R)^2 - (\mathrm{E}(R))^2$.

Note (i) standard deviation of $R = \mathrm{SD}\ (R) = \sqrt{\mathrm{Var}(R)} = \sigma$

(ii) $\mathrm{Var}(R) \geq 0$ since $(R - \mu)^2 \geq 0$, so always check $\mathrm{E}(R^2) \geq (\mathrm{E}(R))^2$.

Example The random variable R is defined by the probability distribution:

r	1	2	3	4	5
$\mathrm{P}(R = r)$	0.1	0.2	0.4	0.2	0.1

Find: **a** $\mathrm{E}(R)$

b $\mathrm{Var}(R)$ using both formulas

c $\mathrm{SD}(R)$.

a Notice the probability distribution is symmetrical so $\mathrm{E}(R)$ can easily be found by symmetry in this case, i.e. $\mathrm{E}(R) = 3 = \mu$.

b $\mathrm{Var}(R) = \mathrm{E}((R - \mu)^2)$ is a useful method with spreadsheets:

r	1	2	3	4	5
$R - \mu$	-2	-1	0	1	2
$(R - \mu)^2$	4	1	0	1	4
$\mathrm{P}(R = r)$	0.1	0.2	0.4	0.2	0.1

$\mathrm{E}((R - \mu)^2) = (4 \times 0.1) + (1 \times 0.2) + (0 \times 0.4) + (1 \times 0.2) + (4 \times 0.1) = 1.2$

Using $\text{Var}(R) = \text{E}(R^2) - (\text{E}(R))^2$:

$\text{E}(R^2) = (1^2 \times 0.1) + (2^2 \times 0.2) + (3^2 \times 0.4) + (4^2 \times 0.2) + (5^2 \times 0.1) = 10.2$

$\text{E}(R^2) - (\text{E}(R))^2 = 10.2 - 3^2 = 1.2$

c $\text{SD}(R) = \sqrt{\text{Var}(R)} = \sqrt{1.2} = 1.10$

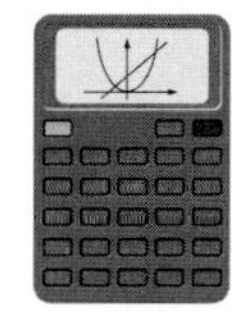

Try checking your answers using the mean and standard deviation facilities on your calculator (if it has these facilities). Input the values of the random variable as 'data' and the probabilities as 'weights' or 'frequencies'! (Standard deviation of a random variable is a population measure so use σ_n not σ_{n-1}.)

EXERCISE 4.4A

1 Find $\text{E}(R)$, $\text{E}(R^2)$, $\text{Var}(R)$ and $\text{SD}(R)$ for the random variable with the following probability distribution:

r	0	1	2
$\text{P}(R = r)$	0.2	0.3	0.5

2 Traffic records for a particular stretch of road on summer bank holidays show that on 70% of such days there are no accidents, on 25% there is one accident and on the remaining 5% there are two accidents. The number of days when there were more than two accidents is negligible. Find the mean, variance and standard deviation of the number of such accidents.

3 A discrete random variable R has a probability distribution given by the following formula:

$$\text{P}(R = r) = \begin{cases} a(r+1) & r = 0, 1, 2, 3 \\ 0 & \text{otherwise} \end{cases}$$

Find: **a** the constant a **b** $\text{E}(R)$ **c** $\text{Var}(R)$ **d** $\text{SD}(R)$.

4 To get to school in the mornings, I can either walk which takes 35 minutes, catch a bus which takes 9 minutes or get a lift which takes 6 minutes. Find the mean and standard deviation of my journey time, if I walk 20% of the time, catch a bus 70% of the time and get a lift 10% of the time.

EXERCISE 4.4B

1 In Statland each adult who is liable to tax must pay an annual 'poll tax' of £300. The probability distribution of the number of taxable adults per household, T, is:

t	1	2	3	4	5
$\text{P}(T = t)$	0.2	0.5	0.15	0.1	0.05

a Find $\text{E}(T)$, $\text{Var}(T)$.

b If B = annual 'poll tax' bill per household, construct the probability distribution for B and hence find $\text{E}(B)$ and $\text{Var}(B)$.

c Express B in terms of T. Using your answers to **a** and **b** complete:

$\text{Var}(B) = \text{Var}(\ldots \times \ldots) = \ldots \text{Var}(T)$

$\text{SD}(B) = \sqrt{\text{Var}(B)} = \sqrt{\ldots \text{Var}(T)} = \ldots \sqrt{\text{Var}(T)} = \ldots \text{SD}(T)$

2 A petrol station sells different types of fuel at the following prices per litre: 59.9p, 60.9p, 64.9p. Let F denote the price per litre paid by a randomly selected customer.

The probability distribution of F is:

f	59.9	60.9	64.9
$\text{P}(F = f)$	0.25	0.62	0.13

a Find $\text{E}(F)$, $\text{Var}(F)$.

b The Chancellor now imposes a new fuel tax of 5p per litre on all fuels. If N = new price per litre, and assuming the same distribution as before, find $\text{E}(N)$, $\text{Var}(N)$.

c Express N in terms of F. Using your answers to **a** and **b** complete:
$\text{Var}(N) = \text{Var}(\ \dots + \ \dots) = \text{Var}(F)$
$\text{SD}(N) = \sqrt{\text{Var}(N)} = \sqrt{\text{Var}(\ \dots)} = \text{SD}(F)$

Note We saw previously that if a random variable is multiplied by a constant factor a, the mean will also be multiplied by a. Similarly, deviations from the mean would also be multiplied by a, and so the squares of these deviations would be multiplied by a^2, i.e. $\text{E}(aR) = a\text{E}(R)$ but $\text{Var}(aR) = a^2\,\text{Var}(R)$.
We also saw that if a constant b is added to a random variable then the mean will also be changed by adding b. The variance, or spread, however would be unaltered since deviations from the mean would remain the same, i.e. $\text{E}(R + b) = \text{E}(R) + b$ but $\text{Var}(R + b) = \text{Var}(R)$ and in general, for any random variable X, if a and b are constants, $\text{E}(aR + b) = a\text{E}(R) + b$ but $\text{Var}(aR + b) = a^2\,\text{Var}(R)$.

Make use of these general results in the next two questions.

3 The discrete random variable X has a mean of 52 and a variance of 8. Find the mean and variance of: **a** $3X$ **b** $\frac{X}{4}$ **c** $X + 5$ **d** $\frac{(X - 10)}{2}$.

4 In order to compare values of two random variables it can be useful to 'standardise' each variable. The 'standardised value' of a random variable R is given by Z where $Z = \frac{R - \mu}{\sigma}$.

a Find $\text{E}(Z)$, $\text{Var}(Z)$.
b Find the standardised value of a mathematics mark of 89% if the mean mark of all the students who took the test is 72% with a standard deviation of 12%.
c Find the standardised value of an English mark of 76% if the mean mark of all the students who took the test is 56% with a standard deviation of 10%.
d Which mark is better relative to the general distribution of marks among students who sat these papers?

5 An investor has the opportunity to invest in two different investment schemes. Initially she invests in one scheme. If it is successful, she also invests in the second scheme. Assuming the investments are each successful with probability p, independently of one another, find an expression for the expectation and variance of the number of successful investments.

Simulation

Random variables are often used to model experimental data. We shall now consider how to use the probability distribution of a random variable in a simulation.

A useful technique is to use a **cumulative probability distribution**, which gives the probability that a random variable takes any value *up to* a certain value.

Consider the manager of a new car hire company who wishes to simulate the number of limousines required on a daily basis for a 30-day period. He believes that M, the number of limousines hired out per day, has the distribution:

m	0	1	2	≥ 3
$\text{P}(M = m)$	0.1	0.6	0.3	0

The cumulative probability distribution is given by:

m	0	1	2
$P(M \leq m)$	0.1	0.7	1

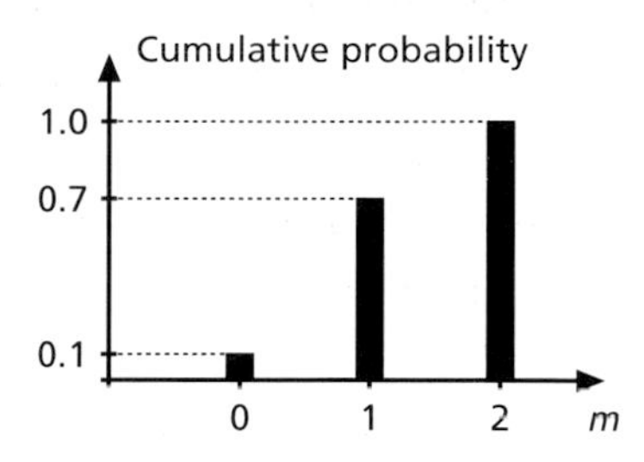

and the cumulative bar diagram looks like this:
(Notice the cumulative probability distribution always takes values from 0 to 1 in ascending order.)

He generates a random number between 0 and 1 on his calculator, $n = 0.459$ say. Each number is taken to represent a value of the cumulative probability, and so identifies a value of M, e.g. 0.459 represents 1 limousine and values of n can be split into these three intervals which give the required probabilities:

$$0 \leq n < 0.1 \quad \Rightarrow m = 0$$
$$0.1 \leq n < 0.7 \quad \Rightarrow m = 1$$
$$0.7 \leq n < 1 \quad \Rightarrow m = 2$$

(We choose $n < 1$ because the random number generator on a calculator will not give 1.000.)

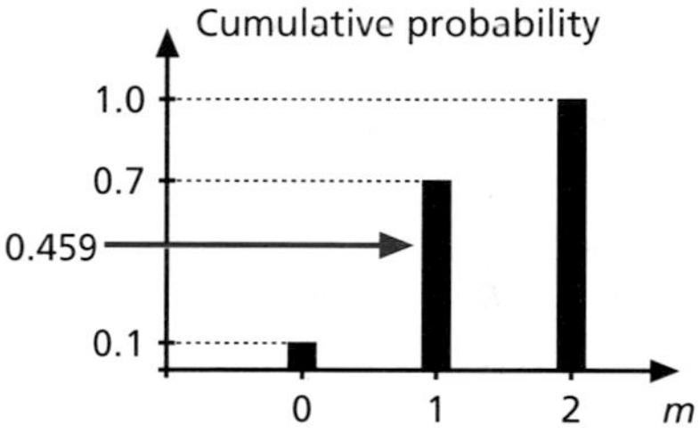

His numbers are:

0.459 0.72 0.869 0.724 0.247 0.171 0.953 0.961 0.716 0.678
0.286 0.992 0.235 0.891 0.923 0.286 0.657 0.133 0.029 0.325
0.599 0.882 0.646 0.032 0.249 0.131 0.099 0.201 0.22 0.843

giving values of M:

1 2 2 2 1 1 2 2 2 1
1 2 1 2 2 1 1 1 0 1
1 2 1 0 1 1 0 1 1 2

To summarise the results, there are: 3 days with no limousines hired out
16 days with one limousine hired out
11 days with two limousines hired out.

Remember simulations do not necessarily give the exact results predicted in theory (3, 18, 9).

EXERCISE 4.5

1 Repeat the simulation of the number of limousines required for another 30-day period.

2 If X has a probability distribution given by:

x	0	1	2	3	4	5	6	7
$P(X = x)$	0.08	0.13	0.22	0.23	0.18	0.09	0.04	0.03

find the cumulative probability distribution.

3 Show that the cumulative probability distribution for the random variable H, the number of heads when two coins are tossed, is given by:

h	0	1	2
$P(H < h)$	0.25	0.75	1

Draw a cumulative bar diagram and use it to simulate 30 trials of tossing two coins.

4 The probability distribution of the random variable W, the amount won in £ on one ticket in a lottery, is given by:

w	0	10	50	100
$P(W = w)$	0.96	0.03	0.008	0.002

Find the cumulative probability distribution and use it to simulate amounts won with 50 tickets. Did you ever win with your 50 tickets?

Choose the simplest way of doing the simulations in questions **5** and **6**.

5 The defective rate in a particular type of silicon chips is 24%. Use your calculator to 'open' an imaginary consignment of 20 silicon chips. How many were defective in your consignment? Now 'open' a second consignment. Did you get the same number of defectives?

6 A tea company produces a set of four different cards showing tea clippers. Each packet of tea contains a randomly selected card. Find the average number of packets opened until a complete set is obtained. (Perform 20 simulations, but combine your results with others to get a better estimate.)

Continuous random variables

Remember, whereas a discrete random variable can only take isolated values on the number line, a continuous random variable can take any value within an interval or on the real number line. For example, the discrete random variable D, the number of people in a randomly selected household, can be counted and will take integral values. To each value of D it is possible to assign a probability by estimating from data collected from surveys. However, the continuous random variable X, the birth weight of a child, must be measured. How can probabilities be assigned?

Background: Probability density curve

The frequency distribution for a sample of babies can be illustrated as a histogram showing relative frequency density (the relative frequency per unit value of weight) against weight.

Now relative frequency density

$$= \frac{\text{relative frequency}}{\text{width of interval}}$$

so relative frequency

$= \text{relative frequency density} \times \text{width of interval}$

$= \text{height of bar} \times \text{width of bar}$

$= \text{area of bar}$

i.e. area of each rectangle corresponds to relative frequency.

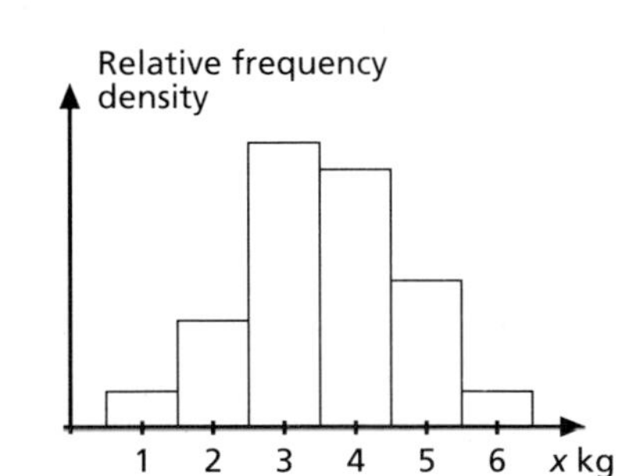

For large samples, the relative frequency density becomes the **probability density** and the **area** of each rectangle corresponds to the probabilities associated with each interval. The total area of all the rectangles is 1 (since the total of relative frequencies is 1).

Now this weight will not be recorded precisely because in practice the measurement will probably be taken to the nearest gram. Suppose the weights were recorded to the nearest (i) kilogram (ii) 100 grams. The probability distributions might look like:

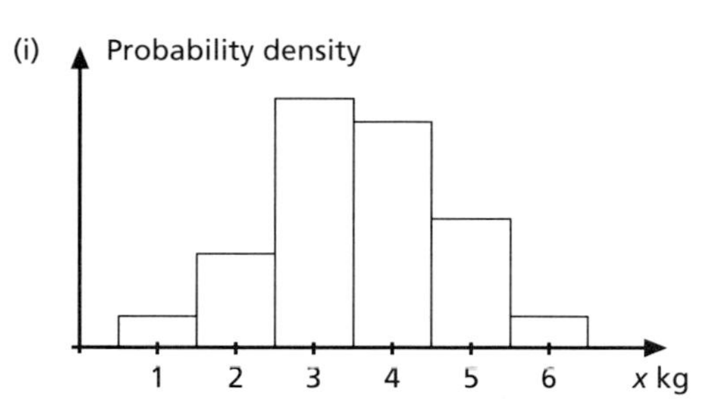

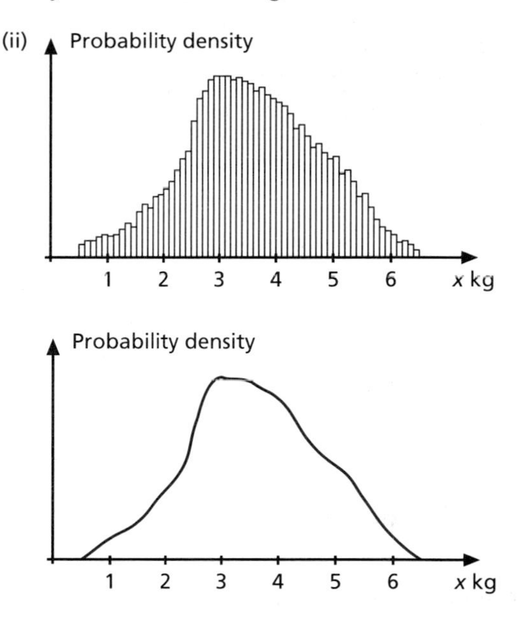

As the accuracy of measurement is increased the overall shape of the distribution approaches a smooth curve. The area under the curve is still 1.
The more accurate the measurements become the greater the number of values, until there are an uncountable number of possible weights. So it becomes impossible to assign a probability to each individual weight as can be done with a discrete random variable.

So for a continuous random variable X, the probability that X falls in a particular interval can be specified by calculating the area under the probability density curve in that interval.
Consider the following example. An eccentric maths teacher prides herself in always finishing the lesson on time. She has a policy of finishing the lesson at any time during the last five minutes. Suppose X is the amount of time between finishing the lesson and the end of the period. Any value of X is just as likely to occur as any other. The probability distribution would look like this:

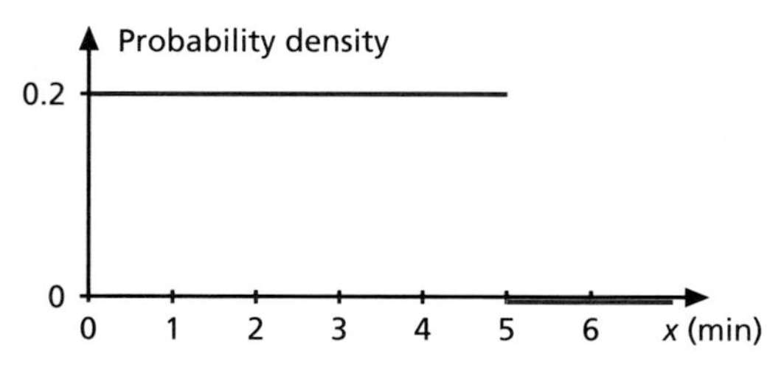

Probability density is constant over the interval 0–5 minutes and has value 0 above 5 minutes. (This is in fact an example of a continuous **uniform** distribution.) Since the total area under the 'curve' is 1 and the 'curve' only has a positive height when x is between 0 and 5, this height must be 0.2 since

$$\text{total area} = \text{base} \times \text{height} = 5 \times 0.2 = 1.$$

Now to find the probability that the teacher finishes between 2 and 4 minutes before the end of the period, i.e. $P(2 < X < 4)$, it is only necessary to find the area under the 'curve' in the interval $2 < x < 4$.

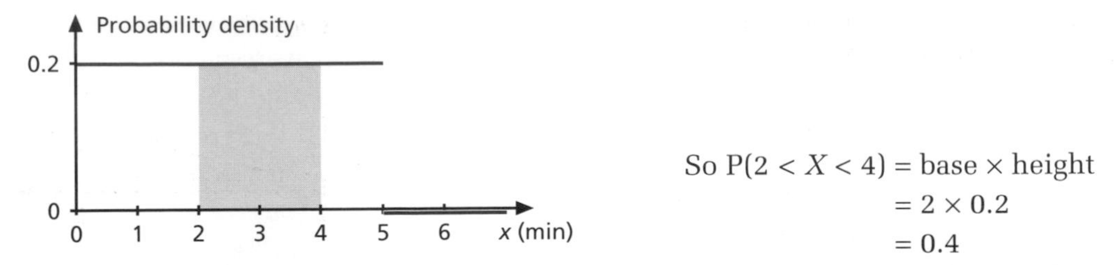

So $P(2 < X < 4) = \text{base} \times \text{height}$
$= 2 \times 0.2$
$= 0.4$

or on 40% of occasions the lesson is finished between 2 and 4 minutes before the period ends.

Note $P(2 \leq X \leq 4)$ has an identical value to $P(2 < X < 4)$ since $P(X = 2)$ and $P(X = 4)$, both areas at a single point, are 0, or in general, for any **continuous** random variable X,

$$\mathbf{P(x_1 \leq X \leq x_2) = P(x_1 < X < x_2)}$$

Now in the preceding example, the area under the 'curve' was easy to find since it was a rectangle. This geometrical approach can be used when the area is either a rectangle, a triangle or a combination of these shapes.

When the shape of the distribution is a curve, if a formula for the height of the curve is known, this formula is called a **probability density function** or **pdf**. Integration of this function can then be used to find areas under the curve and hence probabilities.

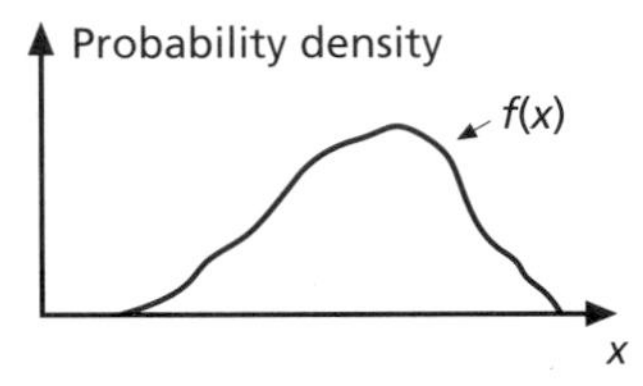

If X is a continuous random variable and there is a function $f(x)$ such that

$P(x_1 \leq X \leq x_2) = \int_{x_1}^{x_2} f(x)\mathrm{d}x$ then $f(x)$ is the probability density function of X, or pdf of X.

What conditions must $f(x)$ satisfy?

(i) $\boldsymbol{f(x) \geq 0}$ for all values of x. (Probability is never negative, so probability density and hence the probability density function cannot be negative.)

(ii) $\boldsymbol{\int_a^b f(x)\mathrm{d}x = 1}$ where the random variable is defined on the interval $[a, b]$.

If the random variable is defined over an infinite interval, for example from negative infinity to infinity, then $\int_{-\infty}^{\infty} f(x)\mathrm{d}x = 1$

So, for the required interval, the total area under the curve is 1.

Example A continuous random variable X is thought to have a probability density function (pdf) given by

$$f(x) = \begin{cases} \frac{1}{12}(x^2 + 1) & 0 \leq x \leq 3 \\ 0 & \text{otherwise} \end{cases}$$

a Show that $f(x)$ is indeed a pdf and sketch the function.
b Find (i) $P(0 < X < 1)$ (ii) $P(X \geq 1.8)$ (iii) $P(X = 1)$.

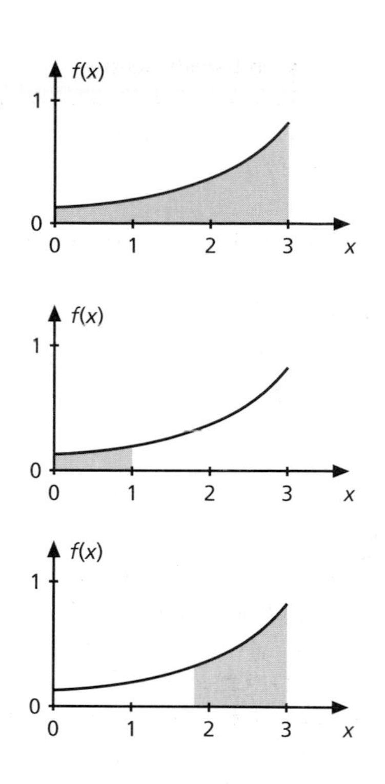

a $\displaystyle\int_0^3 \frac{1}{12}(x^2+1)\mathrm{d}x = \frac{1}{12}\left[\frac{x^3}{3}+x\right]_0^3$

$\displaystyle = \frac{1}{12}\left[\left(\frac{27}{3}+3\right)-\left(0+0\right)\right] = 1$

and $f(x) > 0$ for all x, so $f(x)$ is a pdf.
The shaded area represents the integral.

b (i) $\displaystyle P(0 < X < 1) = \int_0^1 \frac{1}{12}(x^2+1)\mathrm{d}x = \frac{1}{12}\left[\frac{x^3}{3}+x\right]_0^1$

$\displaystyle = \frac{1}{12}\left[\left(\frac{1}{3}+1\right)-\left(0\right)\right] = \frac{1}{9}$

(ii) $\displaystyle P(X \geq 1.8) = \int_{1.8}^3 \frac{1}{12}(x^2+1)\mathrm{d}x = \frac{1}{12}\left[\frac{x^3}{3}+x\right]_{1.8}^3$

$\displaystyle = \frac{1}{12}\left[\left(\frac{3^3}{3}+3\right)-\left(\frac{1.8^3}{3}+1.8\right)\right] = 0.688$

(iii) $\displaystyle P(X = 1) = \int_1^1 \frac{1}{12}(x^2+1)\mathrm{d}x = 0$ as expected.

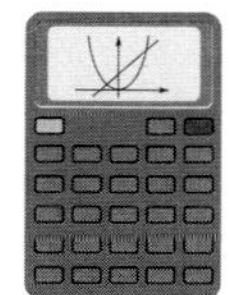

To sketch the pdf on a graphics calculator, select the range so that you can see at least $a \leq x \leq b$ and $y \geq 0$ where $[a, b]$ is the interval over which the pdf is defined. You can check your probability answers if your graphics calculator will do a definite integral!

EXERCISE 4.6A

1 The diagram shows a pdf for the random variable X defined over the range $0 \leq x \leq 4$.

a Given that the triangular area under the curve in the interval over which the pdf is defined must be 1, find the height of the triangle.

b The pdf is of the form $f(x) = \begin{cases} kx & 0 \leq x \leq 4 \\ 0 & \text{otherwise} \end{cases}$. Find k.

2 **a** Show that $f(x)$ is a pdf for the random variable X if $f(x) = \begin{cases} \dfrac{x}{50} & 0 \leq x \leq 10 \\ 0 & \text{otherwise} \end{cases}$

b Sketch the pdf.

c Find (i) $P(X < 6.5)$ (ii) $P(4 \leq X \leq 8)$.

3 Suppose $f(x)$ is the pdf for the random variable X, and $f(x) = \begin{cases} k(4-x) & -1 \leq x \leq 4 \\ 0 & \text{otherwise} \end{cases}$

By integrating $f(x)$, find the constant k, and sketch the pdf.

4 For each of the following functions, decide whether the function could be a pdf over the specified range. If yes, find the value of the constant k. If no, explain why not.

a $f(u) = \begin{cases} \dfrac{k}{u^2} & 2 \le u \le 4 \\ 0 & \text{otherwise} \end{cases}$ **b** $f(x) = \begin{cases} k(x^2 - 1) & 0 \le x \le 2 \\ 0 & \text{otherwise} \end{cases}$

c $f(t) = \begin{cases} k\sqrt{t} & 0 \le t \le 3 \\ 0 & \text{otherwise} \end{cases}$

EXERCISE 4.6B

1 Suppose a random variable X has the pdf $f(x) = \begin{cases} 3x^p & 0 \le x \le 1 \\ 0 & \text{otherwise} \end{cases}$

where p is a constant. Find the value of p and sketch the pdf.

2 The continuous random variable T, the time taken to complete a task, has the pdf

$$f(t) = \begin{cases} t & 0 \le t \le 1 \\ k - t & 1 < t \le 2 \\ 0 & \text{otherwise} \end{cases}$$

a Find the value of the constant k and sketch the pdf.
b Find also (i) $P(T \le 0.5)$ (ii) $P(T \le 1.5)$.

3 The daily demand for diesel at a particular garage, in thousands of litres, X is a continuous random variable whose density function is

$$f(x) = \begin{cases} ax + b & 0 \le x \le 2 \\ 0 & \text{otherwise} \end{cases}$$

where a, b are constants. Given that the probability of the demand on a randomly chosen day will be less than 1000 litres is 0.4, find the constants a, b and the pdf. Find also $P(X > 1.5)$.

What can you tell from the shape of a pdf?

In Chapter 1 we saw that a bar diagram or histogram gave a 'snapshot' of a data set and indicated some important features such as:

- Is the data set symmetrical or skewed?
- Is there a value which has a higher frequency than other values?
- Does the data set have one or several modal values?

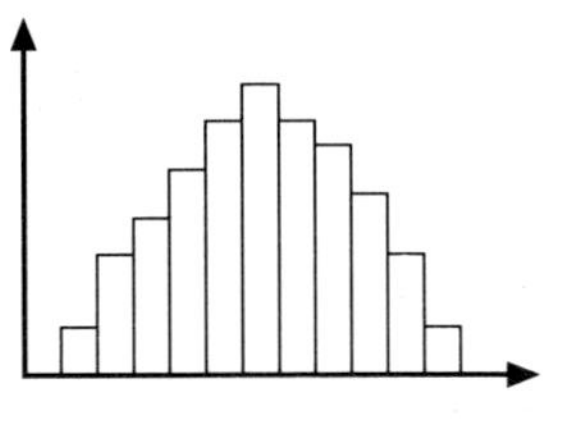

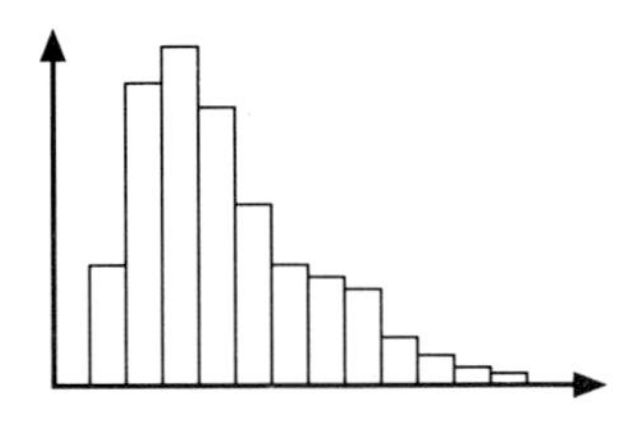

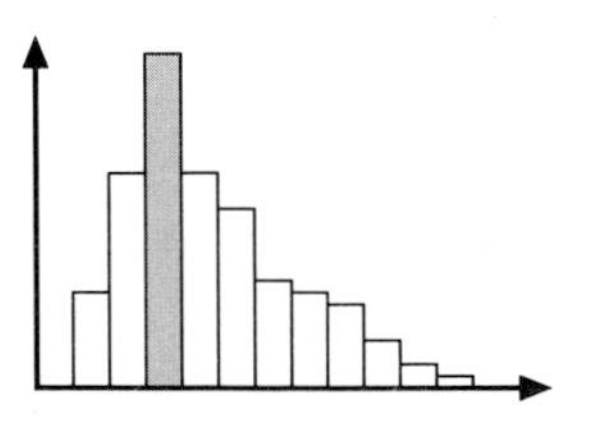

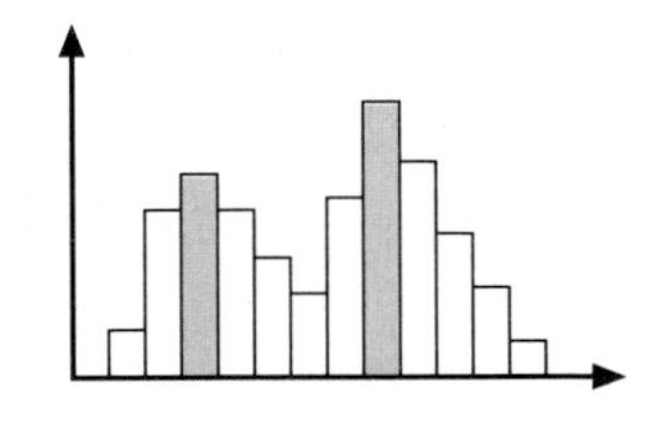

In exactly the same way, a sketch of the pdf of a continuous random variable can illustrate some important features of the distribution. Consider the following questions:

- Is the pdf a simple geometrical shape?

We saw in the previous exercise that areas under curves, and hence probabilities, may be easier to calculate using geometrical ideas than by integrating.

- Is the pdf symmetrical?

We saw in Exercise 4.3 that if the probability distribution of a discrete random variable is symmetrical, then E(X) is usually at the centre of the distribution. The same is true for continuous random variables.

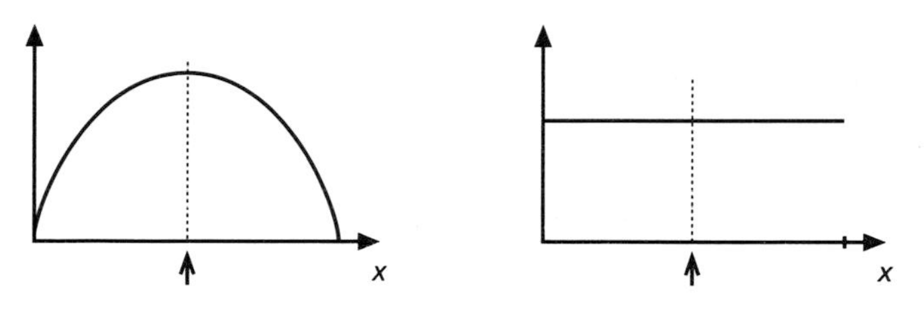

- Does the pdf have a local maximum turning point?

At a local maximum point, the probability density takes the highest value locally and therefore indicates a modal value.

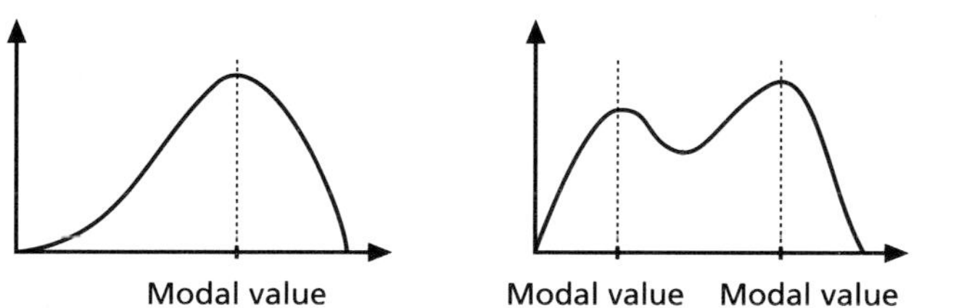

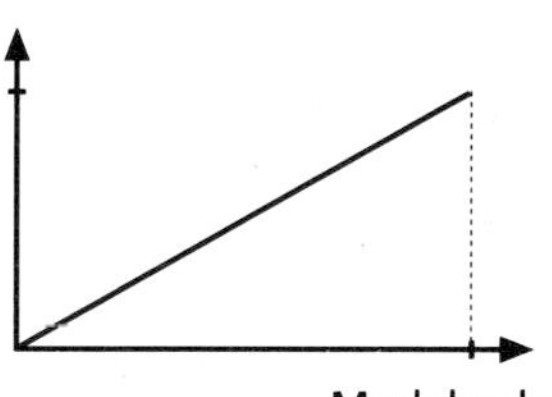

Example 1 The random variable X has a pdf given by

$$f(x) = \begin{cases} \frac{2}{9}x(3-x) & 0 \le x \le 3 \\ 0 & \text{otherwise} \end{cases}. \text{ Find E}(X).$$

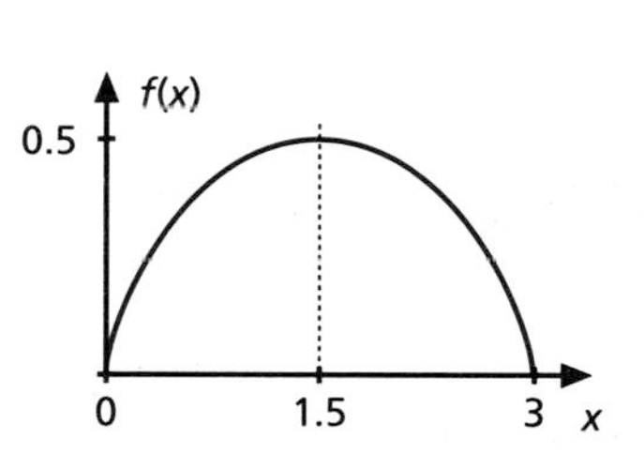

The graph of the pdf is a parabola which cuts the x-axis when $\frac{2}{9}x(3-x) = 0$, i. e. $x = 0$ or $x = 3$.

So the graph has a line of symmetry $x = 1.5$ and E(X) = 1.5.

Example 2 Find the modal value of the continuous random variable X when the pdf is

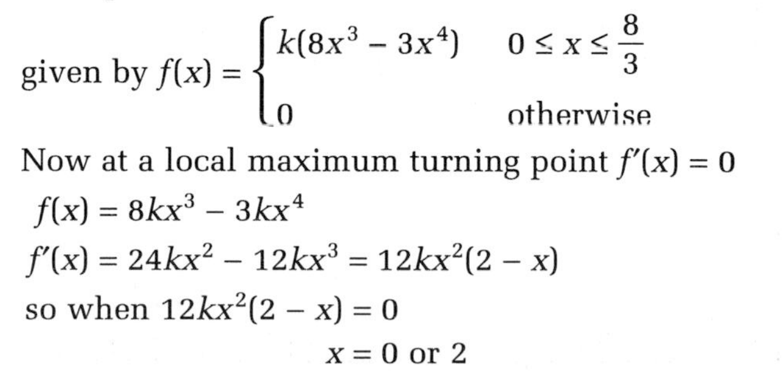

given by $f(x) = \begin{cases} k(8x^3 - 3x^4) & 0 \le x \le \frac{8}{3} \\ 0 & \text{otherwise} \end{cases}$

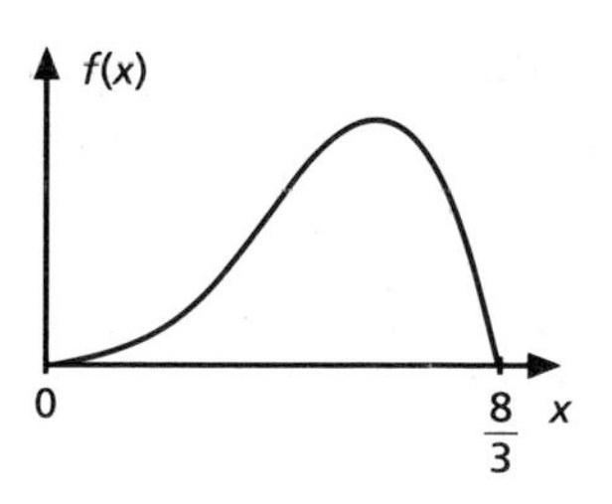

Now at a local maximum turning point $f'(x) = 0$

$f(x) = 8kx^3 - 3kx^4$

$f'(x) = 24kx^2 - 12kx^3 = 12kx^2(2-x)$

so when $12kx^2(2-x) = 0$

$x = 0$ or 2

A sketch shows that $f(0) = 0$, so 0 is not a modal value.

But $x = 2$ is a local maximum. Therefore X has a modal value at $x = 2$.

x	1	2	2.5
$f'(x)$	+	0	−
Shape	/	—	\

EXERCISE 4.7B

1 The random variable X has a pdf given by $f(x) = \begin{cases} 2 & 0 \le x \le 0.5 \\ 0 & \text{otherwise} \end{cases}$

Sketch the pdf. Find $P(X < 0.2)$ using a geometrical method, and $E(X)$.

2 The pdf of T, the random variable describing the time taken in minutes for a machine to do a particular task, is shown in the sketch. Find:

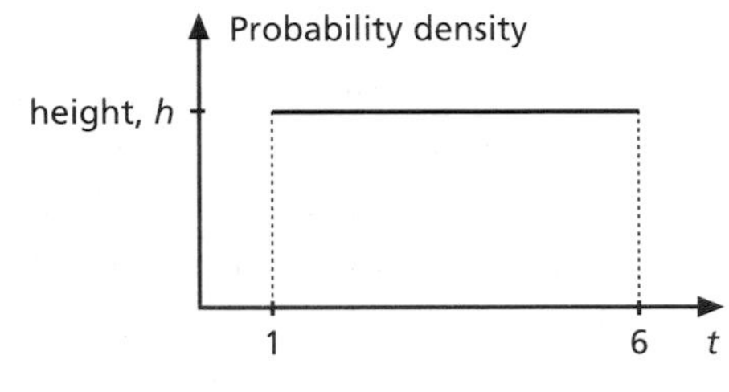

a the height of the rectangle
b the probability that the machine takes less than 3 minutes to do the task
c $E(T)$
d how many tasks from a total of 300 performed by this machine would be expected to take more than 5 minutes.

3

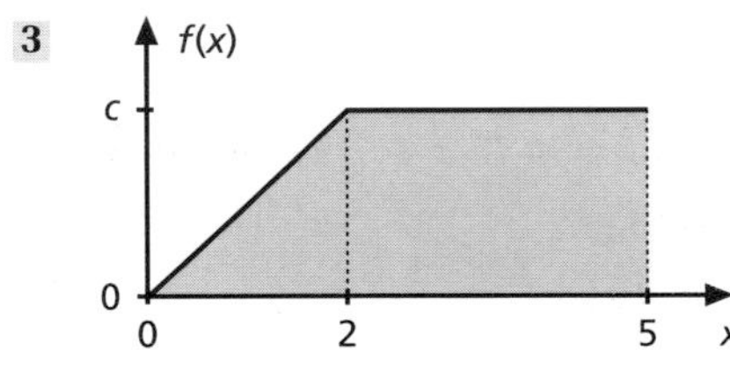

The diagram shows the pdf of a continuous random variable which is of the form

$$f(x) = \begin{cases} kx & 0 \le x \le 2 \\ c & 2 < x \le 5 \\ 0 & \text{otherwise} \end{cases}$$

By considering the area of the trapezium, find k and c.

Check your answer by showing $\int_0^2 f(x)\mathrm{d}x + \int_2^5 f(x)\mathrm{d}x = 1$.

4 The error, $R\%$, in the measurement of a particular length is a random variable whose pdf is shown in the sketch ($R = \frac{\text{error}}{\text{actual length}} \times 100$). Find:

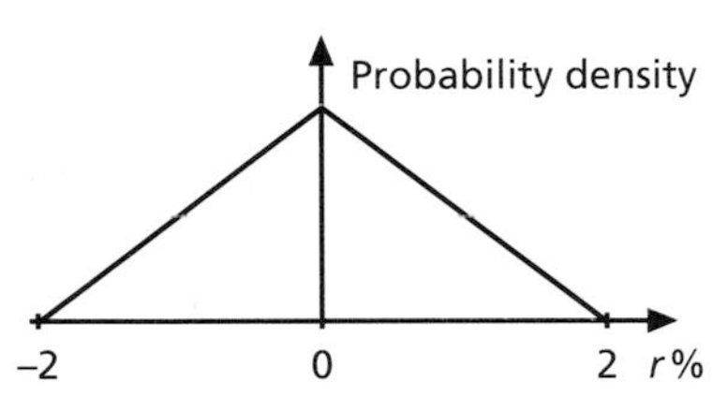

a the height of the triangle
b the probability that the measured length is greater than 201 cm, given the actual length is 200 cm
c the probability that the percentage error in the measurement is less than 1%, i.e. $-1 < r < 1$.

5 The random variable X has a pdf given by $f(x) = \begin{cases} 2x & 0 \le x \le 1 \\ 0 & \text{otherwise} \end{cases}$

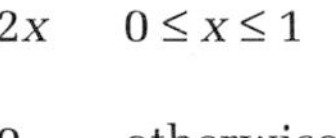

a Sketch the pdf.
b Find $P(X < 0.5)$ using a geometrical method.
c Find any modal value.

6 The random variable X has a pdf as shown in the sketch. Find:

a the height of the triangle
b the mode
c $P(X \le 4)$.

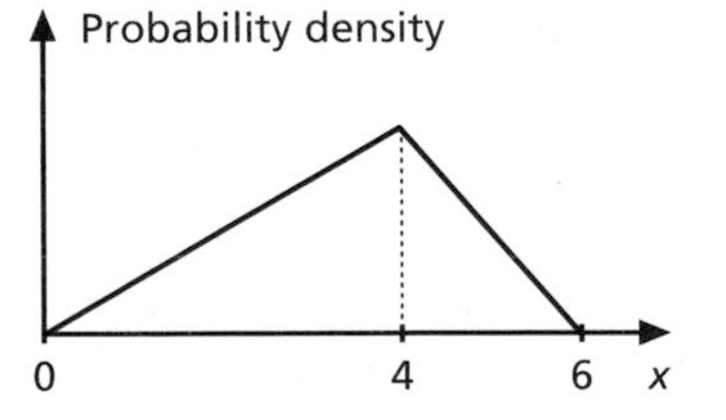

7

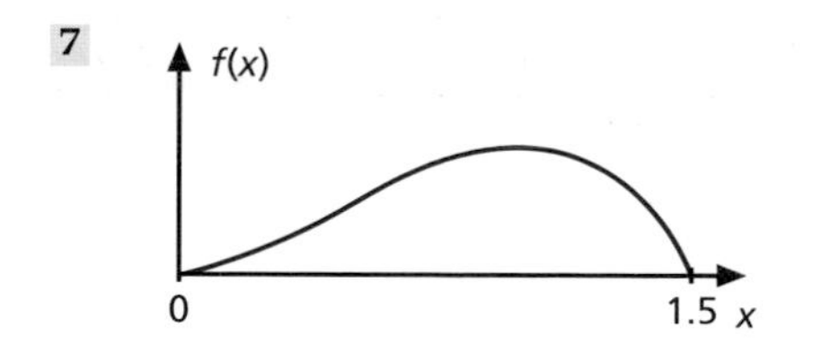

Find the mode of the random variable X whose pdf is given by

$$f(x) = \begin{cases} kx^2(3 - 2x) & 0 \le x \le 1.5 \\ 0 & \text{otherwise} \end{cases}$$

The mean or expected value and variance of a continuous random variable

When the distribution is symmetrical, the expected value can be found by symmetry at the centre of the distribution. However, when this is not the case a different argument must be used. Consider the similarity between a probability distribution for a discrete random variable and a probability distribution for a continuous random variable defined on the interval $[a, b]$, where:

Discrete		*Continuous*
$\Sigma p_i = 1$	$\rightarrow$	$\int_a^b f(x)\mathrm{d}x = 1$

Therefore, replacing Σ with $\int \ldots \mathrm{d}x$, and p_i with $f(x)$, when X is continuous $\mathrm{E}(X)$ and $\mathrm{E}(X^2)$ can be defined in a similar way as when X is discrete.

Discrete		*Continuous*
$\mathrm{E}(X) = \Sigma x_i p_i$	$\rightarrow$	$\mathrm{E}(X) = \int_a^b x f(x)\mathrm{d}x$
$\mathrm{E}(X^2) = \Sigma (x_i)^2 p_i$	$\rightarrow$	$\mathrm{E}(X^2) = \int_a^b x^2 f(x)\mathrm{d}x$

and $\mathrm{Var}(X)$:

$$\mathrm{Var}(X) = \Sigma (x_i - \mu)^2 p_i \quad \rightarrow \quad \mathrm{Var}(X) = \int_a^b (x - \mu)^2 f(x)\mathrm{d}x$$

and the alternative formula for $\mathrm{Var}(X)$ is the same in both cases:

$$\mathrm{Var}(X) = \mathrm{E}(X^2) - (\mathrm{E}(X))^2$$

Example A continuous random variable X has a pdf given by $f(x) = \begin{cases} 2x & 0 \le x \le 1 \\ 0 & \text{otherwise} \end{cases}$

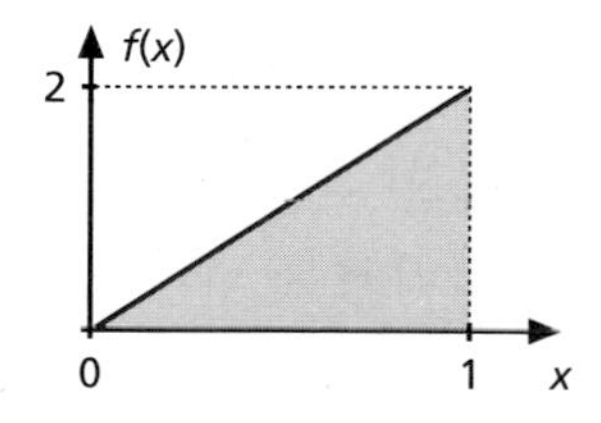

Find: **a** $\mathrm{E}(X)$ and $\mathrm{E}(X^2)$ **b** $\mathrm{Var}(X)$ and $\mathrm{SD}(X)$.

a $\mathrm{E}(X) = \int_0^1 x f(x)\mathrm{d}x = \int_0^1 x(2x)\mathrm{d}x = \int_0^1 2x^2\mathrm{d}x = 2\left[\frac{x^3}{3}\right]_0^1 = \frac{2}{3}$

$\mathrm{E}(X^2) = \int_0^1 x^2 f(x)\mathrm{d}x = \int_0^1 x^2(2x)\mathrm{d}x = \int_0^1 2x^3\mathrm{d}x = 2\left[\frac{x^4}{4}\right]_0^1 = \frac{1}{2}$

b Using the alternative formula $\text{Var}(X) = \text{E}(X^2) - (\text{E}(X))^2$

$$\text{Var}(X) = \frac{1}{2} - \left(\frac{2}{3}\right)^2 = \frac{1}{18}$$

$$\text{SD}(X) = \sqrt{\frac{1}{18}} = 0.236 \text{ to 3 significant figures.}$$

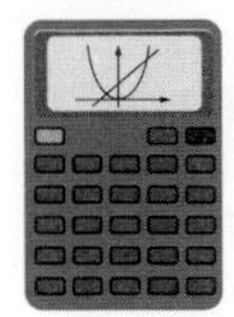

The integration required for $\text{E}(X^2)$ can be quite demanding. You should check your answers if you have a graphics calculator which will do a definite integral.

EXERCISE 4.8A

1 A continuous random variable X has a pdf given by

$$f(x) = \begin{cases} 0.5x & 0 \le x \le 2 \\ 0 & \text{otherwise} \end{cases}$$

Find:

a $\text{E}(X)$, using $\int_0^2 xf(x)\text{d}x$ **b** $\text{E}(X^2)$, using $\int_0^2 x^2 f(x)\text{d}x$

c $\text{Var}(X)$, using $\text{Var}(X) = \text{E}(X^2) - (\text{E}(X))^2$.

2 A continuous random variable Z has a pdf given by $f(z) = \begin{cases} 0.25 & -2 \le z \le 2 \\ 0 & \text{otherwise} \end{cases}$

Sketch the pdf. Find: **a** $\text{E}(Z)$ **b** $\text{E}(Z^2)$ **c** $\text{SD}(Z)$.

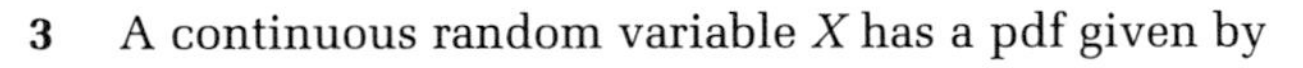

3 A continuous random variable X has a pdf given by

$$f(x) = \begin{cases} kx(1-x) & 0 \le x \le 1 \\ 0 & \text{otherwise} \end{cases}$$

Find:

a k, using the fact that the area under the curve is 1

b $\text{E}(X)$ and $\text{E}(X^2)$ **c** $\text{Var}(X)$ and $\text{SD}(X)$.

4 A continuous random variable W has a pdf given by $f(w) = \begin{cases} k\sqrt{w} & 0 \le w \le 1 \\ 0 & \text{otherwise} \end{cases}$

Find: **a** k and sketch the pdf **b** $\text{E}(W)$ **c** $\text{SD}(W)$.

EXERCISE 4.8B

1 In a particular industry, it is believed that the weekly wage in £ of a semi-skilled worker is a random variable, S, where S has a probability density function given by

$$f(s) = \begin{cases} \dfrac{80\,000}{3s^3} & 100 < s < 200 \\ 0 & \text{otherwise} \end{cases}$$

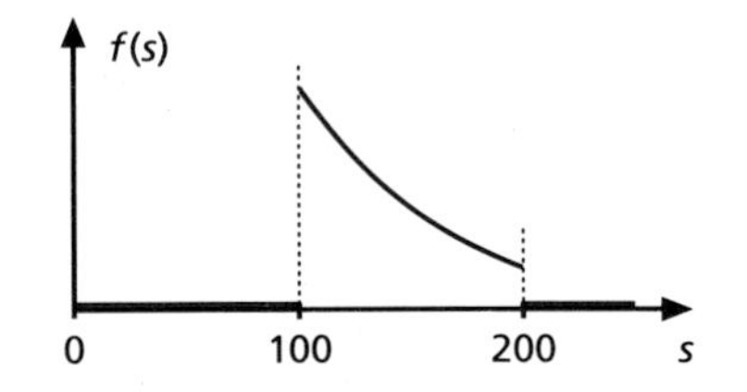

Find the expected value of the weekly wage of a semi-skilled worker in this industry.

2 A continuous random variable Y has a pdf given by $f(y) = \begin{cases} k(1 + y + y^2) & -1 \le y \le 1 \\ 0 & \text{otherwise} \end{cases}$

Find: **a** k and sketch the pdf **b** $\mu = \text{E}(Y)$ **c** $\text{Var}(Y)$ **d** $\text{P}(Y \ge \mu)$.

3 The diagram shows the pdf for the continuous random variable X where

$$f(x) = \begin{cases} \frac{1}{9}(x+1) & -1 \le x \le 2 \\ \frac{1}{9}(5-x) & 2 \le x \le 5 \\ 0 & \text{otherwise} \end{cases}$$

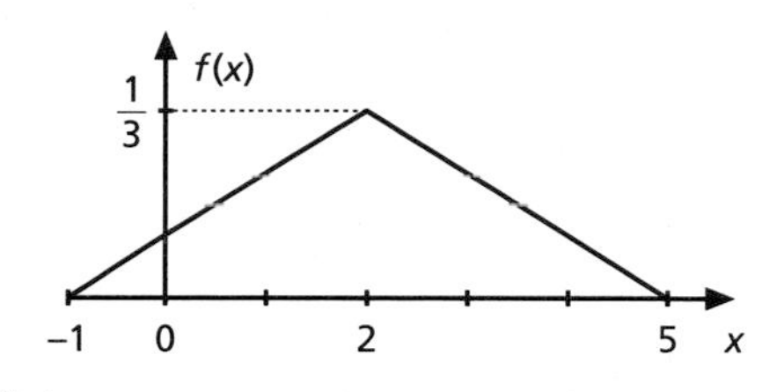

Find: **a** $\text{P}(X < 0)$ **b** $\text{E}(X)$ (using symmetry) **c** $\text{E}(X^2)$ (using two separate integrals) **d** $\text{Var}(X)$.

4 S, the proportion of dye in a particular dyeing solution, is a random variable with pdf

$$f(s) = \begin{cases} 20s^3\,(1-s) & 0 < s < 1 \\ 0 & \text{otherwise} \end{cases}$$

Find: **a** $\text{E}(S)$ **b** $\text{Var}(S)$ **c** $\text{P}(S$ is less than the mean value$)$.

5 The annual growth, in per cent, which certain investment funds differ from a specific target can be modelled by the random variable G with $f(g) = \begin{cases} 0.006(25 - g^2) & -5 \le g \le 5 \\ 0 & \text{otherwise} \end{cases}$

where positive values indicate growth above target and negative values indicate growth below target.

a Find the probability that an investment fund chosen at random has an annual growth (i) 3% or more above target (ii) within 1% of target.

b Calculate the mean and standard deviation of the annual growth about the target annual growth.

Cumulative distributions

In Chapter 1 we saw how cumulative frequency for a data set could be used to record how many observations fall below a particular value. Additionally, if the number of observations below a particular value was exactly half, then this gave a convenient way of finding the median of the distribution, particularly for continuous data sets, e.g.

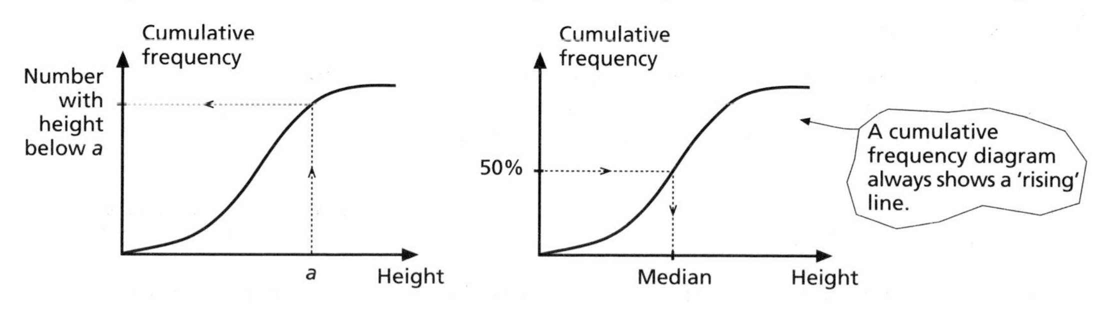

In exactly the same way, we can define and use the **cumulative distribution function** for a continuous random variable. Consider the following example.

Find the probability that the random variable X takes any value up to a particular value x_0, $P(X \leq x_0)$ where

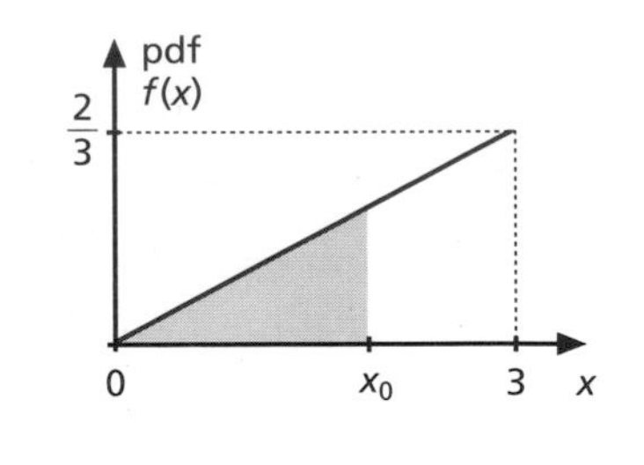

$$f(x) = \begin{cases} \frac{2}{9}x & 0 < x < 3 \\ 0 & \text{otherwise} \end{cases}$$

$$P(X \leq x_0) = \int_0^{x_0} f(x)dx = \int_0^{x_0} \frac{2}{9}x dx = \frac{2}{9}\left[\frac{x^2}{2}\right]_0^{x_0} = \frac{{x_0}^2}{9}$$

so $\quad P(X \leq 0) = \frac{0^2}{9} = 0 \Rightarrow$ no probability below the value $x = 0$

$\quad P(X \leq 3) = \frac{3^2}{9} = 1 \Rightarrow$ all probability is taken up by $x = 3$.

Now $P(X \leq x)$ is the cumulative distribution function of X denoted by $F(X)$.

So the cumulative distribution function $F(x) = \frac{x^2}{9}$ looks like this:

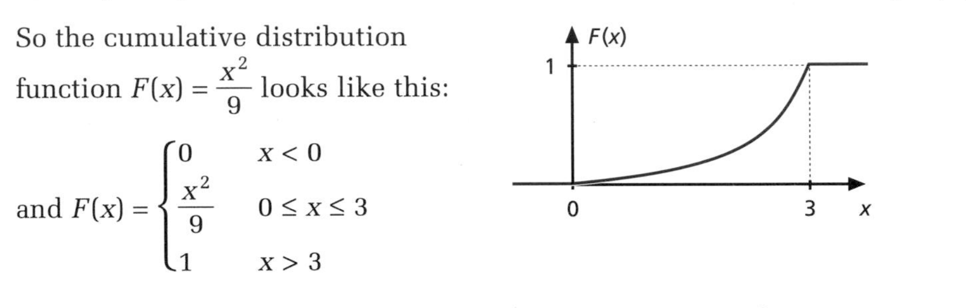

$$\text{and } F(x) = \begin{cases} 0 & x < 0 \\ \frac{x^2}{9} & 0 \leq x \leq 3 \\ 1 & x > 3 \end{cases}$$

In general, for a continuous random variable X with pdf $\begin{cases} f(x) & a < x < b \\ 0 & \text{otherwise} \end{cases}$

the cumulative distribution function of X, called $F(x)$, gives $P(X \leq x)$ and

$$F(x) = \int_a^x f(u)du$$

(u is a dummy variable, since x has already been used as the upper limit of integration), i.e. $F(x_0)$ gives the accumulated probability of all the values of X up to the particular value x_0 and therefore $F(x)$ never decreases.

Now remember the **median** is the value below which half the distribution lies. This can be expressed simply using $F(x)$, i.e.

$$\text{if } m = \text{median value, } F(m) = P(X \leq m) = \tfrac{1}{2}$$

In the above example therefore, the median m satisfies $F(m) = \frac{m^2}{9} = \frac{1}{2}$

$$m^2 = \tfrac{9}{2}$$

$$\text{therefore } m = 2.12$$

(The median must be between 0 and 3, not negative.)

Note The cumulative distribution function $F(x)$ can be found from the pdf $f(x)$ by integrating. It follows that the pdf $f(x)$ can be found by differentiating $F(x)$, i.e. $f(x) = F'(x)$.

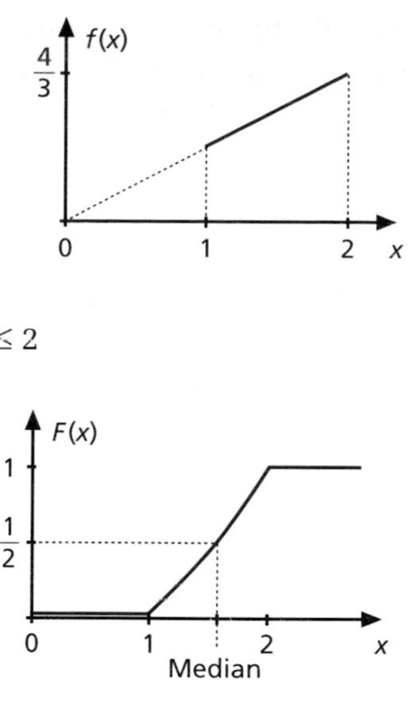

Example 1 If the continuous random variable X has

$$\text{pdf } f(x) = \begin{cases} \dfrac{2x}{3} & 1 \le x \le 2 \\ 0 & \text{otherwise} \end{cases}$$

Find: **a** the cumulative distribution function $F(x)$
b $P(X \le 1.5)$ **c** the median.

a $F(x) = \int_1^x \frac{2}{3}u\,du = \frac{2}{3}\left[\frac{u^2}{2}\right]_1^x = \frac{2}{3}\left[\frac{x^2}{2} - \frac{1}{2}\right] = \frac{x^2}{3} - \frac{1}{3}$ for $1 \le x \le 2$

b $P(X \le 1.5) = F(1.5) = \frac{1.5^2}{3} - \frac{1}{3} = 0.417$

c $F(m) = \frac{m^2}{3} - \frac{1}{3} = \frac{1}{2}$

multiplying by 6, $2m^2 - 2 = 3$

$m^2 = \frac{5}{2}$

$m = 1.58$

Example 2 The cumulative distribution function for a continuous random variable X

$$\text{is } F(x) = \begin{cases} 0 & x < 1 \\ \dfrac{1}{45}(-x^2 + 20x - 19) & 1 \le x \le 4 \\ 1 & x > 4 \end{cases}$$

Find $f(x)$ and sketch the pdf.

$$f(x) = F'(x) = \begin{cases} 0 & x < 1 \\ \dfrac{1}{45}(-2x + 20) & 1 \le x \le 4 \\ 0 & x > 4 \end{cases}$$

$$\text{i.e. } f(x) = \begin{cases} \dfrac{2}{45}(10 - x) & 1 \le x \le 4 \\ 0 & \text{otherwise} \end{cases}$$

EXERCISE 4.9A

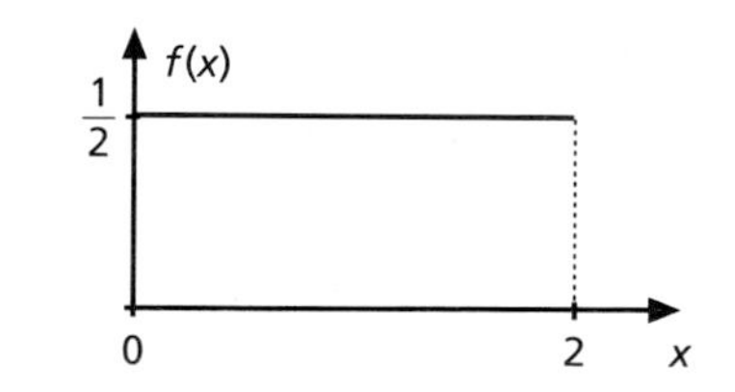

1 Find and sketch the cumulative distribution function for the random variable X where $f(x) = \begin{cases} \frac{1}{2} & 0 \le x \le 2 \\ 0 & \text{otherwise} \end{cases}$

2 Find the cumulative distribution function for the following random variables with pdfs given by:

a $f(x) = \begin{cases} \frac{1}{18}x & 0 \le x \le 6 \\ 0 & \text{otherwise} \end{cases}$

b $f(x) = \begin{cases} \frac{3}{32}x(4 - x) & 0 \le x \le 4 \\ 0 & \text{otherwise} \end{cases}$

c $f(x) = \begin{cases} \frac{3}{10}(2 - x^2) & -1 \le x \le 1 \\ 0 & \text{otherwise} \end{cases}$

3 Given the following cumulative distribution functions $F(x)$, find $f(x)$ and sketch the pdfs.

a $F(x) = \begin{cases} 0 & x < 0 \\ \frac{x}{2} & 0 \le x \le 2 \\ 1 & x > 2 \end{cases}$

b $F(x) = \begin{cases} 0 & x < -1 \\ \frac{x^2}{8} + \frac{x}{2} + \frac{3}{8} & -1 \le x \le 1 \\ 1 & x > 1 \end{cases}$

c $F(x) = \begin{cases} 0 & x < -2 \\ \frac{x^3}{16} + \frac{1}{2} & -2 \le x \le 2 \\ 1 & x > 2 \end{cases}$

4 $F(X)$ is the cumulative distribution function for the random variable X and $F(x) = \begin{cases} 0 & x < -1 \\ \frac{1}{4}(x+1) & -1 \le x \le 3 \\ 1 & x > 3 \end{cases}$

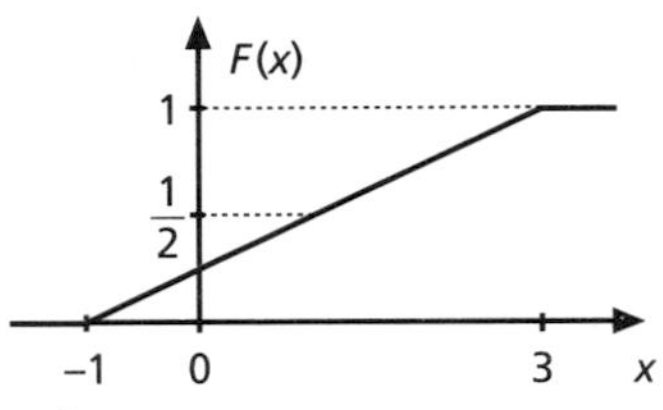

a Explain why the median $m = 1$ from the symmetry of the graph.

b Check that $F(m) = \frac{1}{2}$.

EXERCISE 4.9B

1 Find the median value of the random variable X when the cumulative distribution function is:

a $F(x) = \begin{cases} 0 & x < 0 \\ \frac{x^2}{144} & 0 \le x \le 12 \\ 1 & x > 12 \end{cases}$

b $F(x) = \begin{cases} 0 & x < 0 \\ \frac{x^3}{8} & 0 \le x \le 2 \\ 1 & x > 2 \end{cases}$

2 In an efficiency study, the time in minutes between consecutive customers arriving in a bank queue, T, is found to be a random variable with pdf given by

$$f(t) = \begin{cases} 1 - \frac{t}{2} & 0 \le t \le 2 \\ 0 & \text{otherwise} \end{cases}$$

a Sketch the pdf.

b Find and sketch the cumulative distribution function $F(t)$.

c Find the probability that the time between consecutive customers is more than 30 seconds.

3 For the random variable X, an angle measured in radians, whose pdf is given by

$$f(x) = \begin{cases} k(\pi - x) & 0 < x < \pi \\ 0 & \text{otherwise} \end{cases}$$

a find k and $E(X)$

b find the cumulative distribution function of X

c calculate $P(X < \frac{\pi}{4})$.

4 For the random variable X, an angle measured in radians, whose pdf is given by

$$f(x) = \begin{cases} kx(\pi - x) & 0 < x < \frac{\pi}{2} \\ 0 & \text{otherwise} \end{cases}$$

a find the cumulative distribution function of X

b calculate $P(X > \frac{\pi}{4})$.

CHAPTER 4 REVIEW

1 A supermarket's records of 4000 customers show that the frequency of the number of magazines or newspapers purchased per customer is as follows:

Number of magazines/newspapers						
0	1	2	3	4	5	≥5
Frequency						
1684	832	656	408	332	88	0

Find:

a an estimate of the probability distribution of M, the number of magazines/newspapers purchased per customer

b $P(1 \le M \le 4)$ **c** $P(M \ge 2)$.

2 If D is the discrete random variable defined by the formula: $P(D = d) = \begin{cases} k & d = 0, 1, 2 \\ kd & d = 3, 4 \end{cases}$

find:

a k, and so the values in probability distribution of D

b $E(D)$ **c** $Var(D)$ using the formula $Var(D) = E(D^2) - (E(D))^2$.

3 20% of fish at a fish farm are infected with a parasite. The farm manager samples four fish daily. Let F = the number of fish infected with the parasite from a sample of four. By drawing a tree diagram, find the probability distribution of F and the cumulative probability distribution.

4 The random variable X has a pdf given by

$$f(x) = \begin{cases} \frac{1}{4}(x+1) & 0 \le x \le 2 \\ 0 & \text{otherwise} \end{cases}$$

a Sketch the function and show that $f(x)$ satisfies the conditions for a pdf.

b Find: (i) $P(X > 1)$ (ii) $E(X)$ (iii) $Var(X)$ and $SD(X)$.

5 Find and sketch the cumulative distribution function for X when $f(x) = \begin{cases} \frac{1}{8} & -4 \le x \le 4 \\ 0 & \text{otherwise} \end{cases}$

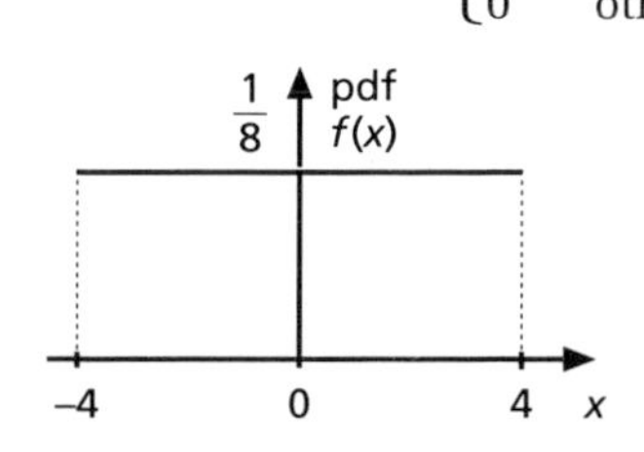

6 The time T seconds between vehicles passing over a particular bridge is thought to be modelled by the pdf

$$f(t) = \begin{cases} \frac{1}{50}(10 - t) & 0 \le t \le 10 \\ 0 & \text{otherwise} \end{cases}$$

a Find the average or expected time between vehicles passing over the bridge.

b By considering the cumulative distribution function, find the probability that the time between vehicles is less than average.

7 Find the pdf of the random variable X when the cumulative distribution function is given by

$$F(x) = \begin{cases} 0 & x < -2 \\ \frac{(x+2)}{3} & -2 \le x \le 1 \\ 1 & x > 1 \end{cases}$$

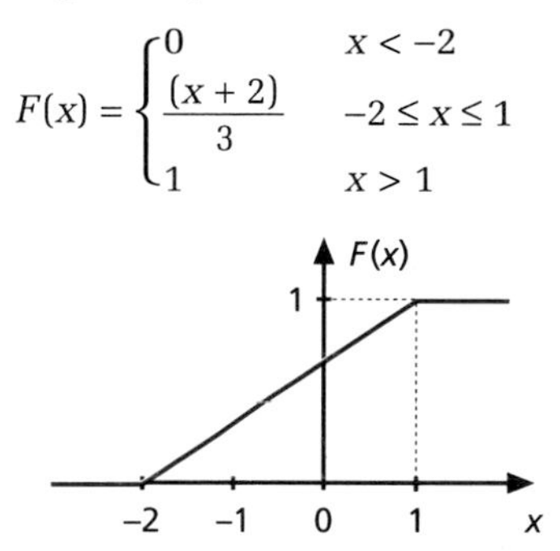

8 Seeds of a certain variety of plant are nine times more likely to germinate as not. One seed is sown in each pot. Pots are joined in strips of three. Show that the probability distribution of S, the number of seeds germinating in a strip, is given by:

s	0	1	2	3
$P(S = s)$	0.001	0.027	0.243	0.729

Find the cumulative probability distribution of S and use it to simulate the sowing of seeds in ten strips.

CHAPTER 4 SUMMARY

Random variable, R (continuous or discrete)
A quantity, R, whose value depends on the outcome of a random experiment.

Probability distribution of a discrete random variable
A table or formula giving the probabilities p_i associated with each value of a random variable where $0 \le p_i \le 1$, $\Sigma p_i = 1$.

Expected value or mean of a discrete random variable, D
μ or $\mathrm{E}(D)$ is a representative or average value of the random variable D.
$\mathrm{E}(D) = \Sigma p_i d_i$

Variance of a discrete random variable, D
σ^2 or $\mathrm{Var}(D)$ indicates the spread of the random variable D about the mean.
$\mathrm{Var}(D) = \Sigma p_i (d_i - \mu)^2$ or
$\mathrm{Var}(D) = \mathrm{E}(D^2) - (\mathrm{E}(D))^2$
where $\mathrm{E}(D^2) = \Sigma p_i (d_i)^2$

Standard deviation of a discrete random variable
$\sigma = \sqrt{\mathrm{Var}(D)}$ measures the spread of the random variable D about the mean, in the same units as D.

Probability density function or pdf of a continuous random variable X, $f(x)$
If $f(x)$ is the pdf of X, then

$$P(x_1 \le X \le x_2) = \int_{x_1}^{x_2} f(x)\mathrm{d}x$$

$f(x) \ge 0$ for all x, and $\int_{-\infty}^{\infty} f(x)\mathrm{d}x = 1$.

Expected value or mean of a continuous random variable X
μ or $\mathrm{E}(X)$ is a representative value or average of the random variable X.

$\mathrm{E}(X) = \int_a^b xf(x)\mathrm{d}x$ where the pdf $f(x)$ is defined on the interval $a \le x \le b$.

Variance of a continuous random variable X
σ^2 or $\mathrm{Var}(X)$ indicates the spread of the random variable X about the mean.
$\mathrm{Var}(X) = \mathrm{E}(X^2) - (\mathrm{E}(X))^2$

where $\mathrm{E}(X^2) = \int_a^b x^2 f(x)\mathrm{d}x$ and the pdf $f(x)$ is defined on the interval $a \le x \le b$.

Cumulative distribution function of a continuous random variable X, $F(x)$

$F(x) = \mathrm{P}(X \le x)$ or $\mathrm{P}(X < x) = \int_a^x f(u)\mathrm{d}u$

where the pdf $f(x)$ is defined on the interval $a \le x \le b$.
$F(x)$ is a non-decreasing function.

Median of a continuous random variable X
If m is the median of the random variable X, $F(m) = \frac{1}{2}$.

Mode of a continuous random variable X
The mode, if it exists, is the value of x which occurs with the highest probability density and may be at a local maximum point.

5 Correlation and Regression

In Chapter 2 we saw how useful a scatter diagram is in deciding whether or not a relationship exists between two variables. For example, the bivariate data, height and weight of boys in Class 1B in June 1996 showed a moderately strong positive relationship, i.e. boys who are taller also tend to be heavier.

In this example the relationship is approximately **linear**, i.e. the relationship could be summarised by a 'best fitting' *straight line.* There are many other forms of relationship such as quadratic, exponential, logarithmic, and so on. This chapter is only concerned with linear relationships.

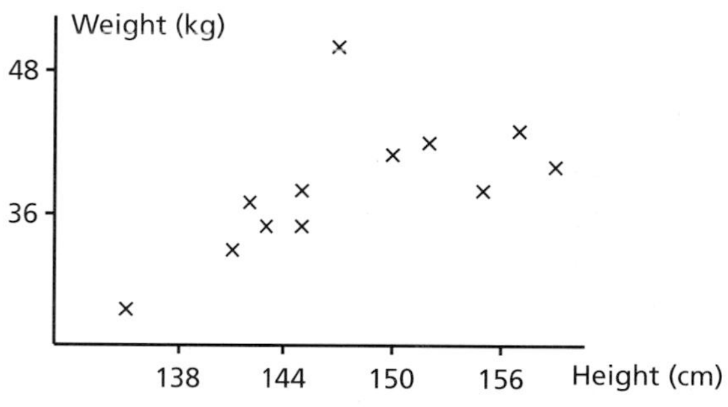

When a scatter diagram shows evidence of a linear relationship, the experimenter would often want to know more:

- Can the strength of any linear relationship be measured?
- If the relationship is strong and points on the scatter diagram lie approximately on a straight line, can the equation of the line be found and used for prediction?

In this chapter we learn how to find a correlation coefficient (a measure of the strength of a linear relationship) and how to find a linear regression line (the equation of a line of best fit).

Correlation

The scatter diagram is *always* the first step in deciding the amount of association or correlation in a linear relationship. Then, without any calculation, it is possible to describe the relationship as positive, negative or non-existent, and the strength of the relationship as strong, moderate or weak. Here are some examples.

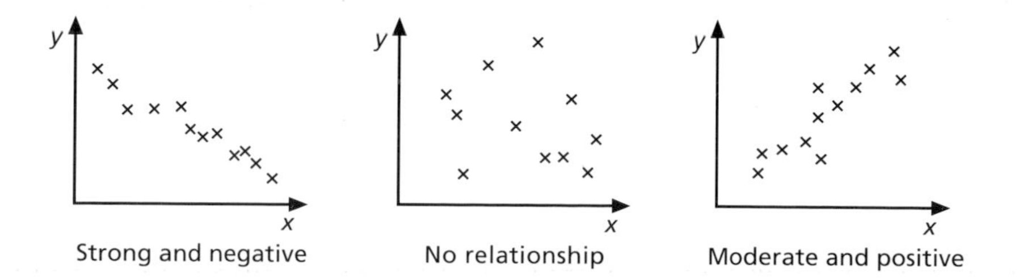

The scatter diagram also indicates whether the relationship is non-linear, in which case there may be no point in looking further for a measure of the linear correlation. This diagram shows a strong non-linear relationship, possibly a quadratic relationship. A numerical value to describe the extent of **linear correlation** in a data set, the **correlation coefficient *r***, is calculated in such a way that it takes a value between –1 and 1 where:

$r = -1$ indicates perfect negative linear correlation (all points lie exactly on a straight line with negative gradient)

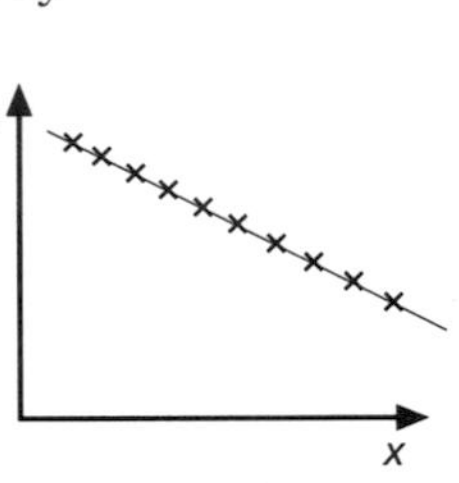

$r = 0$ indicates no linear correlation, e.g.

$r = 1$ indicates perfect positive linear correlation (all points lie exactly on a straight line with positive gradient).

Other values of r can be described using this **correlation guide**:

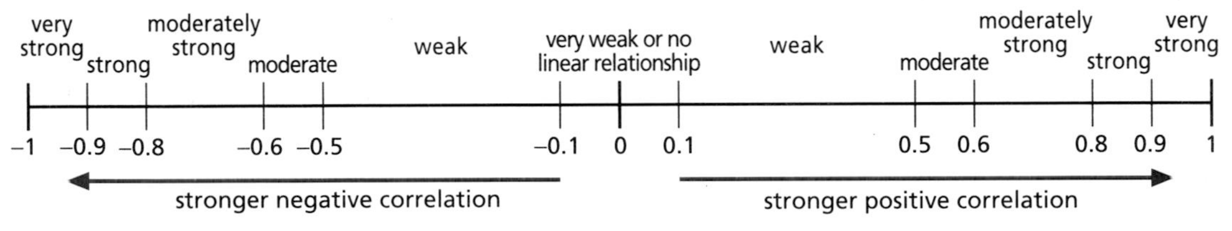

Note The value of r:

(i) is not the gradient of the line

(ii) does not depend on the units of measurement, e.g. weight could be measured in kilograms or grams

(iii) does not depend on which of the two variables is labelled as x.

Usually data are collected so that some inference can be made about a population. The correlation coefficient, r, is calculated for a sample and therefore gives an estimate of the population correlation coefficient.

EXERCISE 5.1

1 What kind of linear correlation do you think there is between the following variables: positive, negative or none?

a exam results and the time spent on homework

b age of smoker and number of cigarettes smoked

c money spent on national lottery tickets and the jackpot prize
d number of policemen on the beat and amount of vandalism
e marks in a physics exam and marks in an art exam

2 Draw a scatter diagram to illustrate the relationship between these pairs of variables. Show at least ten points.
a sales of soft drinks and outside temperature
b weight of school children and their IQ
c number of absences from school and number of A grades in a national exam
d amount of pocket money and age

3 Describe the strength of the correlation shown in the following scatter diagrams using the words perfect, strong, moderate, weak, no relation, positive, negative.

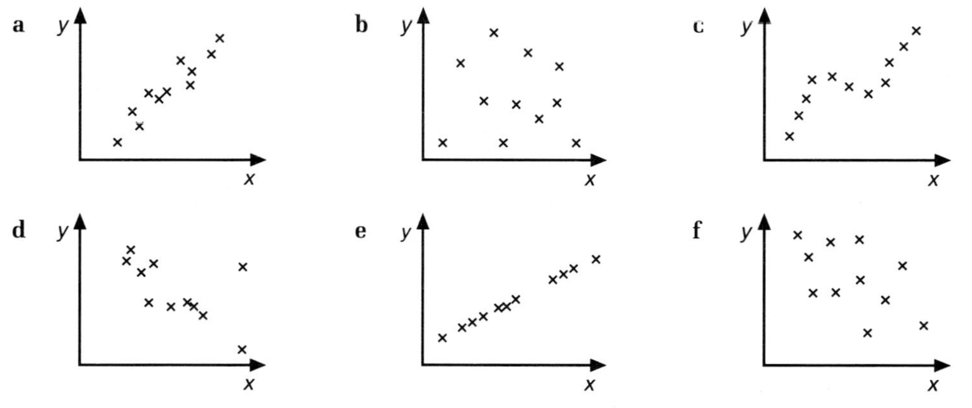

4 Using the given correlation guide, describe the linear correlation between x and y when:
a $r = 0.85$ **b** $r = -0.95$ **c** $r = 0.05$ **d** $r = -0.45$ **e** $r = 0.68$.

Pearson's Product Moment Correlation Coefficient

The most widely used correlation coefficient is **Pearson's Product Moment Correlation Coefficient**. The formula for r comes from considering deviations from the mean in both the x and y variables.

$$r = \frac{\Sigma(x_i - \overline{x})(y_i - \overline{y})}{\sqrt{\Sigma(x_i - \overline{x})^2 \Sigma(y_i - \overline{y})^2}} \text{ or } \frac{S_{xy}}{\sqrt{S_{xx}S_{yy}}}$$

Now $\Sigma(x_i - \overline{x})(y_i - \overline{y})$ is difficult to calculate, but can be simplified as follows:

$$\begin{aligned}\Sigma(x_i - \overline{x})(y_i - \overline{y}) &= \Sigma(x_i y_i - x_i \overline{y} - \overline{x} y_i + \overline{x}\,\overline{y}) \\ &= \Sigma x_i y_i - \Sigma x_i \overline{y} - \Sigma \overline{x} y_i + \Sigma \overline{x}\,\overline{y} \\ &= \Sigma xy - \overline{y}\Sigma x - \overline{x}\Sigma y + n\overline{x}\,\overline{y} \\ &= \Sigma xy - \frac{\Sigma y}{n}\Sigma x - \frac{\Sigma x}{n}\Sigma y + \not{n}\frac{\Sigma x}{\not{n}}\frac{\Sigma y}{n} \\ &= \Sigma xy - \frac{\Sigma x \Sigma y}{n} \text{ (a theoretical proof!)}\end{aligned}$$

and similarly it can be shown that $\Sigma(x_i - \overline{x})^2 = \Sigma x^2 - \dfrac{(\Sigma x)^2}{n}$

and $\Sigma(y_i - \overline{y})^2 = \Sigma y^2 - \dfrac{(\Sigma y)^2}{n}$

giving Pearson's Product Moment Correlation Coefficient:

$$r = \frac{S_{xy}}{\sqrt{S_{xx}S_{yy}}} \quad \text{where} \quad S_{xy} = \Sigma xy - \frac{(\Sigma x)(\Sigma y)}{n}$$

$$S_{xx} = \Sigma x^2 - \frac{(\Sigma x)^2}{n}$$

$$S_{yy} = \Sigma y^2 - \frac{(\Sigma y)^2}{n}$$

Example 1 Draw the scatter diagram and calculate r for the following data set:

x	1	2	3	4
y	1	3	5	5

(This is a simple example to illustrate the method – a larger data set is needed for the sample correlation coefficient to be a good estimate of the population correlation!)

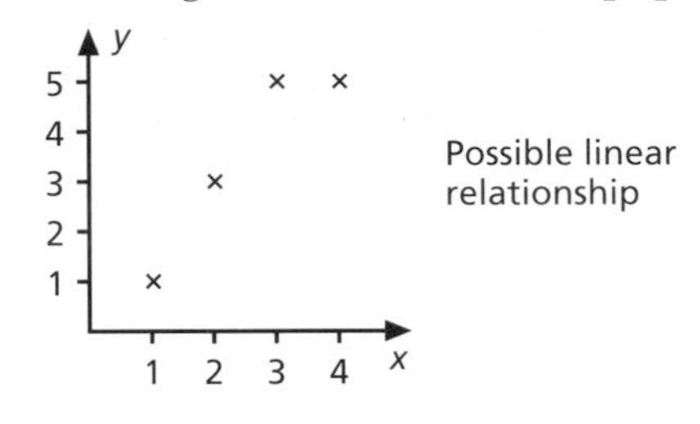

Firstly, since the formula involves several sums, the data may be rearranged to form a table.

	x	y	x^2	y^2	xy
	1	1	1	1	1
	2	3	4	9	6
	3	5	9	25	15
	4	5	16	25	20
Totals	10	14	30	60	42

$n = 4$
$\Sigma x = 10$
$\Sigma y = 14$
$\Sigma x^2 = 30$
$\Sigma y^2 = 60$
$\Sigma xy = 42$

$$S_{xy} = \Sigma xy - \frac{(\Sigma x)(\Sigma y)}{n} = 42 - \frac{(10)(14)}{4} = 7$$

$$S_{xx} = \Sigma x^2 - \frac{(\Sigma x)^2}{n} = 30 - \frac{(10)^2}{4} = 5$$

$$S_{yy} = \Sigma y^2 - \frac{(\Sigma y)^2}{n} = 60 - \frac{(14)^2}{4} = 11$$

$$r = \frac{S_{xy}}{\sqrt{S_{xx}S_{yy}}} = \frac{7}{\sqrt{5 \times 11}} = 0.944,$$ a very strong positive correlation.

Example 2 For the data whose scatter diagram is shown in the introduction on page 109 (height and weight of boys in Class 1B in June 1996), calculate r and comment.

Height (cm)	157	145	159	143	142	152	147	135	141	155	150	145
Weight (kg)	43	35	40	35	37	42	50	28	33	38	41	38

The scatter diagram shows a possible linear relationship so it is appropriate to calculate a correlation coefficient.

	Height x	Weight y	x^2	y^2	xy
	157	43	24 649	1849	6751
	145	35	21 025	1225	5075
	159	40	25 281	1600	6360
	143	35	20 449	1225	5005
	142	37	20 164	1369	5254
	152	42	23 104	1764	6384
	147	50	21 609	2500	7350
	135	28	18 225	784	3780
	141	33	19 881	1089	4653
	155	38	24 025	1444	5890
	150	41	22 500	1681	6150
	145	38	21 025	1444	5510
Totals	1771	460	261 937	17 974	68 162

$$n = 12$$
$$\Sigma x = 1771$$
$$\Sigma y = 460$$
$$\Sigma x^2 = 261\,937$$
$$\Sigma y^2 = 17\,974$$
$$\Sigma xy = 68\,162$$

$$S_{xy} = \Sigma xy - \frac{(\Sigma x)(\Sigma y)}{n} = 68\,162 - \frac{(1771)(460)}{12} = 273.667$$

$$S_{xx} = \Sigma x^2 - \frac{(\Sigma x)^2}{n} = 261\,937 - \frac{(1771)^2}{12} = 566.917$$

$$S_{yy} = \Sigma y^2 - \frac{(\Sigma y)^2}{n} = 17\,974 - \frac{(460)^2}{12} = 340.667$$

$$r = \frac{S_{xy}}{\sqrt{S_{xx}S_{yy}}} = \frac{273.667}{\sqrt{5.66.917 \times 340.667}}$$
$$= 0.623$$

i.e. the correlation coefficient for the height and weight of boys in Class 1B in June 1996 is 0.623, showing a moderately strong positive relationship.

Note (i) S_{xx}, S_{yy} will always be positive, whereas S_{xy} will be positive if the correlation is positive or negative if the correlation is negative.
(ii) Compare S_{xx} with the formula for variance of x given in Chapter 1.

$$s^2 = \frac{\Sigma x_i^2 - (\Sigma x_i)^2/n}{n-1} = \frac{S_{xx}}{n-1}$$ S_{xx} is the numerator!

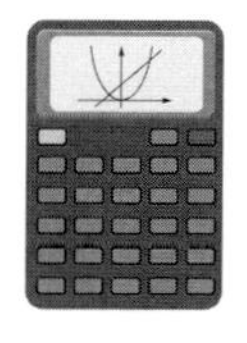

Many scientific and graphics calculators will calculate r directly. All you have to do is input the data. Find out if your calculator will do this. You may need to go into LR mode. For real data, these calculations can be tedious. In exam questions summary totals may be given.
(Graphics calculators and spreadsheet packages will usually also draw scatter diagrams.)

EXERCISE 5.2A

1 For the following data sets, first draw a scatter diagram then calculate r using the formula $r = \frac{S_{xy}}{\sqrt{S_{xx}S_{yy}}}$. Comment on your results.

a

x	1	2	3	4
y	6	10	11	12

b

x	11	12	13	14	15
y	10	9	13	8	6

c

x	2	3	4	5	6	7
y	4	6	9	5	6	8

d

x	0.1	0.2	0.3	0.4	0.5	0.6	0.7
y	9	4	1	0	1	4	9

2 The data set gives backfat thickness (bft) in millimetres, and lean meat content (lmc) in percentages, measured for pig carcasses at Wye College, University of London in the 1970s.

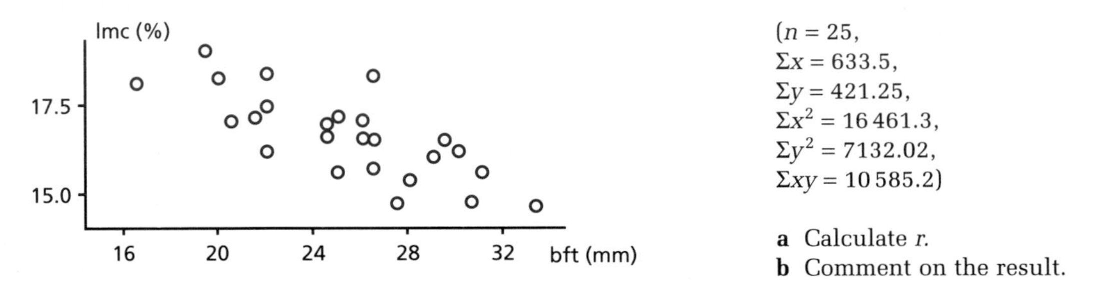

($n = 25$,
$\Sigma x = 633.5$,
$\Sigma y = 421.25$,
$\Sigma x^2 = 16\,461.3$,
$\Sigma y^2 = 7132.02$,
$\Sigma xy = 10\,585.2$)

a Calculate r.
b Comment on the result.

3 This data set is from Slim-Jim's Diet Plan, which you met in Chapter 2, showing initial weight and weight loss after one month.

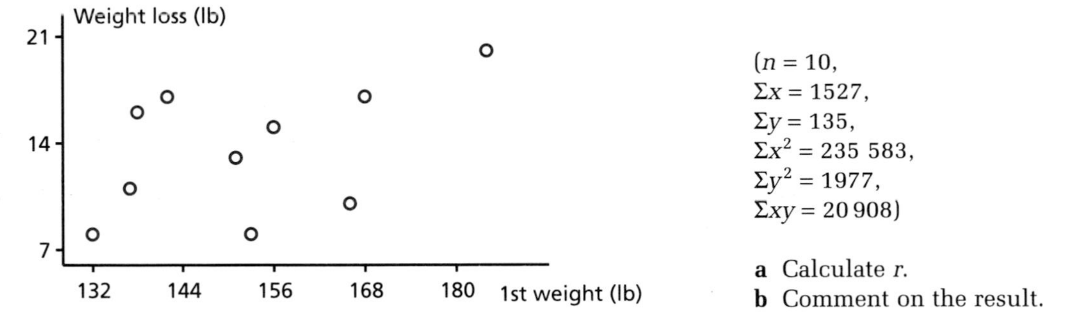

($n = 10$,
$\Sigma x = 1527$,
$\Sigma y = 135$,
$\Sigma x^2 = 235\,583$,
$\Sigma y^2 = 1977$,
$\Sigma xy = 20\,908$)

a Calculate r.
b Comment on the result.

4 The distance as the crow flies and the distance by road between various places in Sheffield are shown in this data set from Chapter 2.

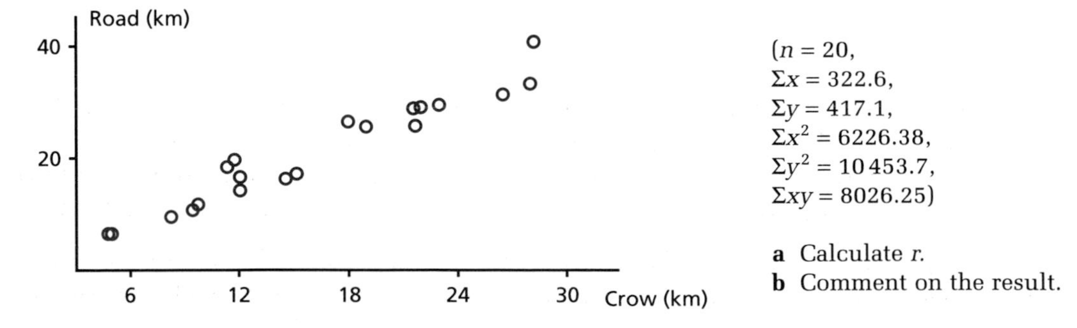

($n = 20$,
$\Sigma x = 322.6$,
$\Sigma y = 417.1$,
$\Sigma x^2 = 6226.38$,
$\Sigma y^2 = 10\,453.7$,
$\Sigma xy = 8026.25$)

a Calculate r.
b Comment on the result.

5 Collect your own data! (Measuring is required.) As a class, collect data on finger span (to the nearest half centimetre) and height (centimetres).
Draw a scatter diagram and calculate the correlation coefficient.
Is there a strong relationship between finger span and height?

EXERCISE 5.2B

1 In Chapter 2, Exercise 2.5A, the scatter diagrams for these data sets showed a linear relationship. For each set calculate r and comment on the relationship.

a Heights and weights of boys, December 1996

Height (cm)	162	154	160	145	146	153	157	136	143	161	157	146
Weight (kg)	44	41	43	34	40	40	48	29	38	43	43	38

b Toy car experiment

X (cm)	10	10	10	20	20	20	30	30	30	40	40	40	50	50	50	60	60	60
Y (cm)	53	48	45	55	58	56	70	66	68	73	88	89	96	96	96	103	105	109

c Heights and weights again!

Weight (kg)	41	43	34	40	40	48	29	38	43	43	38	44
Height (m)	1.54	1.60	1.45	1.46	1.53	1.57	1.36	1.43	1.61	1.57	1.46	1.62

2 The secondhand prices and ages of various Ford Fiesta 1.1 motorcars were noted from a local newspaper in 1997 as follows:

Year	1985	1989	1987	1989	1995	1992	1992	1990	1988	1991	1993	1994
Age (years)	12	8	10	8	2	5	5	7	11	6	4	3
Price (£)	750	2395	975	1950	5195	3695	2850	2250	900	2200	4495	4675

On the basis of these data, comment fully on the relationship between age and price.

3 Collect your own data! (A ruler is required.) Copy the following sentence on a horizontal line in your normal handwriting:

Statistics is not a spectator sport.

Measure the length of the sentence in millimetres. Using all the data from the class, draw a scatter diagram illustrating length of the sentence in millimetres versus finger span to the nearest half centimetre (as measured in Exercise 5.2A).
If two or more data points coincide exactly on the scatter diagram how could you show this?
Comment on the relationship.

Correlation coefficients: beware!

Cause and effect

Although a high value of r may indicate a strong relationship between two variables, it does not necessarily indicate that changes in one variable *cause* changes in the other. There may be a third variable to which both variables are related. Also the relationship may be entirely coincidental, in which case we say there is a **spurious** correlation.

For example, in primary schools there is a strong correlation between the amount of tooth decay and reading ability. However it would never be suggested that allowing teeth to decay improves reading ability, neither does improving reading cause tooth decay. They are both related to the age of the child. The only way a causal relationship can be established is to carry out further investigations where any other variables which might be influencing the study are carefully controlled. A study which considered tooth decay and reading ability of children with the same age would undoubtedly show little relationship.

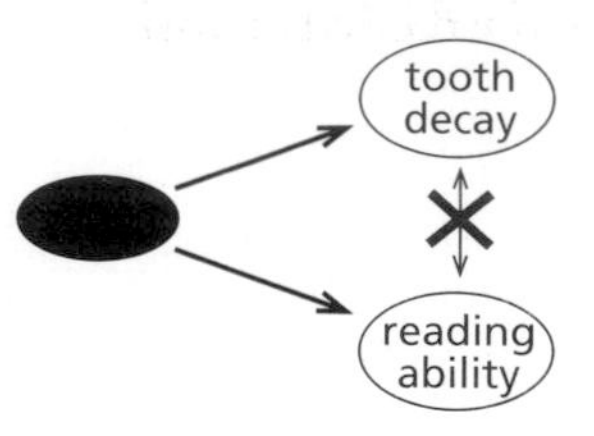

If one variable (x) causes changes in another variable (y) then x is known as the independent or **predictor** or **explanatory** variable and y is known as the dependent or **response** variable. But remember when calculating correlation coefficient it does not matter which variable is labelled x or y.

Outliers

If the scatter diagram exhibits points which are extraordinary in any way, i.e. **outliers**, it is often useful to consider the effect that these points have on the calculation of r. Always consider whether the outlier has been recorded incorrectly, in which case it can be ignored in the calculation of correlation coefficient. If an outlier is indeed a legitimate point then it may well have a considerable effect on the value of the correlation coefficient.

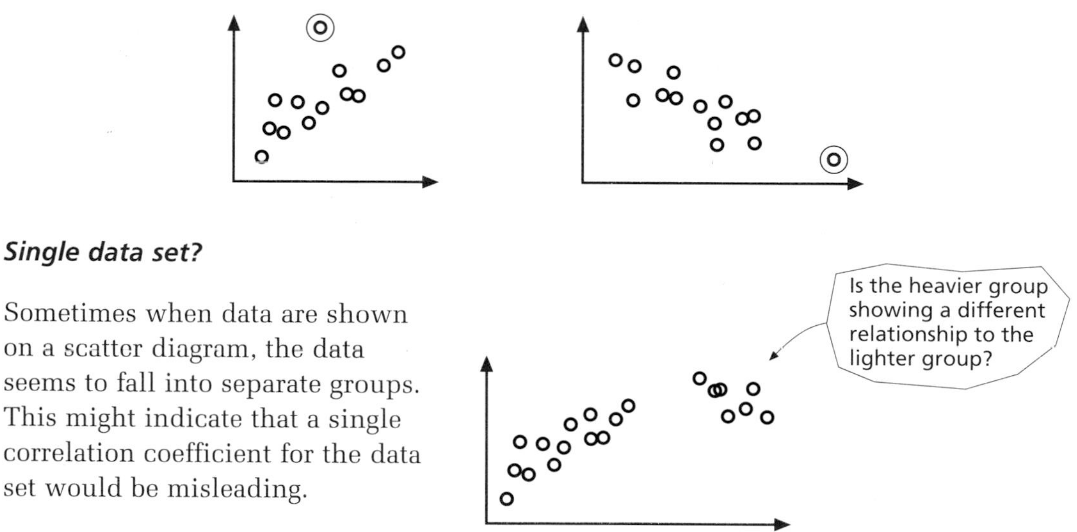

Single data set?

Sometimes when data are shown on a scatter diagram, the data seems to fall into separate groups. This might indicate that a single correlation coefficient for the data set would be misleading.

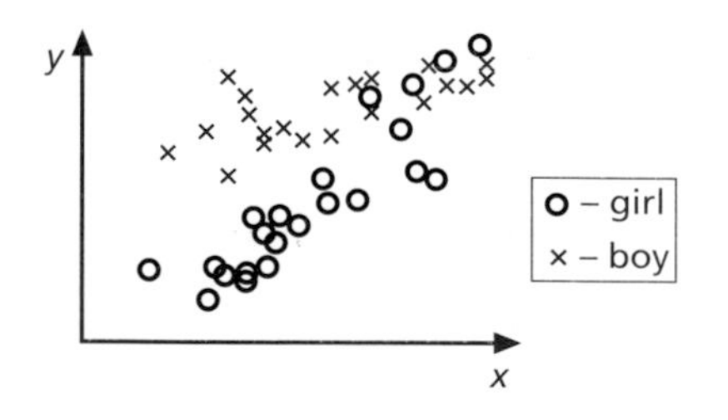

Alternatively, data may appear as a single set in the scatter diagram but in reality represent two different groups. For example, boys and girls may exhibit different trends which become disguised if the data set is plotted as a single group of pupils.

EXERCISE 5.3B

1 For the following variables which are related, say which is the predictor and which is the response variable. If you think the relationship is not causal, suggest a possible variable which is influencing both. For example, for 'amount of sunburn, suntan lotion protection factor' the suntan lotion protection factor is the predictor variable, and the amount of sunburn is the response variable (it depends on the protection factor).

a	exam performance,	amount of revision
b	amount of fertiliser,	crop yield
c	reading ability,	mathematical ability
d	number unemployed,	amount spent on social security
e	lung cancer rates,	number of cigarettes smoked
f	number of doctors in a town,	number of deaths in the town
g	height,	reading ability
h	policemen's salary over a period of years,	amount of crime over a period of years

2 Suppose the boy recorded as being the heaviest in Class 1B in June 1996 (page 112) had inadvertently been weighed with his blazer and shoes on, whereas the other boys had not. This would be justification for ignoring these values and recalculating r.
These data gave $r = 0.623$.

Height (cm)	157	145	159	143	142	152	147	135	141	155	150	145
Weight (kg)	43	35	40	35	37	42	50	28	33	38	41	38

a Recalculate the correlation coefficient ignoring the heavy boy's data.
b Suppose the short boy was actually several months younger than the others. Recalculate the correlation coefficient ignoring his data.
c In each case say what the effect is of removing the outlier.

3 The scatter diagram shows systolic blood pressure (y) measured in millimetres of mercury and the age (x) measured in years for a sample of women considered to be in good health.

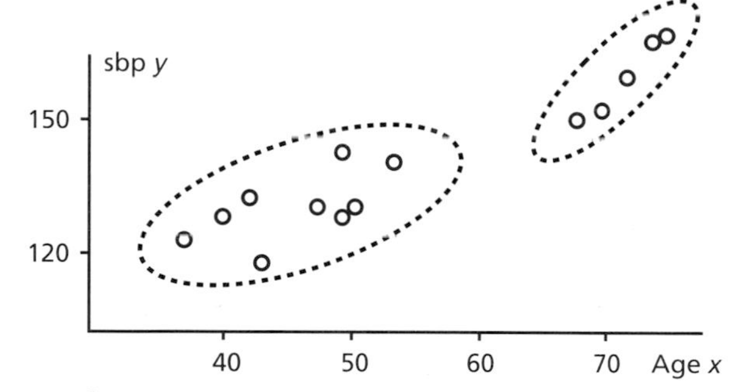

a Calculate the correlation coefficient for each group separately given the summary totals.
Younger group:
$n = 9$, $\Sigma x = 410$, $\Sigma y = 1156$, $\Sigma x^2 = 18\,902$, $\Sigma y^2 = 148\,980$, $\Sigma xy = 52\,873$
Older group:
$n = 5$, $\Sigma x = 354$, $\Sigma y = 790$, $\Sigma x^2 = 25\,096$, $\Sigma y^2 = 125\,114$, $\Sigma xy = 56\,029$
b Is there a different correlation for the younger women than for the older women in this sample? What conclusion can you draw about older and younger women in general?

4 The scatter diagram shows percentage unemployment in eleven regions of Britain in 1987 and the corresponding percentages of household weekly expenditure spent on motoring and travel fares in 1986/7 from Chapter 2.

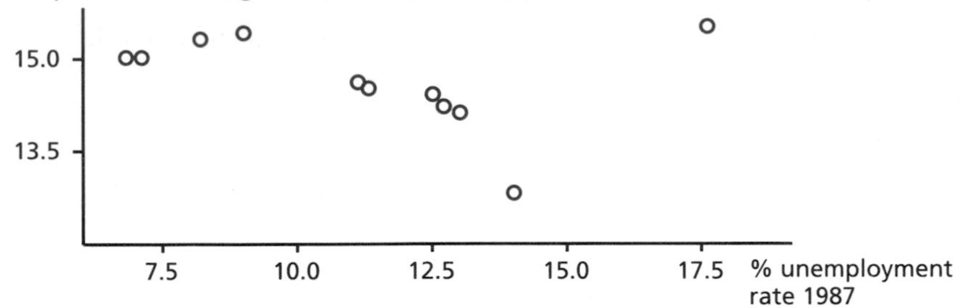

($n = 11$, $\Sigma x = 123.3$, $\Sigma y = 160.8$, $\Sigma x^2 = 1488.09$, $\Sigma y^2 = 2356.56$, $\Sigma xy = 1794.11$)

a Calculate the correlation coefficient for the whole data set.

b The outlier is Northern Ireland whose unemployment rate was 17.6% and average percentage of household weekly expenditure spent on motoring and travel fares was 15.5. Why would it be useful to recalculate r ignoring Northern Ireland? Calculate the revised value of r and comment on the relationship between percentage unemployment and percentage spent on travel.

5 As part of an investigation into the connection between index finger length and height of pupils in first year, the following data were collected by a sixth year class (read the data across):

Boys' height (mm)

1485 1524 1535 1437 1575 1610 1519 1557 1596 1535 1487 1565 1497 1531
1640 1608 1698 1480 1614 1510 1566 1539 1586 1684 1651 1692 1627 1593
1511 1642 1635 1760 1716 1568 1633 1825 1739 1648 1661 1652 1689 1538

Boys' index finger length (mm)

69 73 70 69 67 77 71 73 69 74 71 73 77 73 76 77 75 64 72 68 72
65 72 68 74 74 62 69 74 77 77 90 78 72 75 88 77 75 71 71 80 67

Girls' height (mm)

1615 1620 1542 1672 1732 1651 1557 1630 1596 1739 1740 1582 1713 1733
1574 1690 1673 1518 1533 1720 1625 1626 1740 1638 1763 1663 1580 1637
1568 1696 1609 1626 1642 1665 1613 1743 1511 1717 1649 1566 1599 1575

Girls' index finger length (mm)

77 67 66 70 86 78 76 78 76 74 84 75 77 79 80 75 75 70 76 75 71
81 82 77 86 77 76 75 73 75 77 66 66 72 75 82 72 71 73 74 63 71

giving the following scatter diagrams:

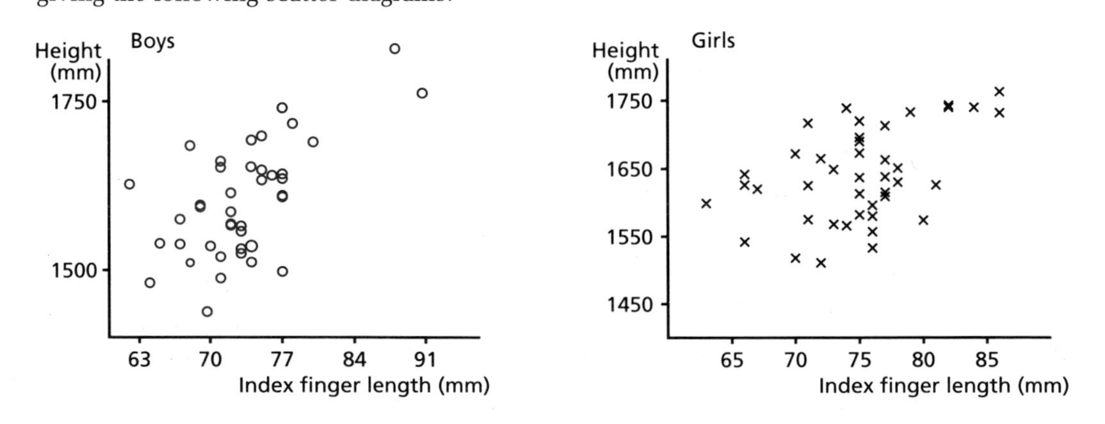

The summary totals for the boys and girls separately are:
Boys
$n = 42$, $\Sigma x = 67\,158$, $\Sigma y = 3066$, $\Sigma x^2 = 107\,678\,576$, $\Sigma y^2 = 225\,008$, $\Sigma xy = 4\,914\,225$
Girls
$n = 42$, $\Sigma x = 68\,881$, $\Sigma y = 3149$, $\Sigma x^2 = 113\,158\,608$, $\Sigma y^2 = 237\,217$, $\Sigma xy = 5\,171\,381$

a Find the correlation coefficient for each data set separately and comment on the strengths of the relationships.
Now the data sets are combined to give the following scatter diagram.

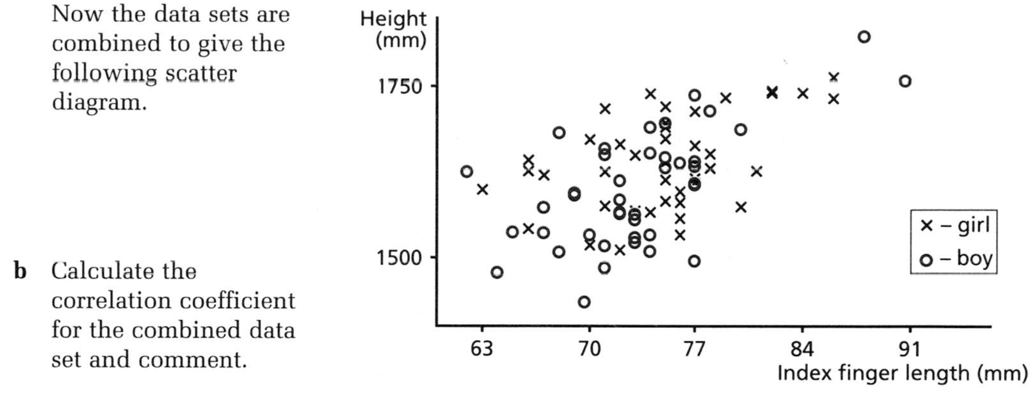

b Calculate the correlation coefficient for the combined data set and comment.

Linear regression – Fitting a linear model

In regression analysis, information on one variable is used to draw some conclusion about another variable. If a data set shows a moderate to strong linear relationship when a scatter diagram is drawn, and it is suspected that changes in one variable cause changes in the other variable, the experimenter or data handler would often be interested in establishing the equation of a best fitting straight line through the data. In this way, it is hoped to model the relationship between the two variables in the population. Conventionally the independent or predictor variable is plotted on the x-axis and the dependent or response variable on the y-axis. So an equation of the form

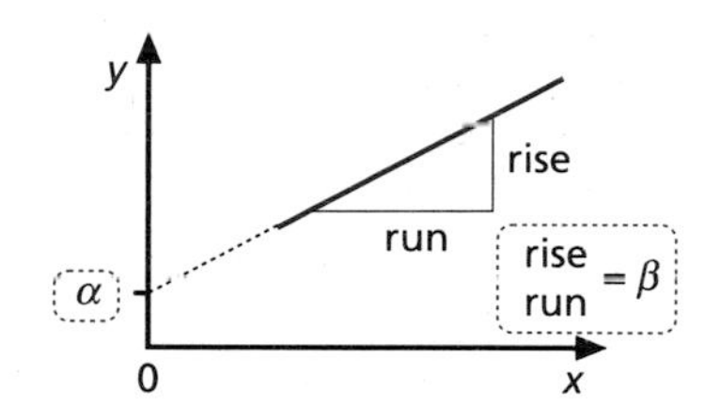

$$y = \alpha + \beta x$$

describing a well-fitting line through the points can be used to predict an *'average'* y value for a given x value. The gradient, β, gives the rate of change of y with respect to x, and α gives the vertical intercept or y intercept.

If there is **perfect linear correlation** between the two variables, then this equation would predict *exactly* the y values for given x values since all the points would lie on the line.
For example, there is perfect linear correlation between °C and °F and the equation is $(°F) = 32 + \frac{9}{5}(°C)$.
This equation can be used to predict exactly the temperature in °F given a temperature in °C and the gradient of the line $\frac{9}{5}$ indicates that a change of 1°C produces a change of $\frac{9}{5}$°F.

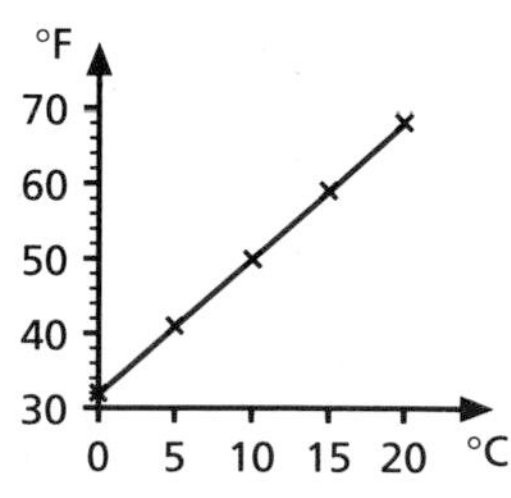

However, when the linear correlation is *less than perfect,* the problem is to try to find the best fitting straight line. One way of finding a best fitting line is by eye. This is a quick and easy method but, unfortunately, one person's judgement of the best fitting line through the points may be different from the next person's. If the points are reasonably close to a straight line this is a satisfactory method, but as the scatter increases it becomes much more difficult to fit a line by eye.

Data handlers need a more objective method of finding a best fitting line. When a data point is not actually on the proposed best fitting line, the y value predicted by the line will be subject to a **residual**, r.
So if $y = \alpha + \beta x$ is the equation of the proposed line, then for a data point (x_i, y_i)

$$y_i = \text{predicted } y + r_i$$

or $$y_i = (\alpha + \beta x_i) + r_i$$

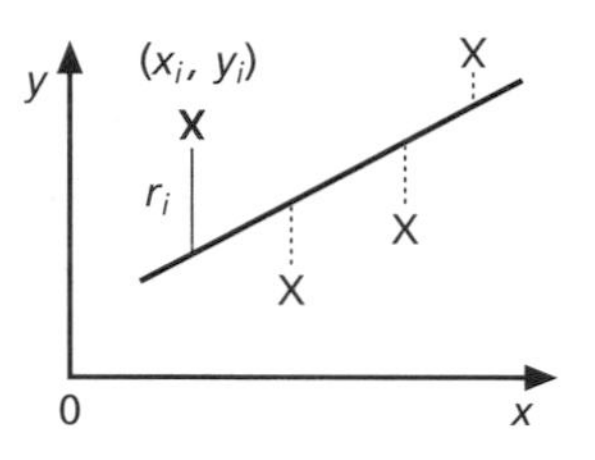

A good line would reduce these residuals as much as possible. Some residuals will be positive, some negative, so the residuals are squared then summed (a technique which has been used before to avoid positive and negative values cancelling each other out in a sum). The closer the points are to the line, the smaller the sum of the (residuals)^2 or $(r_i)^2$, the better the fit of the line!

The resulting process gives the **least squares line of best fit**, and the resulting equation is called the equation of the **regression line of *y* on x**. Working from first principles, using advanced calculus, is time-consuming and hard, but the values of α and β can be found readily using the following formulas.

The formula for the linear regression line of y on x is given by $y = \alpha + \beta x$ where values of α and β are estimated by the following formulas:

$$\hat{\beta} = \frac{S_{xy}}{S_{xx}} \text{ and } \hat{\alpha} = \bar{y} - \hat{\beta}\bar{x}$$

($\hat{\alpha}$ and $\hat{\beta}$ are calculated from the *sample* data set and are therefore estimators of the *population* parameters α and β.)

Note The least squares regression line always passes through the point $(\bar{x}, \bar{y})$. The line of best fit *by eye* can be improved by making it pass through the point $(\bar{x}, \bar{y})$.

Example 1 For this data set seen in an earlier example, find:

x	1	2	3	4
y	1	3	5	5

a the line of best fit by eye
b the linear regression line of y on x and draw it on the scatter diagram.
(This is a simple example to illustrate the method – a reliable line needs a larger data set.)

The required summary totals are: $n = 4$, $\Sigma x = 10$, $\Sigma y = 14$, $\Sigma x^2 = 30$, $\Sigma xy = 42$.

a Make the line of best fit by eye go through $(\bar{x}, \bar{y})$, with a balance of points each side of the line.

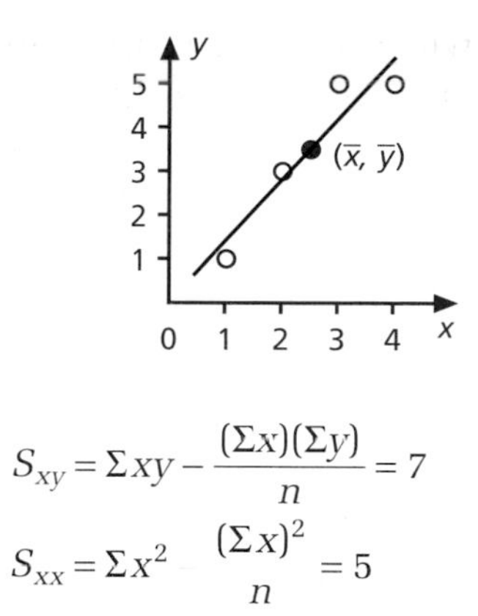

$\bar{x} = \frac{\Sigma x}{n} = \frac{10}{4} = 2.5$

$\bar{y} = \frac{\Sigma y}{n} = \frac{14}{4} = 3.5$

So $(\bar{x}, \bar{y}) = (2.5, 3.5)$

b

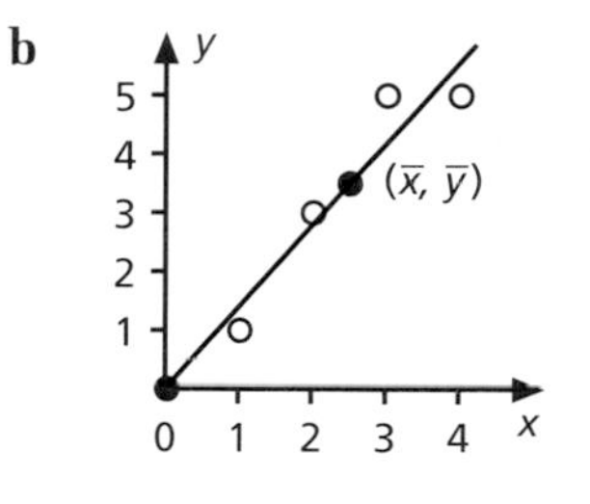

$S_{xy} = \Sigma xy - \frac{(\Sigma x)(\Sigma y)}{n} = 7$

$S_{xx} = \Sigma x^2 \; \frac{(\Sigma x)^2}{n} = 5$

gradient, $\hat{\beta} = \frac{S_{xy}}{S_{xx}} = \frac{7}{5} = 1.4$

vertical intercept, $\hat{\alpha} = \bar{y} - \hat{\beta}\bar{x} = 3.5 - (1.4)2.5 = 0$

and the equation of the regression line is $y = 1.4x$.

When the linear regression line is drawn on the scatter diagram it provides a useful check on the arithmetic as well as the assumption of a linear relationship.

EXERCISE 5.4

1 a Draw a scatter diagram for the following data set:

x	1	2	3	4
y	8	10	9	11

b Copy and complete the calculations to find the equation of the regression line of y on x. First, since the formula involves several sums, the data may be rearranged to form a table.

	x	y	x^2	xy
	1	8	1	8
	2	10	4	20
	3	9		
	4	11		
Totals	10			

$n = 4$
$\Sigma x = 10$
$\Sigma y =$
$\Sigma x^2 =$
$\Sigma xy =$

$S_{xy} = \Sigma xy - \frac{(\Sigma x)(\Sigma y)}{n} =$

$S_{xx} = \Sigma x^2 - \frac{(\Sigma x)^2}{n} =$

$\bar{x} = \frac{\Sigma x}{n} =$

$\bar{y} = \frac{\Sigma y}{n} =$

gradient, $\hat{\beta} = \frac{S_{xy}}{S_{xx}} =$

vertical intercept, $\hat{\alpha} = \bar{y} - \hat{\beta}\bar{x} =$

So the equation of the regression line is $y = \hat{\alpha} + \hat{\beta}x =$

c Draw the regression line on the scatter diagram by plotting $(\bar{x}, \bar{y})$ and $(0, \hat{\alpha})$ and extend the line to cover the range of the data.

2 For the following data sets, (i) draw a scatter diagram (ii) calculate the equation of the regression line of y on x (iii) plot the regression line on the scatter diagram.

a

x	1	2	3	4	5
y	11	10	12	9	6

b

x	2	3	4	5	6	7
y	3	4	7	9	12	10

Linear regression – Using a linear model

With real data sets, the size of the sample is usually larger and the data values can involve larger numbers, so the calculations become tedious. For this reason, in exam questions summary totals may be given. The purpose of finding a linear regression line for a sample data set is to provide a model (equation) which can be used to make predictions about the population.

Example An animal scientist wishes to predict the percentage lean meat content (lmc) of a pig carcass by measuring the backfat thickness (bft). Use the information given in Exercise 5.2 to find a least squares line of best fit. Find the equation of the linear regression line and draw it on a scatter diagram. Give an interpretation of β and use the regression line to predict the average percentage lean meat content for a carcass with backfat thickness of 23 mm.
Now bft is the predictor variable (x) and lmc is the response variable (y) and recall that the summary totals are:
$n = 25$, $\Sigma x = 633.5$, $\Sigma y = 421.25$, $\Sigma x^2 = 16\,461.3$, $\Sigma y^2 = 7132.02$, $\Sigma xy = 10\,585.2$.

$$S_{xy} = \Sigma xy - \frac{(\Sigma x)(\Sigma y)}{n} = 10\,585.2 - \frac{(633.5)(421.25)}{25} = -89.275$$

$$S_{xx} = \Sigma x^2 - \frac{(\Sigma x)^2}{n} = 16\,461.3 - \frac{(633.5)^2}{25} = 408.41$$

$$\overline{x} = \frac{\Sigma x}{n} = \frac{633.5}{25} = 25.34 \qquad \overline{y} = \frac{\Sigma y}{n} = \frac{421.25}{25} = 16.85$$

$$\text{gradient, } \hat{\beta} = \frac{S_{xy}}{S_{xx}} = \frac{-89.275}{408.41} = -0.219$$

and vertical intercept, $\hat{\alpha} = \overline{y} - \hat{\beta}\overline{x} = 16.85 - (-0.219)25.34 = 22.399$
so the equation of the regression line is $y = 22.399 - 0.219x$
or lmc (%) = 22.399 – 0.219 bft (mm)

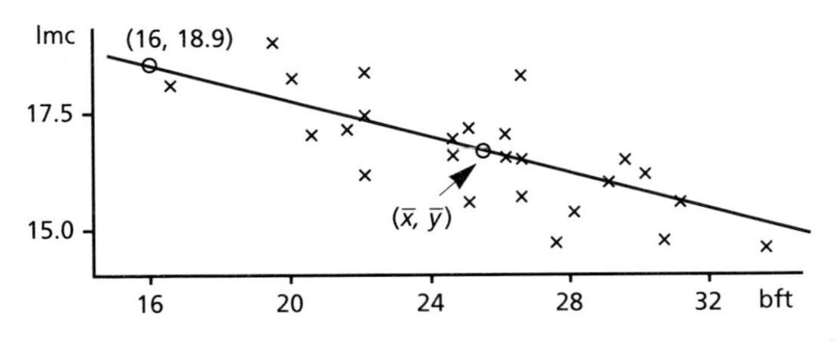

Notice the origin is not necessarily shown in a scatter diagram, so a false impression would be given if the line was extended to cross the vertical axis. So $(0, \hat{\alpha})$ cannot be plotted.
Plot $(\overline{x}, \overline{y})$. Choose another x value at one end of the data set and calculate the predicted y value using the regression equation.
For example, $x = 16$, $y = \hat{\alpha} + \hat{\beta}x = 22.399 - 0.219(16) = 18.895$, so plot (16, 18.9). Join these points and extend the line. A third point with x value at the other end of the data set is useful as a check.
$\hat{\beta} = -0.219$ indicates that for an *increase* of 1 mm in bft, a *reduction* of 0.219% is expected in lmc.

The prediction for lean meat content when the backfat thickness is 23 mm is given by

$$\text{lmc } (\%) = 22.399 - 0.219\ (23) = 17.362 \approx 17.36\%$$

i.e. an *average* value of lmc when bft is 23 mm would be 17.36%.

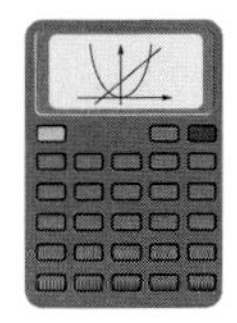

Many scientific and graphics calculators will calculate the equation of the linear regression line directly. All you have to do is enter the data. Find out if your calculator will do this. You may need to go into LR mode. For real data, these calculations can be tedious. In exam questions summary totals may be given.

EXERCISE 5.5A

For the following data sets draw the scatter diagram and calculate the equation of the regression line of y on x. If it is inappropriate to show the origin, draw the regression line by plotting $(\overline{x}, \overline{y})$ and at least one other point with x value taken from one end of the data set and y value predicted by $y = \hat{\alpha} + \hat{\beta}x$.

1 The data set is Forbes' data (see Chapter 2) showing the boiling point of water, x (°F), and the pressure, y (inches of Hg).

Boiling point (°F)	194.5	194.3	197.9	198.4	199.4	199.9	200.9	201.1	201.4
Pressure (in Hg)	20.79	20.79	22.40	22.67	23.15	23.35	23.89	23.99	24.02

Boiling point (°F)	201.3	203.6	204.6	209.5	208.6	210.7	211.9	212.2
Pressure (in Hg)	24.01	25.14	26.57	28.49	27.76	29.04	29.88	30.06

($n = 17$, $\Sigma x = 3450.2$, $\Sigma y = 426$, $\Sigma x^2 = 700\,759.02$, $\Sigma xy = 86\,735.495$)

Predict the average pressure when the boiling point is 212 °F using the linear regression equation and interpret the slope of the line.

2 The data show the study times for a particular statistics assignment and the mark achieved by students in a Higher Maths class.

Time (hours)	2	3	4	2.5	7	6	4	5	3	3.5	5
Mark (out of 20)	10	14	15	12	19	18	16	16	15	16	17

($n = 11$, $\Sigma x = 45$, $\Sigma y = 168$, $\Sigma x^2 = 207.5$, $\Sigma xy = 723$)

Predict the average mark for a study time of three and a half hours using the linear regression equation.

3 The data shows the engine capacity (cc) and the overall fuel consumption (mpg) for seven models of a particular make of cars.

Engine capacity (cc)	954	1124	1360	1427	1427	1995	2664
Fuel consumption (mpg)	33.2	30.6	34.0	25.8	29.2	23.0	18.0

($n = 7$, $\Sigma x = 10\,951$, $\Sigma y = 193.8$, $\Sigma x^2 = 19\,172\,671$, $\Sigma xy = 284\,629.2$)

Predict the average fuel consumption for a 2.4 litre engine using the linear regression equation and interpret the slope of the line.

4 Use your own data!

a Repeat the scatter diagram for the data you have collected on:
(i) finger span and height in your class (Exercise 5.2A)
(ii) finger span and length of sentence (Exercise 5.2B).

b Calculate the regression line and show it on the scatter diagram for:
(i) predicting height from finger span
(ii) predicting finger span from sentence length.

c Predict:
(i) the average height for a person with finger span 190 mm
(ii) the average finger span for a person with sentence length 80 mm.

EXERCISE 5.5B

1 In a development of holiday apartments, the floor area in m^2 is reckoned to be a good predictor of its resale value. The data gives information on nine such apartments found in an estate agent's window in France.

Size (m^2)	26	27	33	29	29	34	30	40	22
Price (FF)	235 000	249 000	267 000	269 000	295 000	345 000	415 000	475 000	195 000

a Draw a scatter diagram, find the correlation coefficient and comment on the relationship.
b Find the regression equation for the data and as a check draw the regression line on the scatter diagram. Express prices as thousands of FF.
c Interpret the slope of the line.
d Use the equation to predict the average price of an apartment of size 26 m^2.

2 An ice-cream manufacturer wished to be able to predict ice-cream consumption. He considered the following data collected over ten fortnightly periods:

Average temp (°C)	13	21	9	17	22	24	16	13	10	19
Consumption of ice-cream (litres/person)	0.21	0.24	0.16	0.22	0.31	0.35	0.19	0.20	0.18	0.26

a Draw a scatter diagram, find the correlation coefficient and comment on the relationship.
b Find the regression equation for the data and as a check draw the regression line on the scatter diagram.
c Predict the average consumption per person for a fortnightly period when the average temperature is 23 °C.

Linear regression: handle with care!

Prediction

In the example on page 122, it was established that the line of best fit for predicting percentage lean meat content from backfat thickness (millimetres) is given by lmc % = 22.399 – 0.219 bft. But can the equation be used to predict lean meat content for *any* backfat thickness? For example, is it possible to have a backfat thickness of 0 mm, and if so would we really expect the lean meat content to be 22.4%? No information was given about bft values below 16 mm so it cannot be assumed that a linear relationship continues to exist below these values or indeed anywhere outside the range of the given values.

In general a linear regression line can only be used for prediction within or close to the range of the data. Prediction within the range of the data set, called **interpolation**, is generally reliable, however prediction outside the range, **extrapolation**, can be dangerous but may be useful in suggesting further lines of enquiry.

Notice also that generally the regression line of y on x is calculated, and used to predict y from x. By interchanging x and y in the formulas, it is possible to find the regression line of x on y. This rarely makes sense. If ever it is appropriate to calculate the regression line of x on y it is usually *not* the same line (contrast with correlation).

Outliers

As with correlation, if an outlier is found it should be given careful consideration. If the data has been erroneously recorded, it should be ignored when calculating the regression equation. However if the data is genuine, including it in the calculations may distort the line. The effect may be to produce a line which does not go through the majority of points, or alternatively it may exert undue influence on the line.

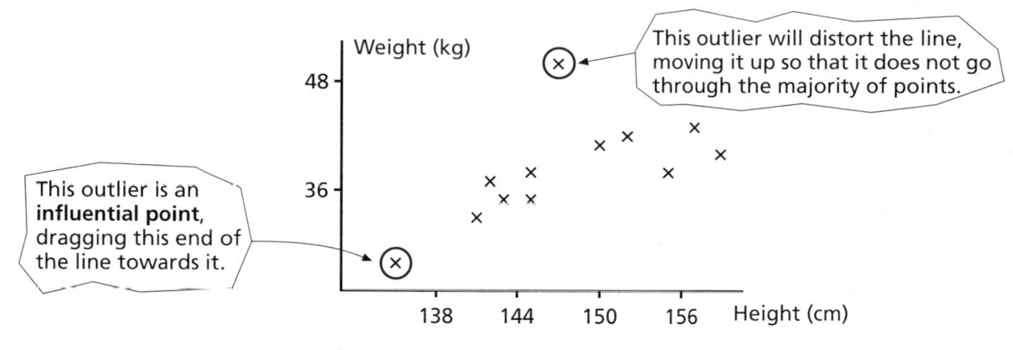

Single data set?

Again careful consideration should be given when a scatter diagram suggests that there may be two subsets within the data. Usually more accurate predictions can be made if the data are treated separately in each subset.

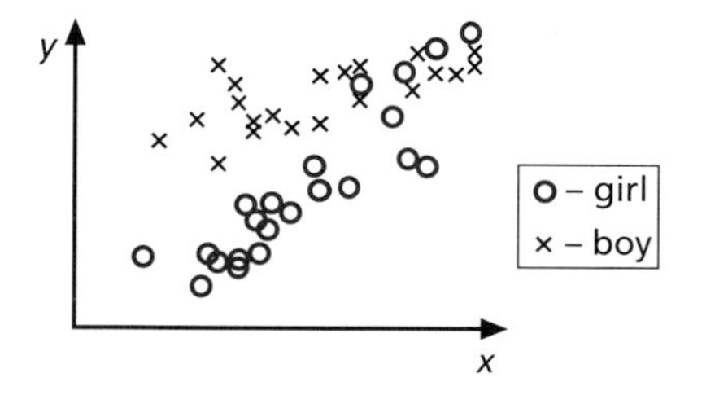

For the data shown, two separate regression equations, one for boys and another for girls, would give more accurate predictions than a single line for all the data.

EXERCISE 5.6B

1 For this data set, the height and weight of boys in Class 1B in June 1996, shown previously, four different regression equations have been calculated.

Height (cm)	157	145	159	143	142	152	147	135	141	155	150	145
Weight (kg)	43	35	40	35	37	42	50	28	33	38	41	38

1 weight = −32.9 + 0.483 height (all boys included)
2 weight = −36.0 + 0.496 height (heavy boy excluded)
3 weight = −10.5 + 0.334 height (small boy excluded)
4 weight = −19.8 + 0.389 height (both boys excluded)

Describe the effect of removing the outliers on the regression equations and comment on the value of predictions in each case.

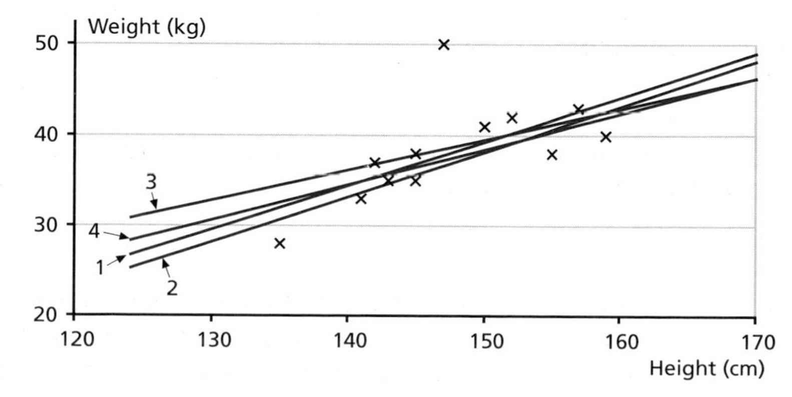

2 This data set showing percentage unemployment and percentage spent on motoring and travel in different regions of Britain was first given in Chapter 2.

% unemployed, x	14.0	11.3	9.0	6.8	7.1	8.2	11.1	12.7	12.5	13.0	17.6
% travel spend, y	12.8	14.5	15.4	15.0	15.0	15.3	14.6	14.2	14.4	14.1	15.5

Northern Ireland (→ 17.6, 15.5)

($n = 11$, $\Sigma x = 123.3$, $\Sigma y = 160.8$, $\Sigma x^2 = 1488.09$, $\Sigma y^2 = 2356.56$, $\Sigma xy = 1794.11$)

a Find the regression equation both with and without the data for Northern Ireland.

b Plot both regression lines on a scatter diagram.

c Predict the percentage travel spend for a region with (i) 15% unemployment (ii) 20% unemployment, using both regression equations and comment on the reliability of the predictions.

3 For the data first given in Chapter 2 showing distances in Sheffield as the crow flies (x) and by road (y), find the linear regression line of y on x.

($n = 20$, $\Sigma x = 322.6$, $\Sigma y = 417.1$, $\Sigma x^2 = 6226.38$, $\Sigma y^2 = 10\,453.7$, $\Sigma xy = 8026.25$)

a Does the line go through the origin?

b Common sense tells us that 0 km as the crow flies means 0 km by road. Explain why the linear regression line is still useful even if it does not go through the origin.

c Give a prediction of the average road distance when the distance as the crow flies is (i) 24 km (ii) 1 km, saying which is the more reliable result.

4 In Exercise 5.3B, data on systolic blood pressure and age for a group of women were given. The data seemed to be divided into two subsets.

a Find the regression equations for the whole data set and for the younger group (ignoring the five oldest women). Plot both the regression lines on a scatter diagram and comment.

sbp	158	139	126	131	128	141	167	116	128	126	148	121	151	166
Age	71	53	40	42	47	49	74	43	50	49	67	37	69	73

($n = 14$, $\Sigma x = 764$, $\Sigma y = 1946$, $\Sigma x^2 = 43\,998$, $\Sigma xy = 108\,902$)

b Predict the average sbp of: (i) a 45-year-old woman (ii) an 85-year-old woman. Comment on your answers.

CHAPTER 5 REVIEW

1 For each of the following data sets:

a

x	4	6	8	10	12
y	3	8	10	11	16

b

x	6	10	12	20	25	28
y	20	14	12	11	8	5

(i) draw the scatter diagram

(ii) find the correlation coefficient and describe the relationship

(iii) find the linear regression line of y on x and draw it on the scatter diagram

(iv) predict the average y value in **a** when $x = 5$ and in **b** when $x = 15$.

2 In an investigation of the relationship between incubation temperature (t) and the amount of antibiotic (y) present in 1 litre of culture fluid at the end of a fixed culture period, the results were as follows:

t (°C)	25	26	27	28	29	30	31	32	33
y (mg)	10.8	11.4	11.6	12.3	12.4	12.9	13.1	13.2	13.7

($n = 9$, $\Sigma t = 261$, $\Sigma t^2 = 7629$, $\Sigma y = 111.4$, $\Sigma y^2 = 1386.16$, $\Sigma ty = 3251.2$)

a Find the least squares regression line of y on t.

b Plot the data and the regression line.

c Interpret the gradient of the regression line.

d Predict the average amount of antibiotic present for a temperature of 28 °C and 20 °C and explain why the prediction for 20 °C is unreliable.

3 The following data come from a study investigating a new method of measuring body composition, and give age in years (x) and percentage body fat (y) for a group of females.

Age	23	39	41	49	50	53	53	54	56	57	58	58	60	61
% fat	27.9	31.4	25.9	25.2	31.1	34.7	42.0	29.1	32.5	30.3	33.0	33.8	41.1	34.5

($n = 14$, $\Sigma x = 712$, $\Sigma x^2 = 37\,600$, $\Sigma y = 452.5$, $\Sigma y^2 = 14\,937.6$, $\Sigma xy = 23\,346.5$)

a (i) How are age and percentage fat related?

(ii) Remove the two outliers highlighted in the diagram. Find a new relationship between age and percentage fat for females.

(iii) Plot both regression equations on a scatter diagram.

(iv) Predict the average percentage fat for both a 30-year-old and a 60-year-old woman and comment.

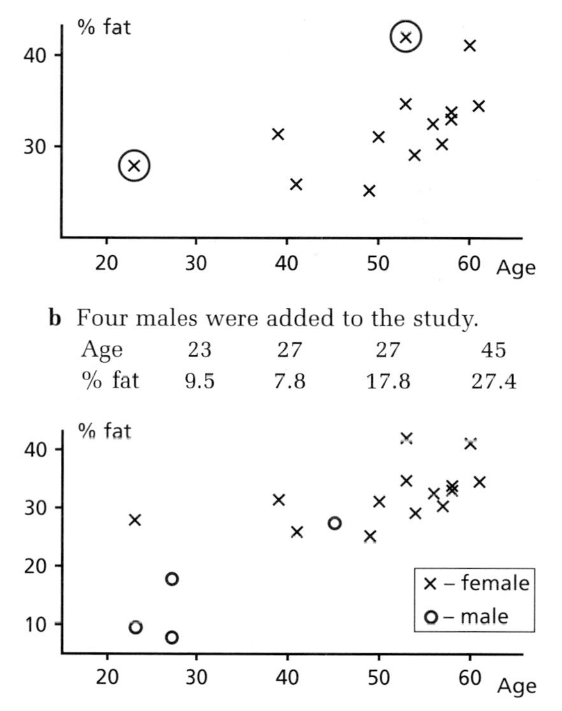

b Four males were added to the study.

Age	23	27	27	45
% fat	9.5	7.8	17.8	27.4

Find the linear regression equation for these males and show it on a new scatter diagram. Do you think the relationship for males is different from females? Why should you be cautious?

CHAPTER 5 SUMMARY

Scatter diagram
A diagram showing each pair of bivariate data as a point with coordinates (x, y). First step in analysing the relationship between two variables.

Cause and effect
The existence of a linear relationship, no matter how strong, does not necessarily indicate causation.

Independent or predictor variable
The variable which is thought to cause variation in some other variable and may be controlled.

Dependent or response variable
The variable which changes as a result of change in the predictor variable.

Pearson's Product Moment Correlation Coefficient, r
Measures the strength of a linear relationship between two variables x and y.

$$r = \frac{S_{xy}}{\sqrt{S_{xx}S_{yy}}} \quad \text{where } S_{xy} = \Sigma xy - \frac{(\Sigma x)(\Sigma y)}{n}$$

$$S_{xx} = \Sigma x^2 - \frac{(\Sigma x)^2}{n}$$

$$S_{yy} = \Sigma y^2 - \frac{(\Sigma y)^2}{n}$$

and r may be interpreted by:

Best fitting line through a data set by eye
A line drawn with a balance of points on each side, may be improved by passing through $(\overline{x}, \overline{y})$.

Linear regression line of y on x
Using the least squares method:
$y = \alpha + \beta x$.
α and β are estimated by:

$$\text{slope, } \hat{\beta} = \frac{S_{xy}}{S_{xx}}$$

$$\text{and vertical intercept, } \hat{\alpha} = \overline{y} - \hat{\beta}\overline{x}$$

Interpolation
Prediction of an average value of the response variable given a value of the predictor variable *within* the range of the data.

Extrapolation
Prediction of an average value of the response variable given a value of the predictor variable *outside* the range of the data. Extrapolation is less reliable than interpolation.

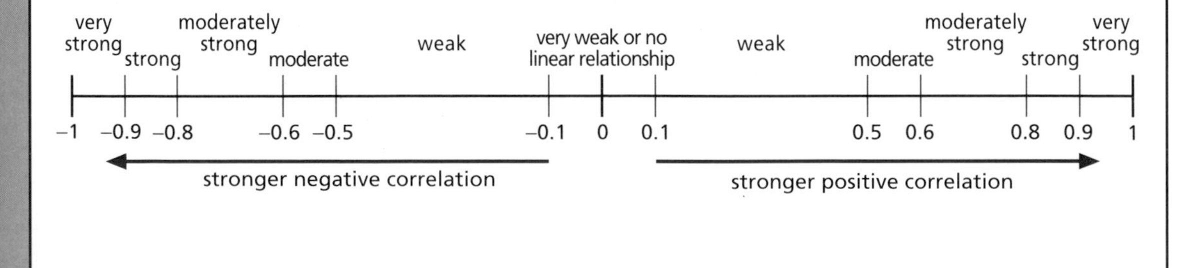

Circles Worksheet

Answers

CHAPTER 1

Page 2 Exercise 1.1

1 **a** Quantitative, continuous
b Qualitative, nominal
c Quantitative, discrete or continuous. (In some situations it is difficult to decide. The final decision will be linked with the choice of mathematical model considered to be most appropriate, for example: a short test marked out of 10 – discrete; a long exam marked out of 100 – continuous.)
d Quantitative, discrete
e Qualitative, ordinal
f Quantitative, continuous
g Qualitative, nominal
h Quantitative, discrete
i Qualitative, nominal

2 Qualitative, nominal
3 Qualitative, ordinal
4 Quantitative, continuous
5 Qualitative, ordinal
6 Quantitative, continuous
7 Qualitative, ordinal
8 Quantitative, discrete
9 Quantitative, continuous

Page 5 Exercise 1.2

1

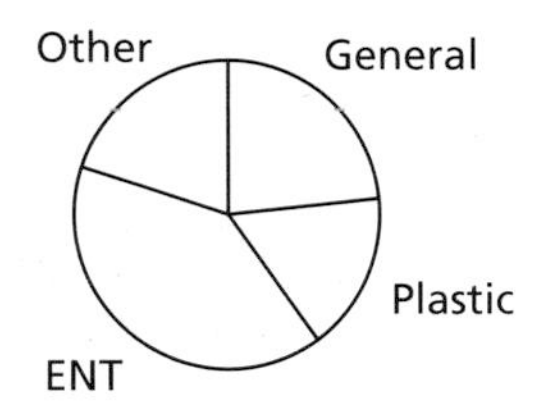

General 84°, plastic 60°, ENT 144°, other 72°

2

3 **a**

Contents	Tally	Frequency
80	//	2
81	////	4
82	////	4
83	////	4
84	///	3
85	////	4
86	~~////~~ ///	8
87	~~////~~	5
88	////	4
89	///	3
90	///	3
91	///	3
92	//	2
93		0
94	/	1
	Total	50

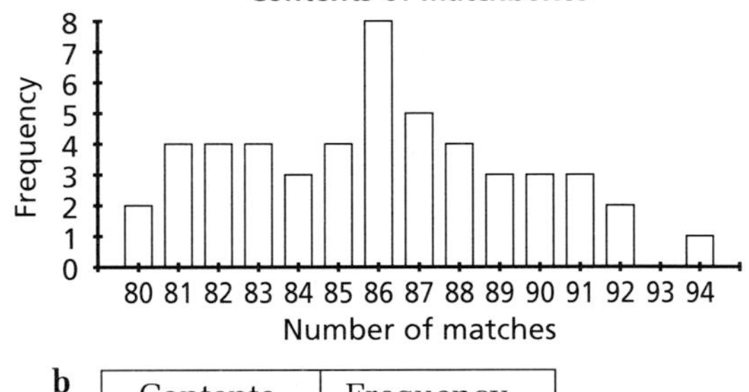

b

Contents	Frequency
78–80	2
81–83	12
84–86	15
87–89	12
90–92	8
93–95	1
Total	50

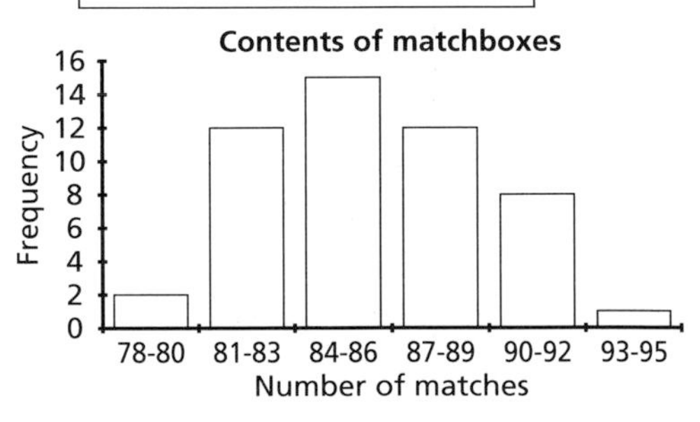

4 Should Britain remain a constitutional monarchy?

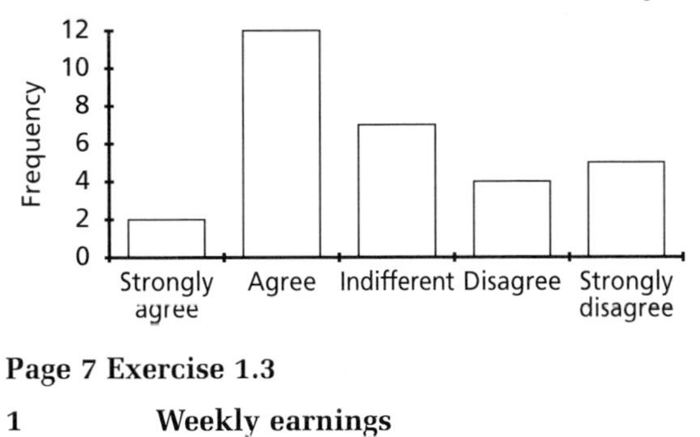

Page 7 Exercise 1.3

1 **Weekly earnings**

8	7
9	3
10	347
11	001339
12	
13	5
14	578

$n = 15$ 14 | 8 represents £148

2 **Weights of eggs**

4	023
4	6689
5	0112234
5	55789
6	044
6	67
7	2

$n = 25$ 7 | 2 represents 72 g

3 **Heights (cm)**

13	56
14	122355577
15	0222445577899
16	06
17	7

$n = 27$ 17 | 7 represents 177 cm

4 **Random numbers**

0	12345
1	15
2	33446
3	004
4	67
5	113
6	0234588
7	666
8	12445888
9	99

$n = 40$ 9 | 9 represents 0.99

Page 10 Exercise 1.4

1

Speed (mph)	Tally	Frequency
$20 \le s < 30$	/	1
$30 \le s < 40$	//	2
$40 \le s < 50$	𝍸 𝍸 𝍸 ////	19
$50 \le s < 60$	𝍸 ///	8
$60 \le s < 70$	///	3
$70 \le s < 80$	/	1
	Total	34

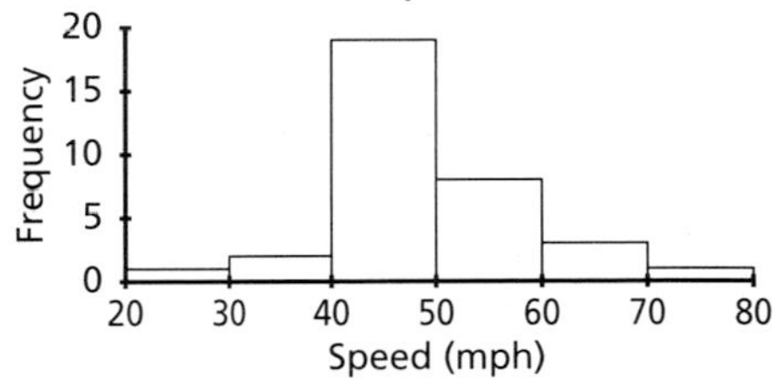

2

Contents	Tally	Frequency
$23.5 \le x < 24.5$	//	2
$24.5 \le x < 25.5$	𝍸 ////	9
$25.5 \le x < 26.5$	𝍸 𝍸 𝍸 𝍸 𝍸	25
$26.5 \le x < 27.5$	𝍸 ////	9
$27.5 \le x < 28.5$	////	4
$28.5 \le x < 29.5$	/	1
	Total	50

3

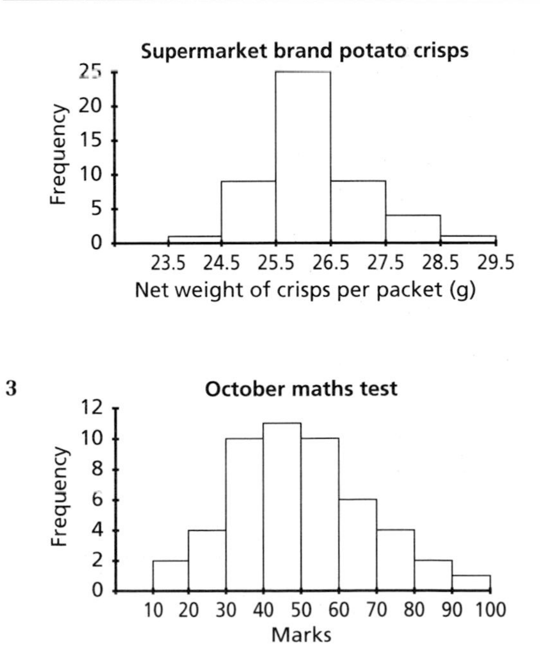

4

Survival time (days)	Frequency
$0 \le x < 365$	9
$365 \le x < 730$	14
$730 \le x < 1095$	6
$1095 \le x < 1460$	4
$1460 \le x < 1825$	3
$1825 \le x < 2190$	4
$2190 \le x < 2555$	3
Total	43

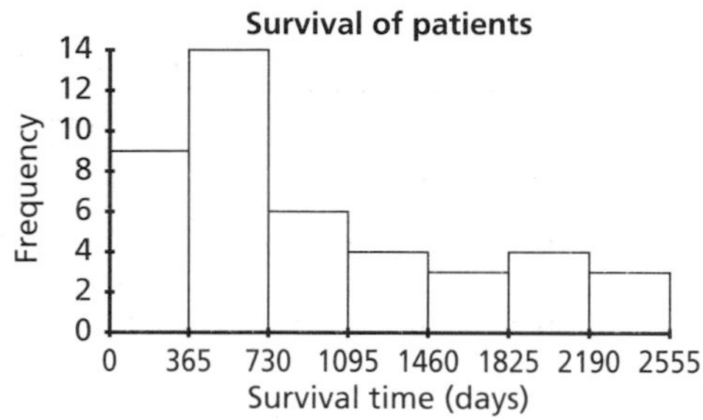

Seven patients survived more than five years.

Page 12 Exercise 1.5A

1 a

Family size	Tally	Frequency	Relative frequency
1	////	4	0.100
2	𝍸 𝍸 𝍸 ///	18	0.450
3	𝍸 𝍸 /	11	0.275
4	𝍸 /	6	0.150
5		0	0.000
6	/	1	0.025
	Total	40	1.000

b 2 children **c** 0.450

2 a

Type	Frequency	Relative frequency	Angle
1	47	0.059	21°
2	93	0.116	42°
3	228	0.285	103°
4	113	0.141	51°
5	147	0.184	66°
6	172	0.215	77°
Total	800	1.000	360°

b Employment survey

Unskilled
Professional
Managers
Semi-skilled
Intermediate
Skilled

c Intermediate and junior non-manual is most likely.

3 a–c

Height	Tally	Frequency	Cumulative frequency
$130 \le x < 135$	///	3	3
$135 \le x < 140$	𝍸 ///	8	11
$140 \le x < 145$	𝍸 𝍸	10	21
$145 \le x < 150$	𝍸 𝍸 /	11	32
$150 \le x < 155$	𝍸 ////	9	41
$155 \le x < 160$	𝍸 //	7	48
$160 \le x < 165$	//	2	50
	Total	50	

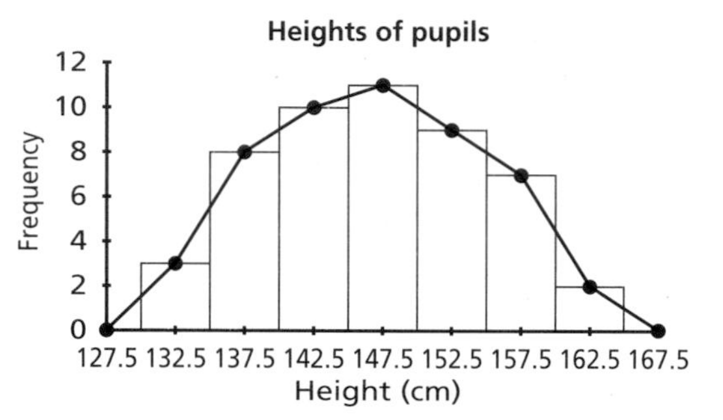

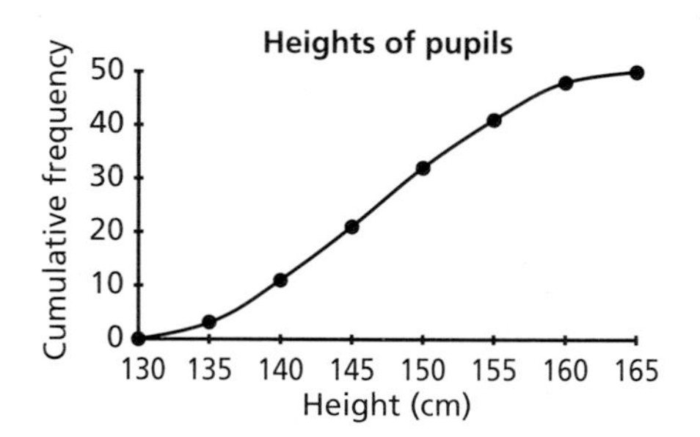

4 a

Contents	Frequency	Cumulative frequency
45	1	1
46	3	4
47	2	6
48	4	10
49	5	15
50	8	23
51	10	33
52	7	40
53	6	46
54	2	48
55	2	50
Total	50	

b

5

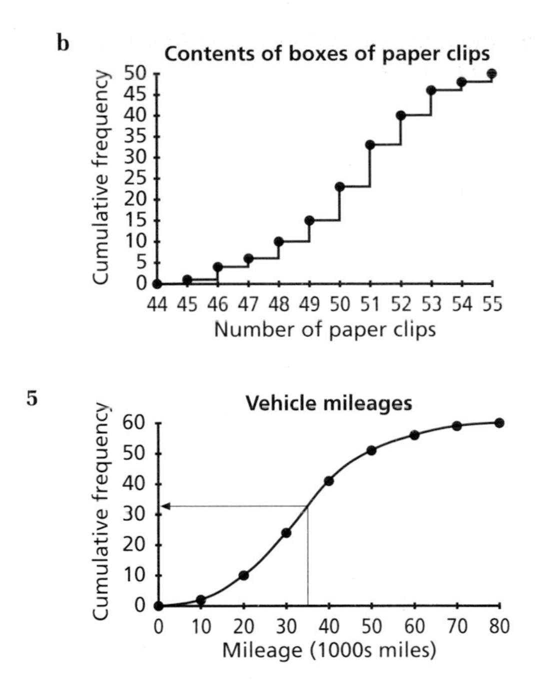

Approx. 34 vehicles have travelled < 36 000 miles.

Page 14 Exercise 1.5B

1 a

Interval	Tally	Frequency	Relative frequency
$0.0 \leq x < 0.1$	~~////~~ //	7	0.200
$0.1 \leq x < 0.2$	//	2	0.057
$0.2 \leq x < 0.3$	~~////~~ //	7	0.200
$0.3 \leq x < 0.4$	////	4	0.114
$0.4 \leq x < 0.5$	//	2	0.057
$0.5 \leq x < 0.6$	/	1	0.029
$0.6 \leq x < 0.7$	////	4	0.114
$0.7 \leq x < 0.8$	///	3	0.086
$0.8 \leq x < 0.9$	//	2	0.057
$0.9 \leq x < 1.0$	///	3	0.086
	Total	35	1.000

b Relative frequencies vary from 0.059 to 0.200. The random number generator may be producing more numbers in some intervals than in others. However, 35 is not a large sample so this variability may well be due to chance.

c (i) 0.1 (ii) 0.5

d (i) 0.628 (ii) 0.372. Generator may produce more numbers < 0.5. However, this may well be due to chance.

e

Interval	Frequency	Relative frequency
$0.0 \leq x < 0.1$	94	0.094
$0.1 \leq x < 0.2$	99	0.099
$0.2 \leq x < 0.3$	88	0.088
$0.3 \leq x < 0.4$	107	0.107
$0.4 \leq x < 0.5$	123	0.123
$0.5 \leq x < 0.6$	115	0.115
$0.6 \leq x < 0.7$	98	0.098
$0.7 \leq x < 0.8$	93	0.093
$0.8 \leq x < 0.9$	88	0.088
$0.9 \leq x < 1.0$	95	0.095
Total	1000	1.000

When 1000 random numbers are tabulated the relative frequencies range from 0.088 to 0.123 which is closer to the expected values. The histogram shows a more uniform distribution.

2 a

Duration	Relative frequencies Planned	Emergency
33	0.006	0.027
34	0.016	0.031
35	0.020	0.049
36	0.033	0.058
37	0.062	0.072
38	0.103	0.157
39	0.201	0.170
40	0.258	0.143
41	0.175	0.121
42	0.087	0.112
43	0.033	0.036
44	0.005	0.022
Total	0.999	0.998

Because of rounding, the relative frequencies do not add to 1.000 in this example.

b

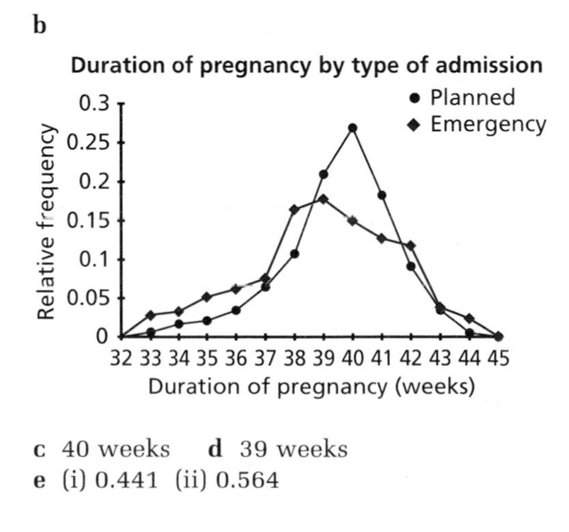

c 40 weeks **d** 39 weeks

e (i) 0.441 (ii) 0.564

f

Duration	Cumulative percentage frequencies Planned	Emergency
33	0.6%	2.7%
34	2.2%	5.8%
35	4.2%	10.7%
36	7.5%	16.5%
37	13.7%	23.7%
38	24.0%	39.4%
39	44.1%	56.4%
40	69.9%	70.7%
41	87.4%	82.8%
42	96.1%	94.0%
43	99.4%	97.6%
44	99.9%	99.8%

g

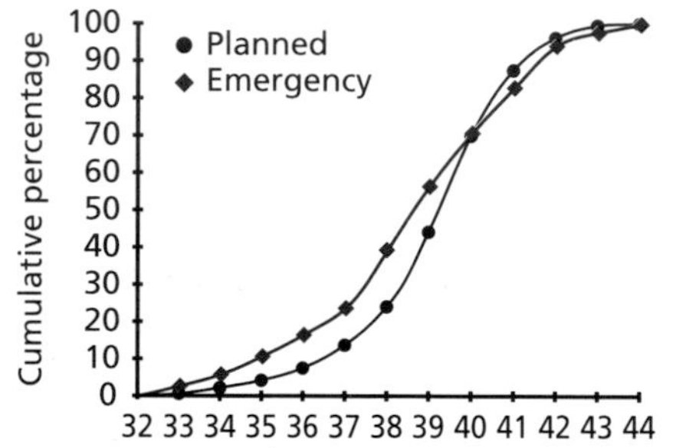

Note how the relative frequency polygon for emergency admissions peaks before the polygon for planned admissions. Also the cumulative percentage line for emergency admissions is above the planned admissions line for short durations up to 40 weeks. These data suggest that those women who were admitted to hospital as an emergency tended to have shorter pregnancies.

Page 18 Exercise 1.6A

1 Mean = 2.8, median = 2, mode = 2

2 Mean ≈ 54.2 g, median = 53 g

3 Mean ≈ $\dfrac{\text{number of clips}}{\text{number of boxes}} = \dfrac{\Sigma xf}{\Sigma f} = \dfrac{2524}{50}$

= 50.48 ≈ 50.5

Median = 51 paper clips

4 **a** Mean = 26.082 ≈ 26.08 g; median = 26.0 g
b Mean = 26.14 g
c Mean = 26.16 g
d Means calculated from frequency tables give estimates because mid-points approximate the average value in each interval. Only the method in part **a** will give an exact answer.

Page 19 Exercise 1.6B

1 **a**

100 125 150 175 200 225 250 275 300 325 350 375 400 425 450 475 500

b Mode = £150 and £175; median = £175; mean = £209 **c** Mode = £150 and £175; median = £175; mean = £197 **d** The mean is reduced by £12 when the large value of £500 is removed. The other two averages do not change in this example. Median and mode are less affected by extreme values.

2 **a** Mean = 925 days (2.5 years approx.); median = 702 days (1.9 years approx.)

b (i) $\frac{17}{43} \approx 0.395$ live longer than the mean

(ii) $\frac{21}{43} \approx 0.488$ live longer than the median

c The answer to part **b** shows that the median is more centrally located than the mean. The value of the mean has been increased by a few very long survival times. It would be more realistic to use the median, as the mean is too optimistic.

Page 22 Exercise 1.7

1 28.5 g, 45 g, 72 g **2** 10.5, 12, 16.5

3

	Lower	Median	Upper
Data Set 1	2.5	5	7.5
Data Set 2	3	5.5	8
Data Set 3	3	6	9
Data Set 4	3.5	6.5	9.5

4 **a** 40 g, 48.5 g, 53 g, 59.5 g, 72 g **b** 5.5 g

c

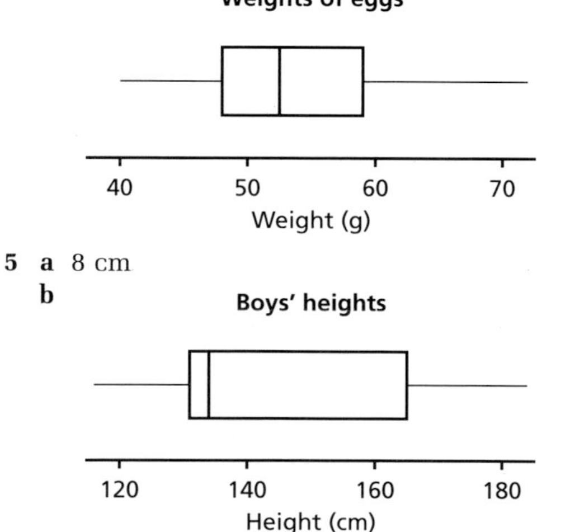

5 **a** 8 cm

b

Page 24 Exercise 1.8

1 Five number summary: 16, 19, 21, 27, 67; fences at 7 and 39 years; possible outliers 48 and 67

Cycle club members

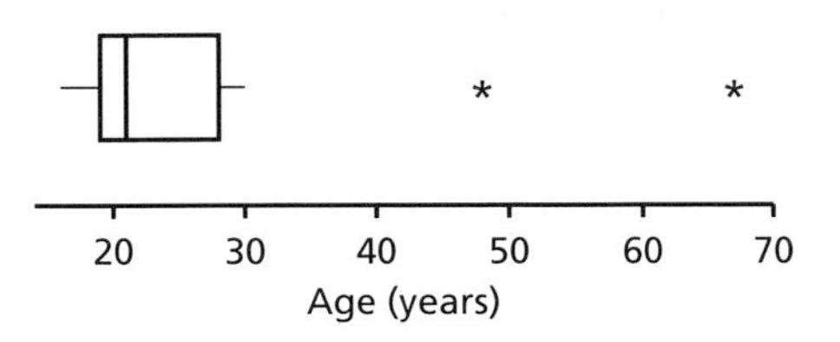

2 Five number summary: 0.55, 1.36, 1.59, 1.69, 2.24 **a** 0.165 **b** Possible outliers are: 0.55, 0.74, 0.77, 0.81, 0.84, 2.24

Strength of glass fibres

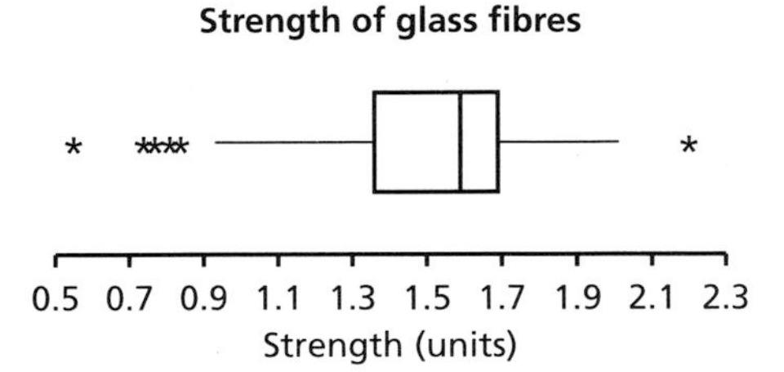

3 **a** 24.1 g, 25.5 g, 26.0 g, 26.6 g, 28.5 g

Contents of packets of crisps

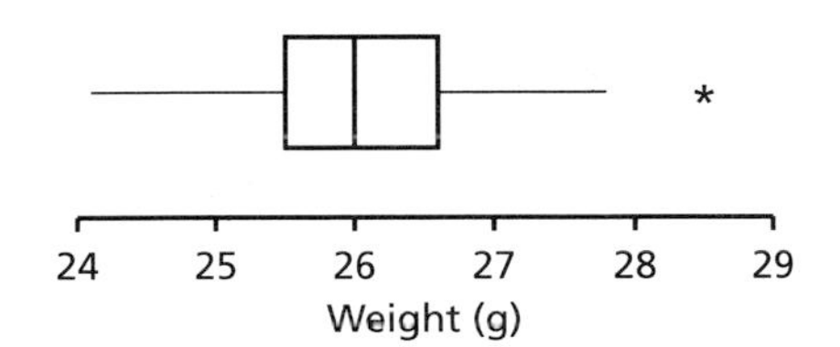

b

Contents	Cumulative percentage
$24.0 \le x < 24.5$	4
$24.5 \le x < 25.0$	10
$25.0 \le x < 25.5$	22
$25.5 \le x < 26.0$	44
$26.0 \le x < 26.5$	72
$26.5 \le x < 27.0$	80
$27.0 \le x < 27.5$	90
$27.5 < x < 28.0$	98
$28.0 \le x < 28.5$	98
$28.5 \le x < 29.0$	100

Page 28 Exercise 1.9A

1 2.3 days

2 **a** $\bar{x} = 11$, $s = 1.6$ **b** $\bar{x} = 11$, $s = 7.9$

3 10.8 cm

Page 28 Exercise 1.9B

1 **a** $\Sigma x^2 f = 127\,686$

b $$s = \sqrt{\frac{\Sigma x^2 f - (\Sigma xf)^2/\Sigma f}{\Sigma f - 1}}$$

$$= \sqrt{\frac{127\,686 - (2524)^2/50}{49}} \approx 2.4$$

2 **a** $\Sigma x^2 f = 34\,215$; $s \approx 1.01$ g

b The actual values in each interval may be slightly different from the mid-point so the answer may not be exactly the same if the data were grouped differently.

Page 30 Chapter 1 Review

1 **a** **Protein content of wheat**

7	7
8	244578
9	2678
10	022478
11	345566
12	6

$n = 24$ 12 | 6 represents 12.6%

b Median = 10.1%; semi-IQR = 1.3%

2 **a**

Star	1	2	3	4	5	Total
Week	0.09	0.38	0.35	0.17	0.01	1.00
Monday	0.09	0.43	0.30	0.09	0.09	1.00

b

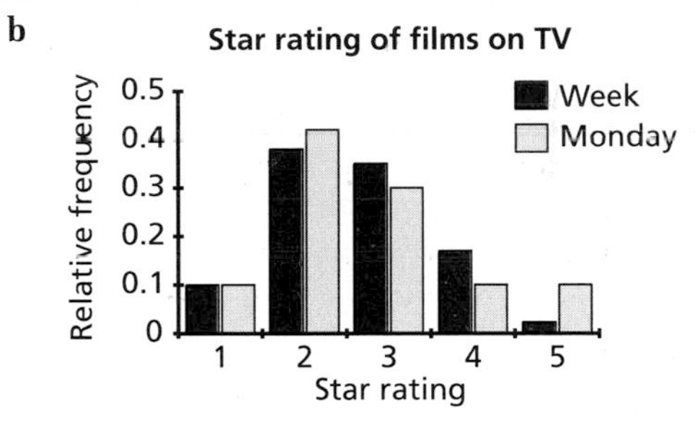

c The relative frequency of 1-star films is the same. There appears to be a slight difference for 2- and 3-star films: 2-star are relatively more, and 3-star relatively less frequent on Monday. The comparison for 4- and 5-star films is more noticeable; there are relatively more 5-star, and relatively fewer 4-star films showing on the Bank Holiday Monday than during an ordinary week. Are these differences due to chance, or are there real differences in the TV film programming? Are the film critics consistent in their ratings?

3 Five number summary: min 85, Q_1 95, median 102, Q_3 110, max 160; lower fence 57.5; upper fence 147.5; outlier 160

Films on TV one Saturday

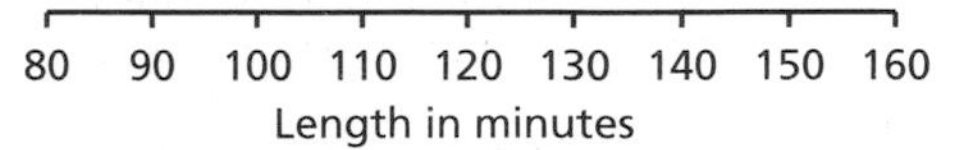

4 $\overline{x} = 296.0$ ml; $s = 5.1$ ml

5

Iron intake (mg)	Tally	Frequency
$6.0 \le x < 8.0$	//	2
$8.0 \le x < 10.0$	////	4
$10.0 \le x < 12.0$	////	4
$12.0 \le x < 14.0$	~~////~~ ///	8
$14.0 \le x < 16.0$	~~////~~ ////	9
$16.0 \le x < 18.0$	~~////~~	5
$18.0 \le x < 20.0$	~~////~~	5
$20.0 \le x < 22.0$	/	1
$22.0 \le x < 24.0$	//	2
	Total	40

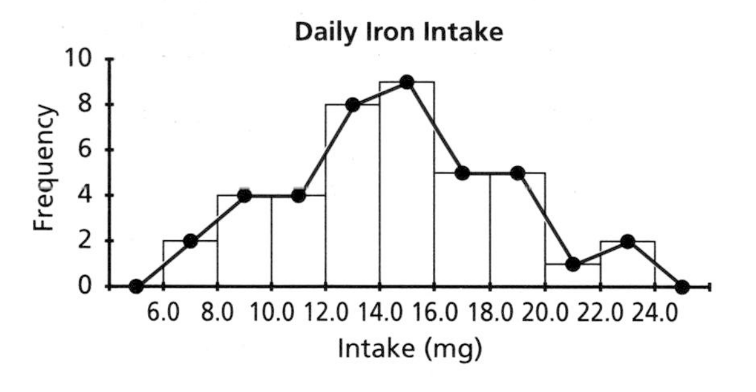

The daily intake < 14.0 mg for 0.45 of these women.

6 Paint drying time < 2 hours in approx. 0.54 of trials.

Time (minutes)	Frequency	Cumulative frequency
$90 \le t < 100$	1	1
$100 \le t < 110$	3	4
$110 \le t < 120$	9	13
$120 \le t < 130$	6	19
$130 \le t < 140$	3	22
$140 \le t < 150$	2	24
Total	24	

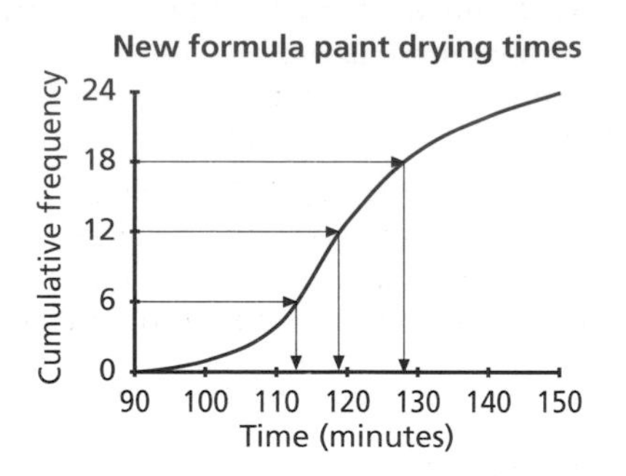

Median = 119 minutes (approx.);
IQR = 128 – 112 = 16 minutes (approx.)

7 (1) Quantitative continuous (2) Qualitative ordinal (3) Quantitative. Although measurements of time are usually considered to be continuous, in this example the rounding is to the nearest 5 minutes which may result in a discrete model being chosen for the data. (4) Quantitative continuous (5) Quantitative continuous (6) Quantitative continuous

CHAPTER 2

Page 33 Exercise 2.1A

The population mean diameter is 1 cm.

Page 35 Exercise 2.1B

1 Suppose components 17, 6, 16, and 4 were randomly chosen, then $\overline{x} \approx 7.08$. The distribution of sample means gathered by one class were:

Stem	Leaf
6	5689
7	000012222234444
7	555566788
8	11

$n = 30$ 8 | 1 represents 8.1 mm

Class's average sample mean ≈ 7.3 mm and the range = 1.6 mm

2 Repeating for Population B gave:

Stem	Leaf
5	59
6	11222
6	5678
7	0344
7	67778
8	022
8	55
9	001
9	77

$n = 30$ 9 | 7 represents 9.7 mm

Average sample mean ≈ 7.5 mm and the range of sample means = 4.2 mm

3 Population A: $\mu = 7.24$; range = 3.6.
Population B: $\mu = 7.535$; range = 7.7.

4 There is more variability in the second population of components and because of this the sample means will give more variable estimates of the population mean.

5 Increasing sample size gives less variable estimates.

Page 37 Exercise 2.2A

1 a

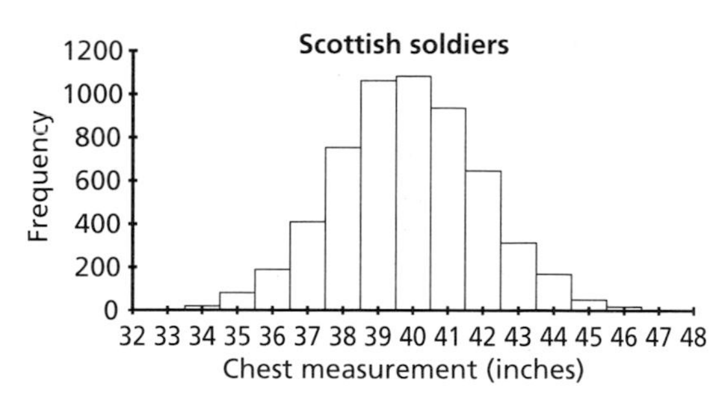

Symmetrical and bell-shaped

b $\overline{x} = 39.8$ inches; $s = 2.1$ inches

c Approx. 99.9% within 3 standard deviations

2

Interval (min)	Frequency
$40 \le t < 45$	1
$45 \le t < 50$	15
$50 \le t < 55$	38
$55 \le t < 60$	22
$60 \le t < 65$	16
$65 \le t < 70$	16
$70 \le t < 75$	26
$75 \le t < 80$	55
$80 \le t < 85$	50
$85 \le t < 90$	40
$90 \le t < 95$	16
$95 \le t < 100$	3
$100 \le t < 105$	0
$105 \le t < 110$	1
Total	299

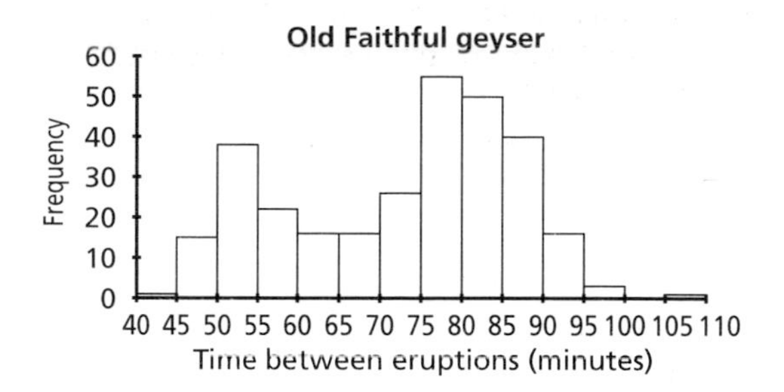

A distinctly bimodal distribution. This suggests there are two types of waiting times; one with a mode slightly less than an hour; the other with a mode of about one and a quarter hours. Geologists might look for mechanisms which explain *short* and *long* waiting times.

3

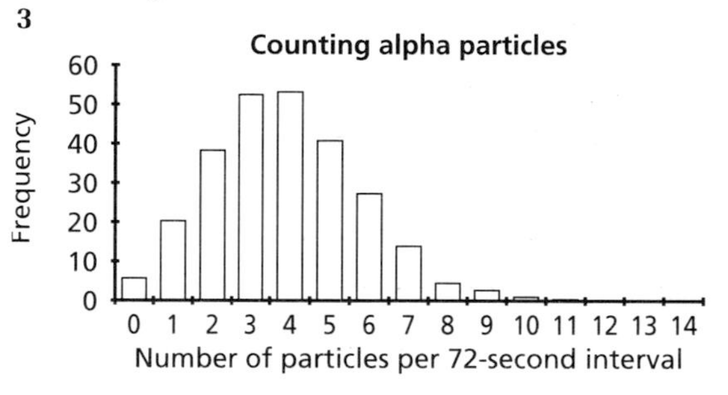

The distribution is very slightly positively skewed (almost symmetrical).
$\overline{x} = 3.9$ particles; $s = 1.9$ particles;
median = 4 particles

Page 38 Exercise 2.2B

1

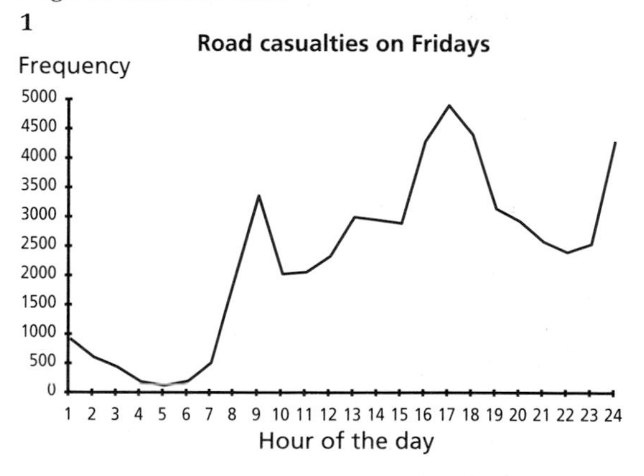

The safest time on the roads is between midnight and 7 am, when the casualty rates are all less than 1000 per hour. The roads are quieter at night. There are distinct peaks between 8 am and 9 am (the rush hour to work and school) and between 4 pm and

5 pm (the rush hour from work and school). High levels (over 2000 casualties per hour) are maintained during business hours. There is a rise in the casualty rate prior to midnight (licensed premises closing?).

2

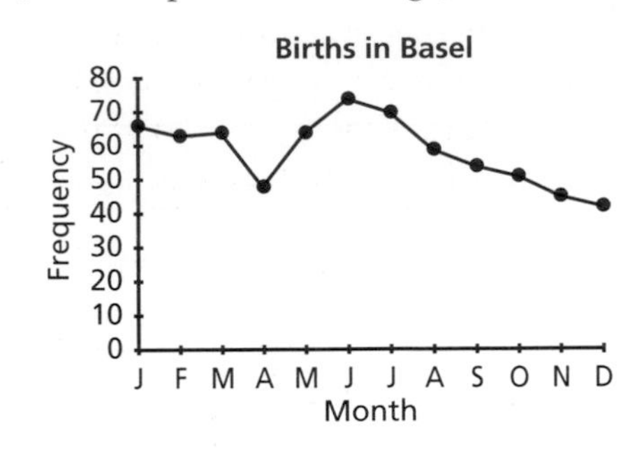

Distribution of births is approaching uniform. $\overline{x} = 58.3$ births; $s = 10.2$ births. Number of births in June and July are the highest (more than 1 standard deviation above the mean). Number of births in November and December are the lowest (more than 1 standard deviation below the mean).

Page 41 Exercise 2.3A

1 a The same number of pupils in each class took the test. The overall mean for the three classes is $\frac{(40.4 + 61.8 + 52.8)}{3} \approx 51.7$ marks.

The class average (mean and median) for Class 1R is the lowest of the three classes and approx. 75% of the pupils in 1R did not exceed the overall average. However, the highest mark among all who took the test was for a pupil in 1R (shown as an outlier). Class 1C had the highest class average. The class mean mark in 1B was about the same as the overall mean but the variability within classes was least in the case of 1B.

b Information may include amongst other things:

- do these classes contain pupils of broadly the same maths ability?
- did these classes perform similarly on previous tests?
- was this test on topics which all the classes were familiar with/taught recently?
- were the tests administered under the same conditions?

2 a (i) **Grip strength**

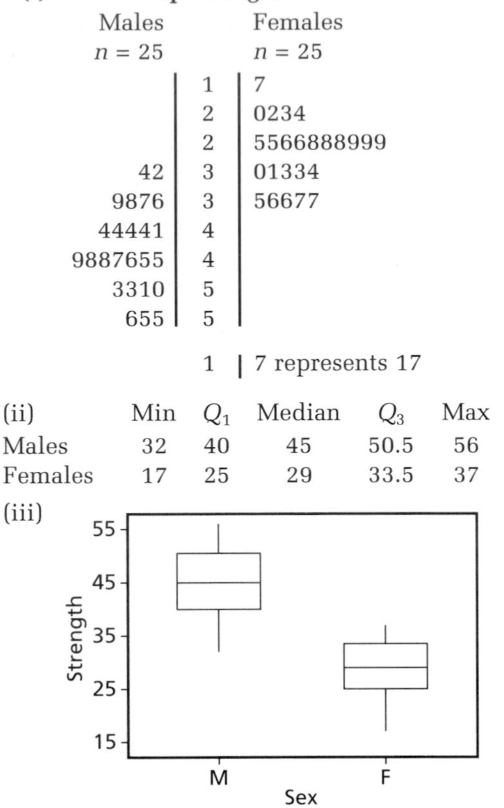

Males $n = 25$		Females $n = 25$
	1	7
	2	0234
	2	5566888999
42	3	01334
9876	3	56677
44441	4	
9887655	4	
3310	5	
655	5	

1 | 7 represents 17

(ii)

	Min	Q_1	Median	Q_3	Max
Males	32	40	45	50.5	56
Females	17	25	29	33.5	37

(iii)

(iv) Males 5.25; females 4.25

(v)

	Males	Females
$\overline{x} =$	45.4	28.8
$s =$	6.7	5.4

(vi) Difficult to be sure with small samples but the distribution of grip strengths seems fairly symmetrical for both males and females.

b On average, males have a much stronger grip than females. The variability within females is slightly less than within the males in these samples.

3

Variable	N	Mean	SD
Type A	20	245.1	36.6
Type B	20	210.3	48.3

	Min	Q_1	Median	Q_3	Max
Type A	181	221	242.5	261	325
Type B	137	179	207	244	344

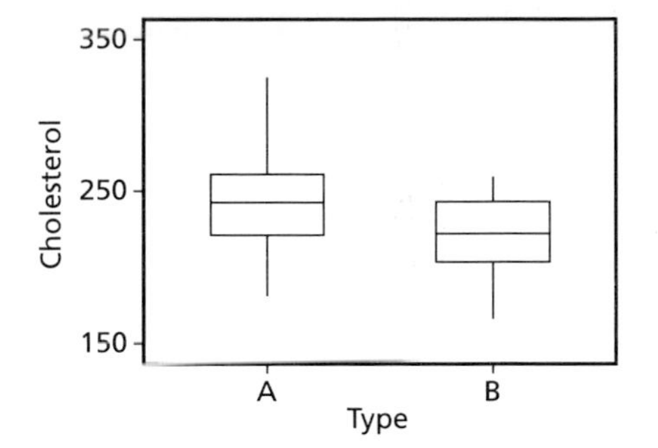

On average, type A men have slightly higher cholesterol levels and slightly less variability in their cholesterol levels. There is so much overlap between the two sets of data it is difficult to say if this difference is associated with behaviour type or due to chance variability.

4 The sample sizes are quite different. Comparing relative frequencies ($n_k/\Sigma n_k$):

k	Hillman	Sussex
1	0.56	0.51
2	0.22	0.23
3	0.10	0.12
4	0.05	0.07
5	0.03	0.04
6	0.02	0.02
7	0.01	0.01

Very similar decreasing distributions.

Page 42 Exercise 2.3B

1 a

Dose	N	Mean	SD
0 mg	10	244.8	2.4
100 mg	10	246.4	2.1
200 mg	10	248.3	2.2

Dose	Min	Q_1	Median	Q_3	Max
0 mg	242	242	244.5	247	248
100 mg	243	245	246.5	248	250
200 mg	245	246	248.0	250	252

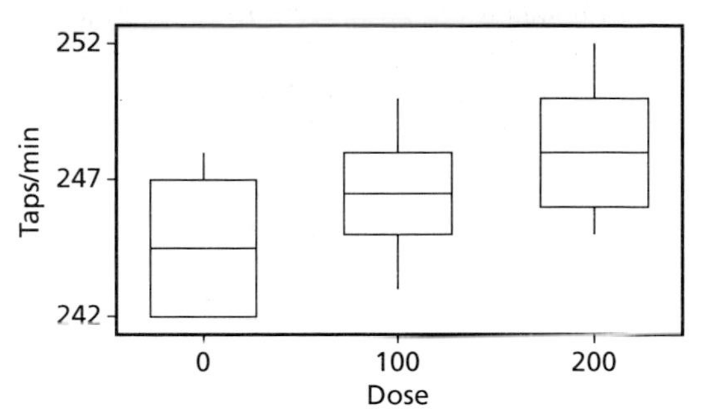

The average tapping rate appears to increase with increasing dose of caffeine. The variability is similar in each group (100 mg group slightly less?).

b Collect tapping rate measurements 'before' and 'after' the dose of caffeine for each person and then relate the difference in tapping rates to the dose.

2

Variable	N	Mean	SD
Jer 2	10	5.340	0.674
Jer M	10	5.245	0.547
H-F 2	10	3.618	0.166
H-F M	10	3.721	0.329
Guer 2	10	5.052	0.466
Guer M	10	4.848	0.503
Can 2	10	4.511	0.348
Can M	10	4.366	0.386
Ayr 2	10	4.117	0.315
Ayr M	10	4.003	0.193

	Min	Q_1	Median	Q_3	Max
Jer 2	4.22	4.85	5.215	5.75	6.55
Jer M	4.49	4.80	5.205	5.41	6.45
H-F 2	3.38	3.55	3.585	3.71	3.94
H-F M	3.30	3.54	3.640	3.93	4.43
Guer 2	4.50	4.59	5.005	5.38	5.97
Guer M	3.88	4.64	4.755	5.18	5.75
Can 2	4.00	4.29	4.415	4.66	5.24
Can M	3.92	4.07	4.330	4.47	5.05
Ayr 2	3.53	3.90	4.180	4.37	4.44
Ayr M	3.74	3.78	4.035	4.11	4.27

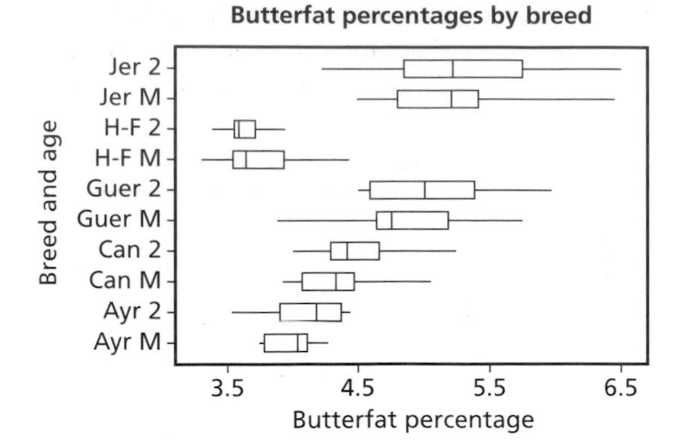

There are considerable differences in butterfat content among breeds but only small differences due to age.

Page 45 Exercise 2.4A

1 a

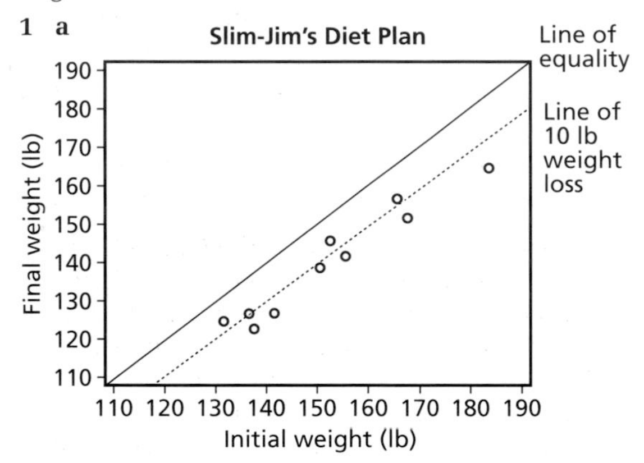

b The following weight losses were reported:

8 15 17 11 16 20 10 17 8 13

c Mean 13.50; SD 4.14

d Although 2 recruits reported weight losses less than 10 lb, the mean weight loss exceeds 10 lb. A more precise rule is needed for deciding whether this is acceptable or not.

2 a

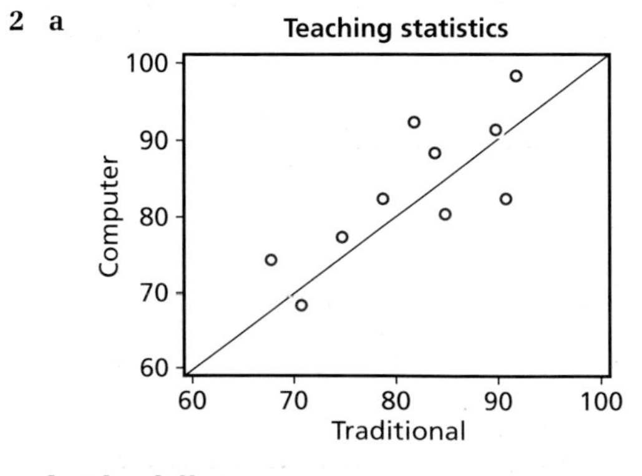

b The differences are:

3 −3 −9 6 6 2 4 10 −5 1

c Mean 1.50; SD 5.72.

d Although the mean difference is positive, indicating that the computer method produced better results, the mean difference is very small compared with the standard deviation. With this uncertainty it would be difficult to justify the expense.

3 a (i) paired data (ii) independent samples

b

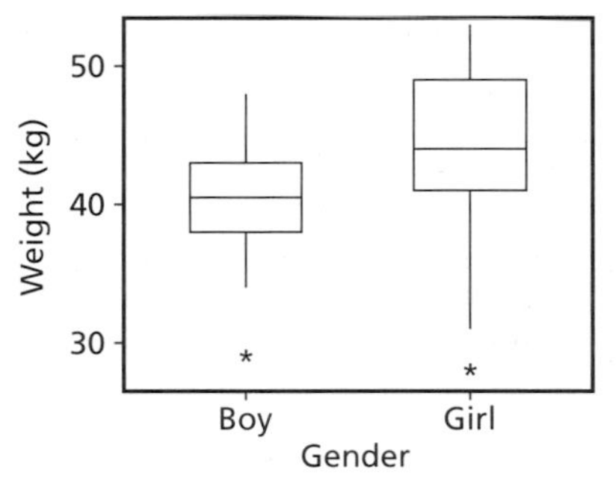

These girls seem to weigh slightly more than the boys and the girls' weights are more variable. There is one boy and one girl who are very light.

c Girls' height in Dec – height in June

N	Mean	SD
15	3.467	3.021

Min	Q_1	Median	Q_3	Max
0.0	2.0	3.0	4.0	12.0

0 1 2 3 4 5 6 7 8 9 10 11 12

Most girls have gained 2 to 4 cm in height. One girl gained 12 cm. Could this be an error?

4 a Paired data

b Differences: Prep 1 – Prep 2

Leaf	1	2	3	4	5	6	7	8
Diff	13	3	4	6	−1	1	5	1

The difference on leaf 1 seems unusually large. The median difference is 3.5 lesions. 7 out of 8 of the differences are positive. It appears that Prep 1 produces more lesions. Can we be sure with so few observations?

Page 46 Exercise 2.4B

1 a Here we are analysing paired data.

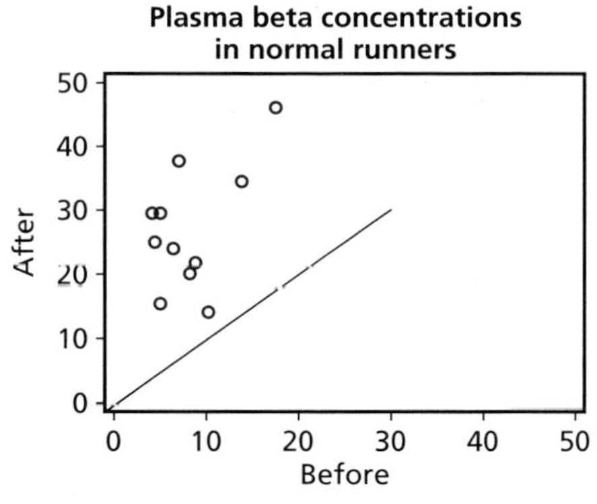

In every case, the plasma beta concentration increases. The increases are:

25.3	20.5	10.3	24.4	17.5	30.6
11.8	12.9	3.8	20.6	28.4	

N	Mean	SD
11	18.74	8.33

Min	Q_1	Median	Q_3	Max
3.8	11.8	20.5	25.3	30.6

Normal runners experience an increase of about 20 units in their plasma beta concentrations.

b The unusually large value of 414 units has been removed from the analysis that follows. The 'After' race concentrations for normal runners are compared with those for the collapsed runners. These are independent samples.

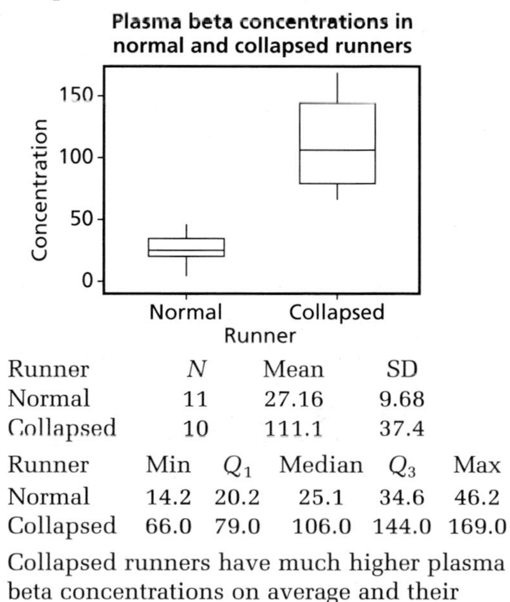

Runner	N	Mean	SD
Normal	11	27.16	9.68
Collapsed	10	111.1	37.4

Runner	Min	Q_1	Median	Q_3	Max
Normal	14.2	20.2	25.1	34.6	46.2
Collapsed	66.0	79.0	106.0	144.0	169.0

Collapsed runners have much higher plasma beta concentrations on average and their concentrations are much more variable.

2 The differences 'After' – 'Before' (weight gained) are calculated for each treatment and these three sets of differences are analysed as independent samples.

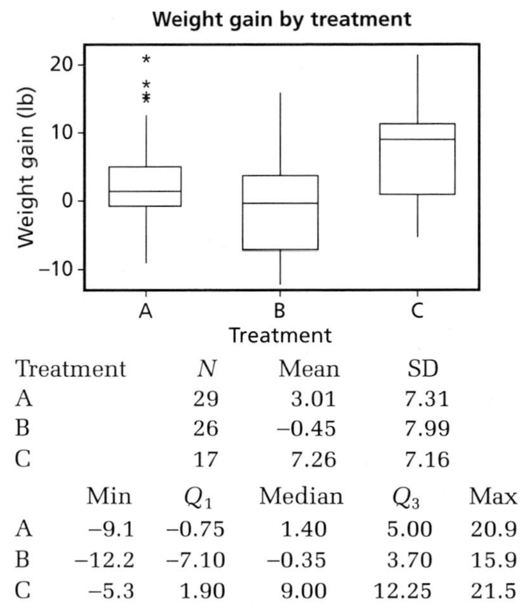

Treatment	N	Mean	SD
A	29	3.01	7.31
B	26	−0.45	7.99
C	17	7.26	7.16

	Min	Q_1	Median	Q_3	Max
A	−9.1	−0.75	1.40	5.00	20.9
B	−12.2	−7.10	−0.35	3.70	15.9
C	−5.3	1.90	9.00	12.25	21.5

Treatment B appears to be the least effective as on average there was almost no weight gain (very slight loss) and approximately as many patients lost weight as gained weight. Treatment A is characterised by some very large weight gains but on average there was a modest weight gain of about 3 lb. Treatment C shows the most favourable weight gain (around 7 to 9 lb) and about 75% of patients achieved a weight gain. It is not possible to generalise these results because we have no details about how the patients were selected for the study or how they were assigned to the different treatments. The within treatment changes can be illustrated using a scatter diagram with a line of equality, for example:

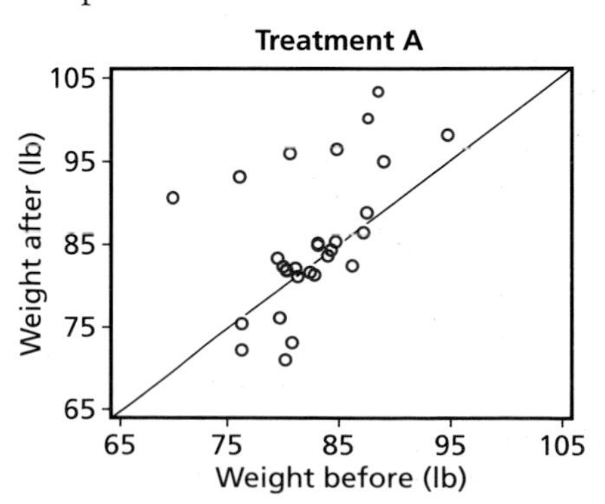

Page 49 Exercise 2.5A

1 A strong positive relationship

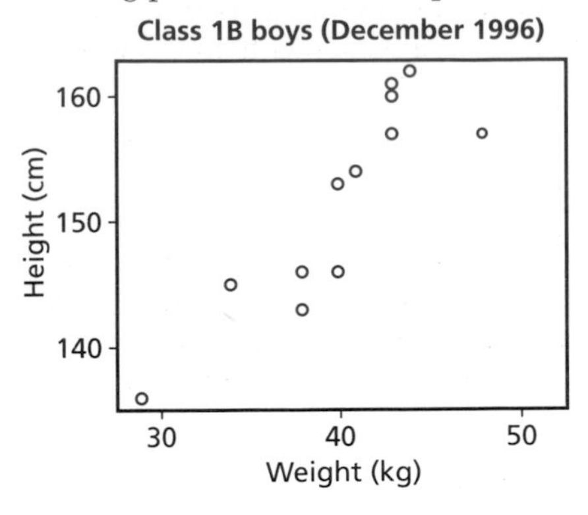

2 A strong positive relationship

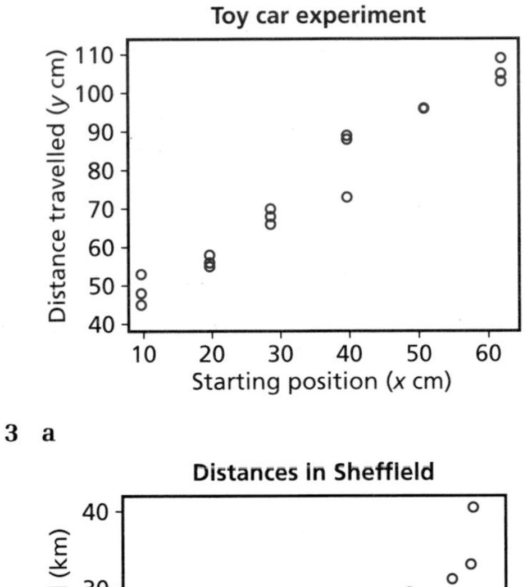

3 **a**

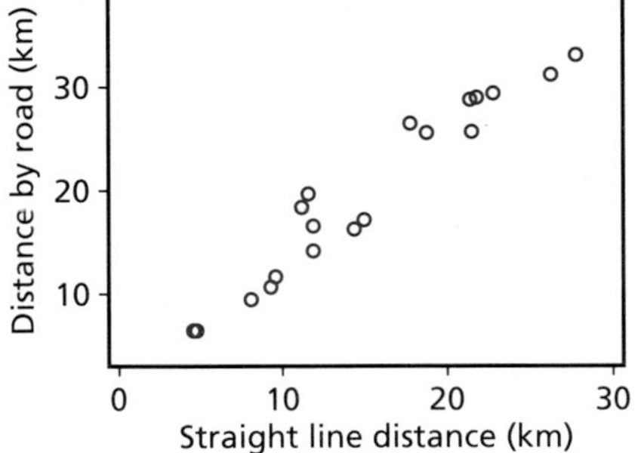

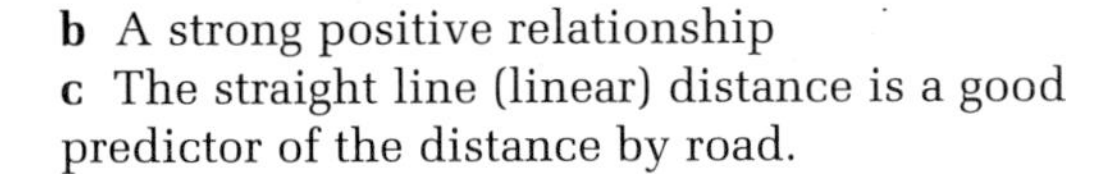

b A strong positive relationship

c The straight line (linear) distance is a good predictor of the distance by road.

4 A strong positive relationship

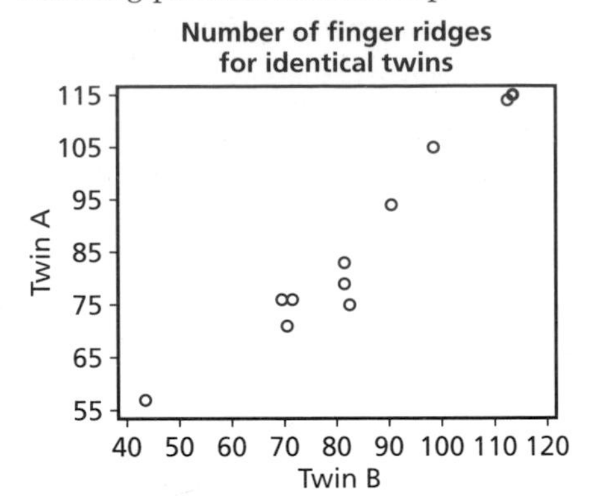

Page 50 Exercise 2.5B

1

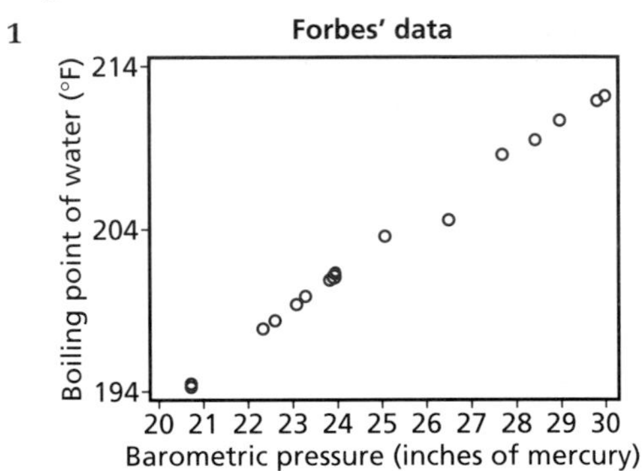

Very strong positive relationship. One value close to the centre seems to be 'out of line'. Is there a very slight curve to the plotted points?

2

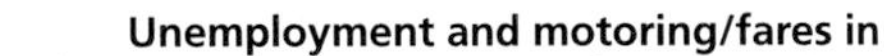

Northern Ireland is a possible outlier. A strong negative relationship if Northern Ireland is ignored.

Page 52 Exercise 2.6B

1

	3 ft	35 ft
Males	0.54	0.63
Females	0.46	0.37
Total	1.00	1.00

At 3 ft above ground the proportion of males in the trap was 0.54, while at 35 ft above ground the proportion of males was 0.63. It seems that males tend to be higher flyers!

2 These proportions have been rounded to 2 decimal places and so may not sum to 1.00 exactly.

Region	Good	Fairly good	Not good	Total
Southampton	0.65	0.30	0.05	1.00
Swindon	0.63	0.32	0.06	1.01
Jersey	0.68	0.26	0.06	1.00
Guernsey	0.64	0.30	0.06	1.00
West Dorset	0.60	0.33	0.07	1.00

These proportions appear remarkably consistent across regions and it is difficult to say whether the small differences that there are result from real differences among regions or to chance variation. The largest difference is between the 'Good' and 'Fairly good' ratings for Jersey and West Dorset.

3

	Wears blazer	Does not wear blazer	Total
Male	5	20	25
Female	10	15	25
Total	15	35	50

	Wearing	Not wearing	Total
Male	0.2	0.8	1.0
Female	0.4	0.6	1.0

The proportion of girls wearing a school blazer is double the proportion of boys with blazers.

Page 55 Chapter 2 Review

1 Product quality: Both large and small customers agree that the company's product quality is high (median score 7.0, semi-IQR 1.0 approx.).
Delivery speed: On average, large customers are more satisfied than small customers (median score 4.0 against 2.5 approx.) although there is about twice the variability amongst large customers.
Price: On average large customers are less satisfied than small customers (median score 2.0 against 3.0). The large customers' views are more consistent (less variable).
Overall: Product quality is highly thought of but other aspects of the company's performance could be improved.

2 The water company lab tends to report higher levels of biochemical oxygen demand and lower levels of suspended solids than the commercial lab. In one case the commercial lab reported a very much higher level of suspended solids than the water company lab.

CHAPTER 3

Probabilities should be given as fractions where the decimal answer is not exact. However, if comparisons are required decimals may be more convenient.

Page 58 Exercise 3.1

1 quite likely **b, c** or **d**; as likely as not **c**; unlikely **b**; fifty-fifty **c**; almost certain **e**; practically impossible **a**

2 certain 1; good chance $0.5 < p < 1$; fair chance difficult to specify because of the different meanings of the word fair; evens 0.5; improbable $0 < p < 0.5$; impossible 0

0 0.5 1

impossible improbable evens fair chance good chance certain

3 **a** {1, 2, 3, 4, 5, 6}; yes **b** no **c** {H, T}; yes **d** no **e** {0, 1, 2, 3, 4, 5}; no

4 **a** 0.1 **b** 0.8 **c** 0.5

5 $\frac{6}{40}$ or $\frac{3}{20}$ or 0.15 , $\frac{34}{40}$ or $\frac{17}{30}$ or 0.85, probably

6 $\frac{2}{20}$ or 0.1, $\frac{11}{50}$ or 0.22, $\frac{17}{100}$ or 0.17, $\frac{35}{200}$ or 0.175, $\frac{70}{500}$ or 0.14; best estimate of probability given by 0.14 (but see next section)

Page 62 Exercise 3.2

1 **a** $\frac{1}{52}$ **b** $\frac{2}{52}$ or $\frac{1}{26}$ **c** $\frac{16}{52}$ or $\frac{4}{13}$

2 **a** $\frac{1}{800}$ or 0.001 **b** $\frac{6}{800}$ or $\frac{3}{400}$ or 0.0075
c $\frac{794}{800}$ or 0.9925
d answer **b** + answer **c** = 1

3 **a** HH, HT, TH, TT; $\frac{1}{2}$ **b** HHH, HHT, HTH, THH, TTH, THT, HTT, TTT; $\frac{3}{8}$

4 **a** $\frac{1}{12}$ **b** $\frac{1}{4}$ **c** $\frac{1}{6}$

5 $\frac{6}{30}$ or $\frac{1}{5}$ or 0.2

6 **a** $\frac{44}{200}$ or 0.22 **b** $\frac{156}{200}$ or 0.78

7 **a** FF only 6, SS only 13, TT only 1
b (i) $\frac{4}{30}$ or 0.133 (ii) $\frac{17}{30}$ or 0.567
(iii) $\frac{13}{30}$ or 0.433

8 a $\frac{5039}{6000}$ or 0.840 **b** $\frac{961}{6000}$ or 0.160

9 $\frac{6}{10}$ or 0.6

10 $\frac{16}{30}$ or 0.53

Page 64 Exercise 3.3

1 a (i) 720 (ii) 720 (iii) 36 (iv) 46656 (v) 64

b $n^2 \leq 2^n < n! < n^n$ for $n \geq 4$

2 a 20 **b** 151 200 **c** 4 **d** 1190

3 720

4 110

5 40 320

Page 65 Exercise 3.4

1

1
1 1
1 2 1
1 3 3 1
1 4 6 4 1
1 5 10 10 5 1
1 6 15 20 15 6 1
1 7 21 35 35 21 7 1
1 8 28 56 70 56 28 8 1
1 9 36 84 126 126 84 36 9 1
1 10 45 120 210 252 210 120 45 10 1

a 2 **b** 5 **c** 21 **d** 21 **e** 210 **f** 1 **g** 1

2 a 35 **b** 28 **c** 45 **d** 126 **e** 6

Page 66 Exercise 3.5

1 a 5 **b** 56 **c** 42 **d** 2520 **e** 4845 **f** 24 **g** 1

2 165

3 990

4 10

5 ${}^{52}C_7 = 133\,784\,560$

6 ${}^{13}C_4 \times {}^{39}C_3 = 6\,534\,385$

7 a (i) 24 (ii) 6 **b** 4

8 14

9 10 **b** 2 **c** 20

10 a $\frac{1}{{}^{20}C_3} = \frac{1}{1140} = 0.0009$

b $\frac{{}^{10}C_3}{{}^{20}C_3}$ or $\frac{{}^{17}C_7 \times {}^{3}C_3}{{}^{20}C_{10}} = 0.1053$

11 a $\frac{4 \times {}^{3}C_3}{{}^{12}C_3} = 0.0182$

b $\frac{3 \times {}^{3}C_3 \times {}^{9}C_1}{{}^{12}C_4} = 0.0545$

12 a $\frac{{}^{197}C_{20}}{{}^{200}C_{20}} = 0.7278$ **b** 0.2722

Page 68 Exercise 3.6

1 a (i) yes (ii) no (iii) no

b (i) no (ii) no (iii) no

2 a (i), (iii) **b** (iii) **c** (iii)

3 a (i) The family runs at most 1 car.

(ii) The family runs 3 or more cars.

b

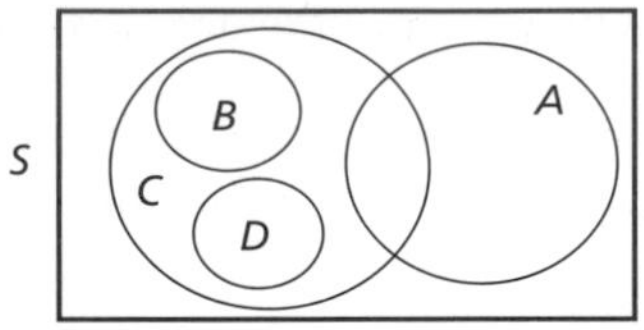

c A, B; A, D; B, D

d (i) A, C (ii) A, B, C or A, C, D or A, B, D

4 a A, B; B, C **b** A, C

5

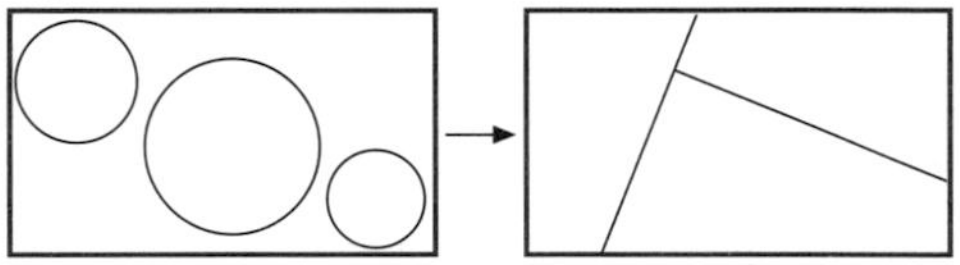

6 a $\overline{A}, \overline{B}$ **b** $\overline{A}, \overline{C}$; $\overline{B}, \overline{C}$ **c** $\overline{A}, \overline{B}$; $\overline{B}, \overline{C}$

7 a $\frac{1}{2}$ **b** $\frac{1}{2}$ **c** $\frac{1}{4}$ **d** $\frac{1}{5}$ **e** $\frac{3}{4}$ **f** $\frac{4}{5}$

Page 70 Exercise 3.7A

1 $\frac{4}{9}, \frac{3}{9}, \frac{7}{9}$

2 a 0.65 **b** 0.2

3 a 0.94 **b** 0.06

4 a 0.5 **b** 0.4

5 0.75

6 a yes **b** no **c** yes, since $P(\overline{X} \text{ or } \overline{Y}) = 1 - P(X \text{ and } Y) =$ $1 -$ P (both occur) so P(both occur) = 0

7 a $\frac{11}{48} \approx 0.229$ **b** $\frac{37}{48} \approx 0.771$

8 a $\frac{6}{11}, \frac{3}{11}, \frac{9}{11}$ **b** $\frac{8}{11}, \frac{1}{11}$

Page 71 Exercise 3.7B

1 a $\frac{8}{20} = 0.4$ **b** $\frac{11}{20} = 0.55$ **c** $\frac{16}{20} = 0.8$

d Events are not mutually exclusive.

e $\frac{3}{20} = 0.15$; $0.4 + 0.55 - 0.15 = 0.8$

2 a $\frac{58}{105} \approx 0.552$ **b** $\frac{74}{105} \approx 0.705$

3 a 0.4 **b** 0.25 **c** 0.15

Page 74 Exercise 3.8A

1 a $\frac{1}{32}$ **b** $\frac{31}{32}$

2 a $\frac{6}{35} \approx 0.171$ **b** $\frac{24}{35} \approx 0.686$

3 0.002; lateness may be caused by same factor, e.g. weather, strikes

4 $\frac{25}{36} \approx 0.694$

5 a No, snow and high winds can occur together. **b** No, the occurrence of one could influence the occurrence of the other.

c (i) $\frac{20}{21} \approx 0.952$ (ii) $\frac{5}{6} \approx 0.794$

6 a 0.92 **b** 0.434

7 a 0.48 **b** 0.08

Page 75 Exercise 3.8B

1 **a** (i) 0.03 (ii) 0.202 (iii) 0.036
b Vehicles may be travelling in convoy.

2 **a** $\frac{4}{15}$ **b** $\frac{2}{5}$ **c** $\frac{4}{15}+\frac{4}{25}+\frac{4}{45}+\frac{4}{75}=\frac{128}{225}$

3 $\frac{32}{663} \approx 0.0483$

Page 76 Exercise 3.9B

1 **a** 0.51 **b** (i) 0.2401 (ii) 0.4998

2 $0.05 \times 0.75 + 0.25 \times 0.95 = 0.275$

3 $\frac{9}{200} = 0.045$

4 **a** 0.09 **b** 0.16 **c** 0.19

5 **a** $\frac{1}{2}$ **b** $\frac{1}{2}$

6 **a** $1-\left(\frac{12}{13}\right)^2 = 0.213$ **b** $\left(\frac{12}{13}\right)^2 = 0.852$
c 0.217 **d** 0.851

7 **a** 0.25 **b** 0.958

Page 78 Exercise 3.10

1 For example, if using decimals, $0 \le n < 0.5 \Rightarrow$ H; $0.5 \le n < 1 \Rightarrow$ T; or use int(2 random + 1) on a graphics calculator; or tabulated random digits $0 \to 4 \Rightarrow$ H; $5 \to 9 \Rightarrow$ T

2 For example, if using random digits, 1, 2, 3 $\Rightarrow$ A; 4, 5, 6 $\Rightarrow$ B; 7, 8, 9 $\Rightarrow$ C; throw 0 away; or use int(3 random + 1)

3 **a** For example, if using decimals, $0 \le n < 0.25 \Rightarrow$ A; $0.25 \le n < 0.5 \Rightarrow$ B; $0.5 \le n < 0.75 \Rightarrow$ C; $0.75 \le n < 1 \Rightarrow$ D; or use int(4 random + 1) **b** For example, if using random digits, 1 $\Rightarrow$ A; 2, 3 $\Rightarrow$ B; 4, 5 $\Rightarrow$ C; 6 $\Rightarrow$ D; throw others away

4 For example,

digits $\begin{cases} 1 \to 9 & \text{produces offspring} \\ 0 & \text{dies} \end{cases}$

ten times, then find total bacteria at end of one-hour period. Repeat using new total.

5 $(1+5+10+10+10+5) \times \left(\frac{2}{5}\right)^5 = 0.317\,44$

Page 79 Statistics in action – Simulating a game

Computer simulations suggest that on average about 44 throws of the die are needed (mean 44, standard deviation 14). See the example in Chapter 2, page 36.

Page 80 Chapter 3 Review

1 $\frac{3}{20} = 0.15$

2 **a** $\frac{2}{3}$ **b** $\frac{1}{12}$

3 **a** (i) $\frac{9}{20} = 0.45$ (ii) $\frac{5}{36} = 0.139$
b independence

4 $\frac{{}^6C_2 \times {}^8C_3}{{}^{14}C_5} = 0.4196$

5 $\frac{1 \times {}^{38}C_2}{{}^{41}C_5} = 0.0009$

6 **a** 0.0002 **b** 0.6485

7 **a** 0.61 **b** 0.81 **c** 0.59 **d** 0.18
e 0.99 **f** 0.25

8 $(1+6+1) \times \left(\frac{2}{5}\right)^4 = 0.2048$

CHAPTER 4

Page 83 Exercise 4.1

1 **a** T, $t = 2, 3, 4, 5, \ldots, 12$
b S, $s = 0, 1, 2, \ldots, n$ **c** C, $c = 0, 1, 2, \ldots, 5$
d M, $0 \le m \le 10$ **e** H, $1.50 \le h \le 2.10$

2 **a** discrete and finite **b** continuous
c discrete and infinite **d** continuous
e discrete and finite

Page 85 Exercise 4.2A

1 **a** no **b** yes **c** yes **d** no

2

t	2	3	4	5	6	7	8	9	10	11	12
$P(T=t)$	$\frac{1}{36}$	$\frac{2}{36}$	$\frac{3}{36}$	$\frac{4}{36}$	$\frac{5}{36}$	$\frac{6}{36}$	$\frac{5}{36}$	$\frac{4}{36}$	$\frac{3}{36}$	$\frac{2}{36}$	$\frac{1}{36}$

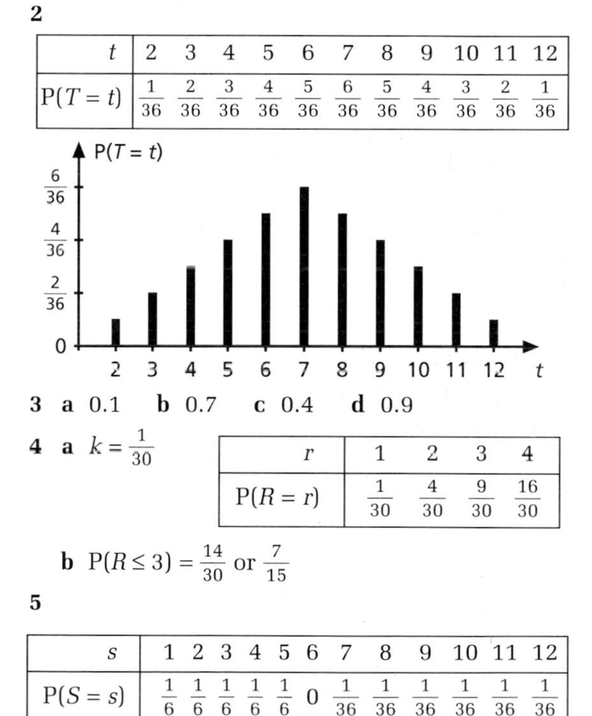

3 **a** 0.1 **b** 0.7 **c** 0.4 **d** 0.9

4 **a** $k = \frac{1}{30}$

r	1	2	3	4
$P(R=r)$	$\frac{1}{30}$	$\frac{4}{30}$	$\frac{9}{30}$	$\frac{16}{30}$

b $P(R \le 3) = \frac{14}{30}$ or $\frac{7}{15}$

5

s	1	2	3	4	5	6	7	8	9	10	11	12
$P(S=s)$	$\frac{1}{6}$	$\frac{1}{6}$	$\frac{1}{6}$	$\frac{1}{6}$	$\frac{1}{6}$	0	$\frac{1}{36}$	$\frac{1}{36}$	$\frac{1}{36}$	$\frac{1}{36}$	$\frac{1}{36}$	$\frac{1}{36}$

Page 86 Exercise 4.2B

1 **a**

s	0	1	2	3	4	5	6	7	8
Rel. freq. $= P(S=s)$	$\frac{12}{180}$	$\frac{15}{180}$	$\frac{19}{180}$	$\frac{24}{180}$	$\frac{30}{180}$	$\frac{25}{180}$	$\frac{23}{180}$	$\frac{20}{180}$	$\frac{12}{180}$
or	.067	.083	.106	.133	.167	.139	.128	.111	.067

Total = 1.001 due to rounding error

b $P(2 < S < 4) = P(3) = \frac{2}{15}$;

$P(2 \leq S \leq 4) = \frac{73}{180} = 0.406$

2

w	1	2	3	4	5
$P(W = w)$	$4k$	$3k$	$2k$	k	0.01

so $k = 0.099$ and

w	1	2	3	4	5
$P(W = w)$	0.396	0.297	0.198	0.099	0.01

3

l	0	1	2	3
$P(L = l)$	$\frac{2}{6}$	$\frac{3}{6}$	0	$\frac{1}{6}$

4

s	0	1	2	3	4
$P(S = s)$	$\frac{1}{16}$	$\frac{4}{16}$	$\frac{6}{16}$	$\frac{4}{16}$	$\frac{1}{16}$

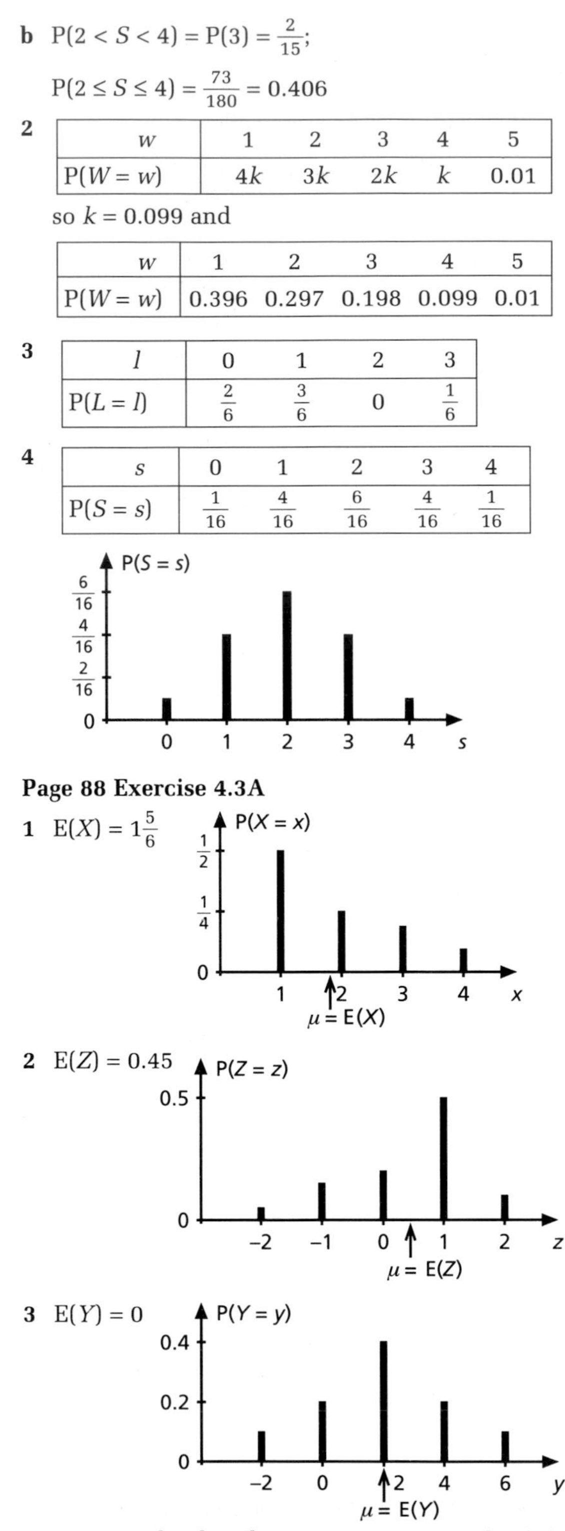

Page 88 Exercise 4.3A

1 $E(X) = 1\frac{5}{6}$

P(X = x); 1/2; 1/4; 0; 1 2 3 4 x; $\mu = E(X)$

2 $E(Z) = 0.45$

P(Z = z); 0.5; 0; −2 −1 0 1 2 z; $\mu = E(Z)$

3 $E(Y) = 0$

P(Y = y); 0.4; 0.2; 0; −2 0 2 4 6 y; $\mu = E(Y)$

Because the distribution is symmetrical, $E(Y)$ takes the value at the centre.

4 $E(T) = 1.533$ tests

5 $E(R) = 4$

6

w	100	0
$P(W = w)$	$\frac{1}{6840}$	$\frac{6839}{6840}$

$({}^{20}P_3 = 6840)$

$E(W) = \frac{100}{6840} = £0.0146$ or 1.46p

Page 88 Exercise 4.3B

1

s	1	2	3	4	5	6
$P(S = s)$	$\frac{11}{36}$	$\frac{9}{36}$	$\frac{7}{36}$	$\frac{5}{36}$	$\frac{3}{36}$	$\frac{1}{36}$

$E(S) = 2\frac{19}{36} \approx 2.528$

2 a $E(C) = 3.13$

b

a	0	250	500	750	1000	1250	1500	1750	2000
$P(A = a)$	0.02	0.09	0.25	0.3	0.18	0.08	0.05	0.02	0.01

$E(A) = £782.50$

c $A = 250C$; $E(A) = E(250C) = 250 \times E(C)$

3 a $E(X) = 1.4$, $E(Y) = 11.4$

b $E(Y) = E(X + 10) = E(X) + 10$

4 a $E(R) = 1.4$, $E(S) = 5.8$

b $E(S) = E(2R + 3) = 2E(R) + 3$

5 a 7.5 **b** 4.5 **c** 8

6 a

v	1	2	3	4	5	6
$P(V = v)$	$\frac{1}{6}$	$\frac{1}{6}$	$\frac{1}{6}$	$\frac{1}{6}$	$\frac{1}{6}$	$\frac{1}{6}$

$E(V) = 3.5$; $(E(V))^2 = 12.25$

b

s	1	4	9	16	25	36
$P(S = s)$	$\frac{1}{6}$	$\frac{1}{6}$	$\frac{1}{6}$	$\frac{1}{6}$	$\frac{1}{6}$	$\frac{1}{6}$

$E(S) = \frac{91}{6} = 15.17$; $E(V^2) \neq (E(V))^2$

7 a 0.3 **b** 1.5

c

$(x + 1)^2$	0	1	4	9
$P(X = x)$	0.1	0.5	0.2	0.2

$E((X + 1)^2) = 3.1$

Page 91 Exercise 4.4A

1 1.3, 2.3, 0.61, 0.781

2 0.35, 0.3275, 0.572

3 a $\frac{1}{10}$ **b** 2 **c** 1 **d** 1

4 13.9 min, 10.59 min

Page 91 Exercise 4.4B

1 a 2.3, 1.11

b

b	300	600	900	1200	1500
$P(B = b)$	0.2	0.5	0.15	0.1	0.05

£690, £^{2}99 900

c $B = 300T$; $\text{Var}(B) = \text{Var}(300 \times T) =$
$300^2\,\text{Var}(T)$ or $90\,000\,\text{Var}(T)$;
$\text{SD}(B) = \sqrt{\text{Var}(B)} = \sqrt{90\,000\,\text{Var}(T)} =$
$300\sqrt{\text{Var}(T)} = 300\,\text{SD}(T)$

2 a 61.17p, 2.2571p^2

b

n	64.9	65.9	69.9
$P(N = n)$	0.25	0.62	0.13

66.17p, 2.2571p^2

c $N = F + 5$; $\text{Var}(N) = \text{Var}(F + 5) = \text{Var}(F)$;
$\text{SD}(N) = \sqrt{\text{Var}(N)} = \sqrt{\text{Var}(F)} = \text{SD}(F)$

3 a 156, 72 **b** 13, 0.5 **c** 57, 8 **d** 21, 2

4 a 0, 1 **b** 1.42 **c** 2
d English better than mathematics

5 $p^2 + p$, $(3p^2 + p) - (p^2 + p)^2$
$= p + 2p^2 - 2p^3 - p^4$

Page 93 Exercise 4.5

1 Answers may differ.

2

x	0	1	2	3	4	5	6	7
$P(X \le x)$	0.08	0.21	0.43	0.66	0.84	0.93	0.97	1

3 Probability distribution is given by

h	0	1	2
$P(H \le h)$	0.25	0.5	0.25

e.g. 0.802 gives 2 heads

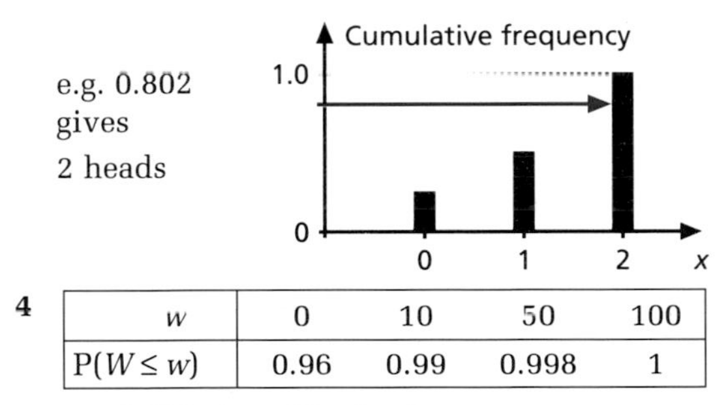

4

w	0	10	50	100
$P(W \le w)$	0.96	0.99	0.998	1

e.g. 0.802 gives £0 winnings

5 $0 \le n < 0.24 \Rightarrow$ defective;
$0.24 \le n < 1 \Rightarrow$ good

6 For example: $0 \le n < 0.25 \Rightarrow$ card 1;
$0.25 \le n < 0.5 \Rightarrow$ card 2;
$0.5 \le n < 0.75 \Rightarrow$ card 3; $0.75 \le n < 1 \Rightarrow$ card 4

Page 97 Exercise 4.6A

1 a $\frac{1}{2}$ **b** $\frac{1}{8}$

2 a $\int_0^{10} \frac{x}{50}\,dx = \left[\frac{x^2}{100}\right]_0^{10} = 1$

and $f(x) = \frac{x}{50} \ge 0$, $0 \le x \le 10$, so $f(x)$ is a pdf.

b

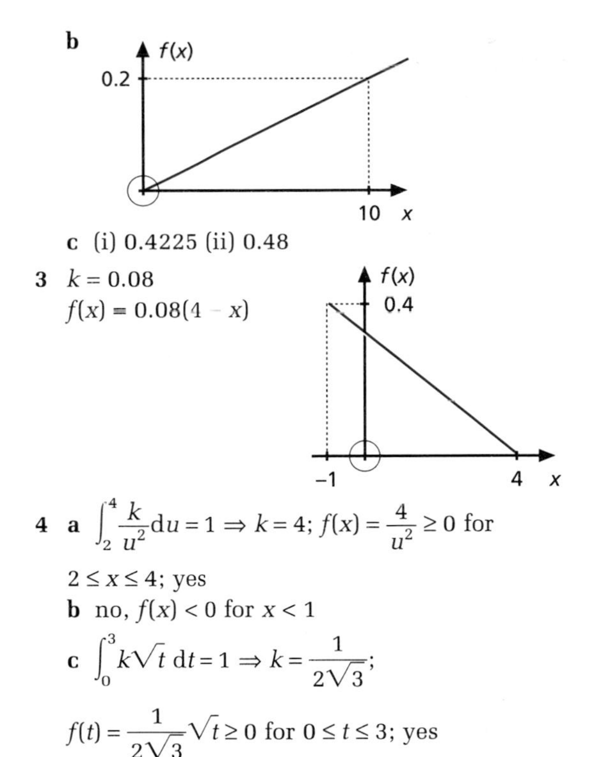

c (i) 0.4225 (ii) 0.48

3 $k = 0.08$
$f(x) = 0.08(4 - x)$

4 a $\int_2^4 \frac{k}{u^2}\,du = 1 \Rightarrow k = 4$; $f(x) = \frac{4}{u^2} \ge 0$ for $2 \le x \le 4$; yes

b no, $f(x) < 0$ for $x < 1$

c $\int_0^3 k\sqrt{t}\,dt = 1 \Rightarrow k = \frac{1}{2\sqrt{3}}$;

$f(t) = \frac{1}{2\sqrt{3}}\sqrt{t} \ge 0$ for $0 \le t \le 3$; yes

Page 98 Exercise 4.6B

1 $\int_0^1 3x^p\,dx = 3\left[\frac{x^{p+1}}{p+1}\right]_0^1 - 1 \Rightarrow p = 2$

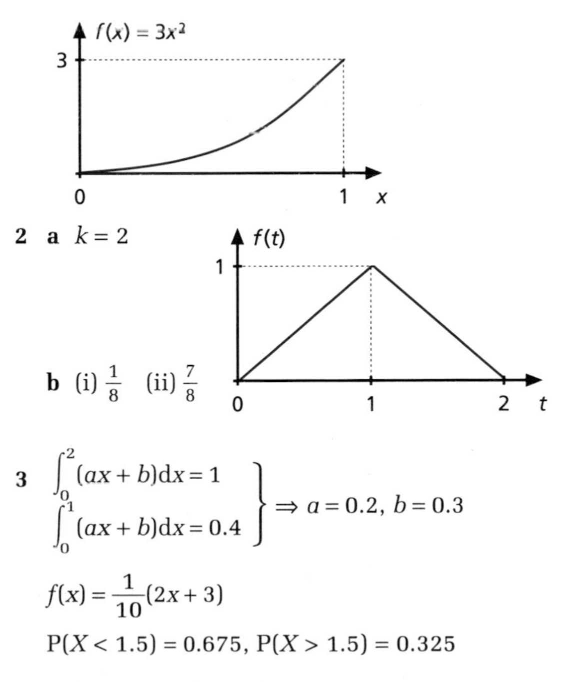

2 a $k = 2$

b (i) $\frac{1}{8}$ (ii) $\frac{7}{8}$

3 $\left.\begin{aligned}\int_0^2 (ax + b)\,dx = 1 \\ \int_0^1 (ax + b)\,dx = 0.4\end{aligned}\right\} \Rightarrow a = 0.2,\ b = 0.3$

$f(x) = \frac{1}{10}(2x + 3)$

$P(X < 1.5) = 0.675$, $P(X > 1.5) = 0.325$

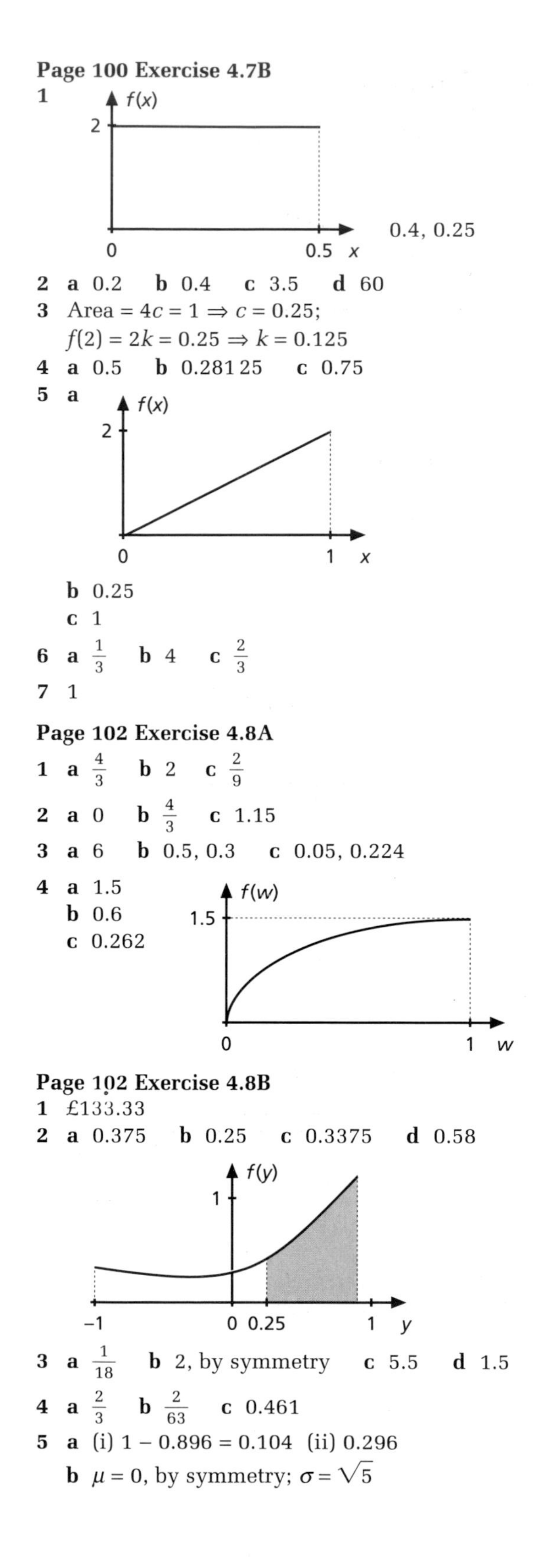

Page 100 Exercise 4.7B

1 0.4, 0.25

2 **a** 0.2 **b** 0.4 **c** 3.5 **d** 60

3 Area = $4c = 1 \Rightarrow c = 0.25$;
$f(2) = 2k = 0.25 \Rightarrow k = 0.125$

4 **a** 0.5 **b** 0.281 25 **c** 0.75

5 **a**

b 0.25
c 1

6 **a** $\frac{1}{3}$ **b** 4 **c** $\frac{2}{3}$

7 1

Page 102 Exercise 4.8A

1 **a** $\frac{4}{3}$ **b** 2 **c** $\frac{2}{9}$

2 **a** 0 **b** $\frac{4}{3}$ **c** 1.15

3 **a** 6 **b** 0.5, 0.3 **c** 0.05, 0.224

4 **a** 1.5
b 0.6
c 0.262

Page 102 Exercise 4.8B

1 £133.33

2 **a** 0.375 **b** 0.25 **c** 0.3375 **d** 0.58

3 **a** $\frac{1}{18}$ **b** 2, by symmetry **c** 5.5 **d** 1.5

4 **a** $\frac{2}{3}$ **b** $\frac{2}{63}$ **c** 0.461

5 **a** (i) $1 - 0.896 = 0.104$ (ii) 0.296
b $\mu = 0$, by symmetry; $\sigma = \sqrt{5}$

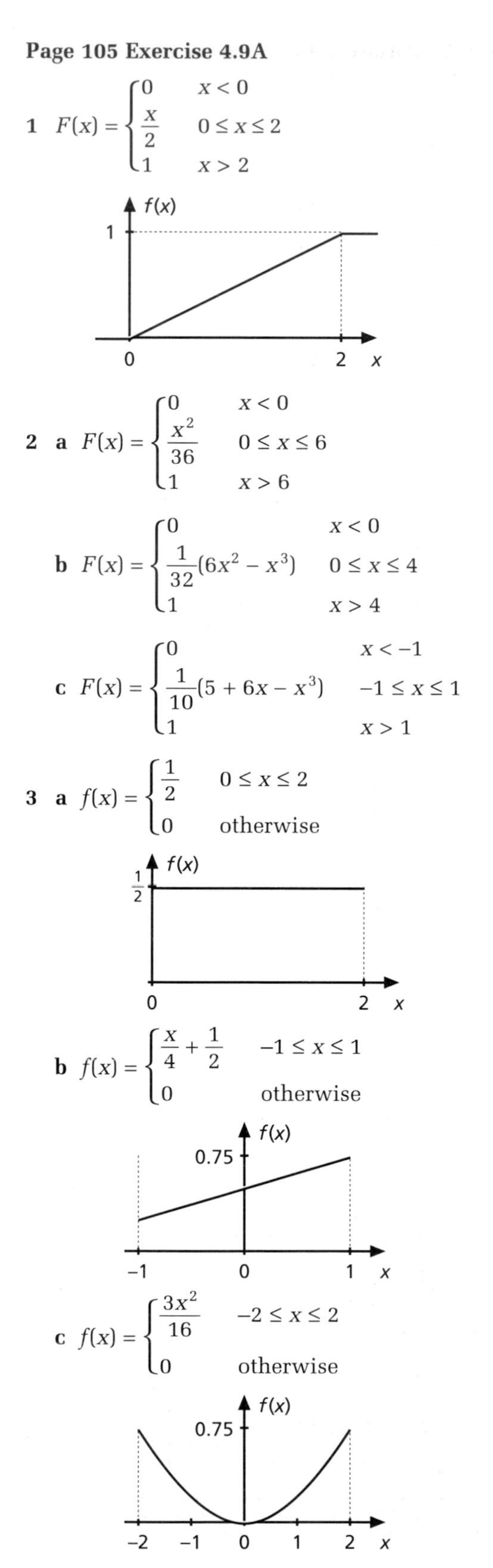

Page 105 Exercise 4.9A

1 $F(x) = \begin{cases} 0 & x < 0 \\ \frac{x}{2} & 0 \le x \le 2 \\ 1 & x > 2 \end{cases}$

2 **a** $F(x) = \begin{cases} 0 & x < 0 \\ \frac{x^2}{36} & 0 \le x \le 6 \\ 1 & x > 6 \end{cases}$

b $F(x) = \begin{cases} 0 & x < 0 \\ \frac{1}{32}(6x^2 - x^3) & 0 \le x \le 4 \\ 1 & x > 4 \end{cases}$

c $F(x) = \begin{cases} 0 & x < -1 \\ \frac{1}{10}(5 + 6x - x^3) & -1 \le x \le 1 \\ 1 & x > 1 \end{cases}$

3 **a** $f(x) = \begin{cases} \frac{1}{2} & 0 \le x \le 2 \\ 0 & \text{otherwise} \end{cases}$

b $f(x) = \begin{cases} \frac{x}{4} + \frac{1}{2} & -1 \le x \le 1 \\ 0 & \text{otherwise} \end{cases}$

c $f(x) = \begin{cases} \frac{3x^2}{16} & -2 \le x \le 2 \\ 0 & \text{otherwise} \end{cases}$

Page 106 Exercise 4.9B

1 **a** 8.49 **b** 1.59

2 **a**

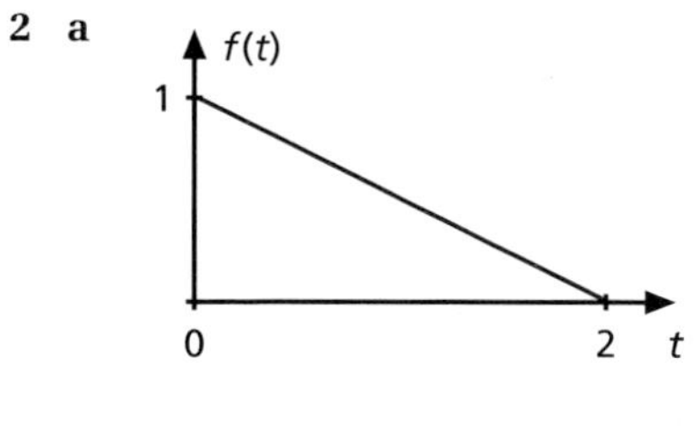

b $F(t) = \begin{cases} 0 & x < 0 \\ t\left(1 - \frac{t}{4}\right) & 0 \le x \le 2 \\ 1 & x > 2 \end{cases}$

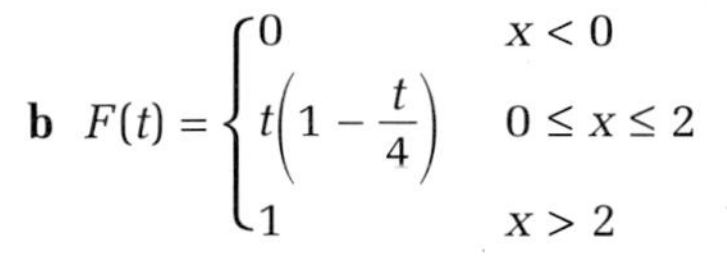

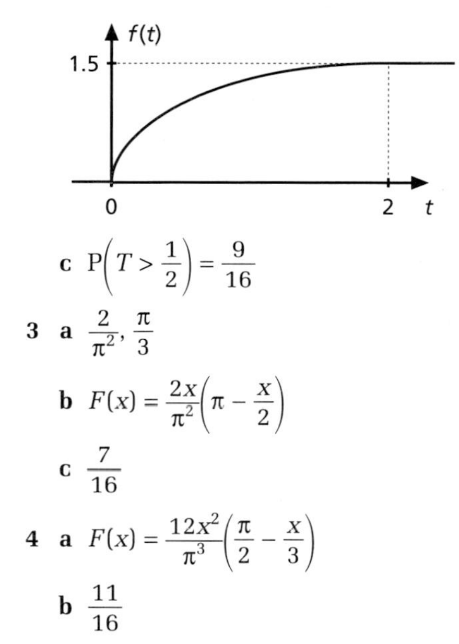

c $\mathrm{P}\left(T > \frac{1}{2}\right) = \frac{9}{16}$

3 **a** $\frac{2}{\pi^2}, \frac{\pi}{3}$

b $F(x) = \frac{2x}{\pi^2}\left(\pi - \frac{x}{2}\right)$

c $\frac{7}{16}$

4 **a** $F(x) = \frac{12x^2}{\pi^3}\left(\frac{\pi}{2} - \frac{x}{3}\right)$

b $\frac{11}{16}$

Page 107 Chapter 4 Review

1 **a**

m	0	1	2	3	4	5	≥5
P($M = m$)	0.421	0.208	0.164	0.102	0.083	0.022	0

b 0.557 **c** 0.371

2 **a**

d	0	1	2	3	4
P($D = d$)	0.1	0.1	0.1	0.3	0.4

b 2.8 **c** 1.76

3

f	0	1	2	3	4
P($F = f$)	0.4096	0.4096	0.1536	0.0256	0.0016

f	0	1	2	3	4
P($F \le f$)	0.4096	0.8192	0.9728	0.9984	1

4 **a** $\int_0^2 \frac{1}{4}(x + 1)\mathrm{d}x = 1$

$f(x) \ge 0$ for all x, $0 \le x \le 2$

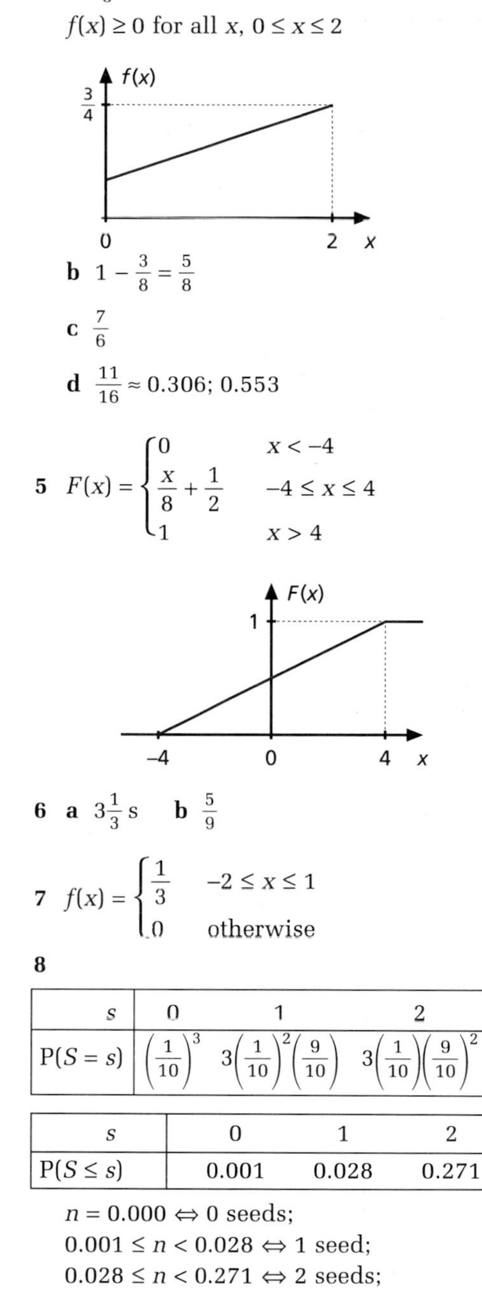

b $1 - \frac{3}{8} = \frac{5}{8}$

c $\frac{7}{6}$

d $\frac{11}{16} \approx 0.306$; 0.553

5 $F(x) = \begin{cases} 0 & x < -4 \\ \frac{x}{8} + \frac{1}{2} & -4 \le x \le 4 \\ 1 & x > 4 \end{cases}$

6 **a** $3\frac{1}{3}$ s **b** $\frac{5}{9}$

7 $f(x) = \begin{cases} \frac{1}{3} & -2 \le x \le 1 \\ 0 & \text{otherwise} \end{cases}$

8

s	0	1	2	3
P($S = s$)	$\left(\frac{1}{10}\right)^3$	$3\left(\frac{1}{10}\right)^2\left(\frac{9}{10}\right)$	$3\left(\frac{1}{10}\right)\left(\frac{9}{10}\right)^2$	$\left(\frac{9}{10}\right)^3$

s	0	1	2	3
P($S \le s$)	0.001	0.028	0.271	1

$n = 0.000 \Leftrightarrow$ 0 seeds;
$0.001 \le n < 0.028 \Leftrightarrow$ 1 seed;
$0.028 \le n < 0.271 \Leftrightarrow$ 2 seeds;
$0.271 \le n < 1 \Leftrightarrow$ 3 seeds

CHAPTER 5

Page 110 Exercise 5.1

1 **a** positive **b** no correlation **c** positive
d negative **e** no correlation

2

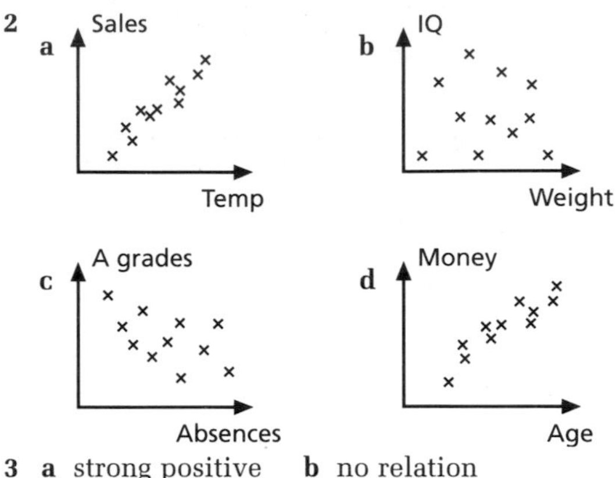

3 **a** strong positive **b** no relation
c positive (may be strong non-linear relation)
d moderate negative **e** perfect positive
f weak negative

4 **a** strong positive **b** very strong negative
c very weak or no linear relation
d weak negative **e** moderately strong positive

Page 114 Exercise 5.2A

1 **a**

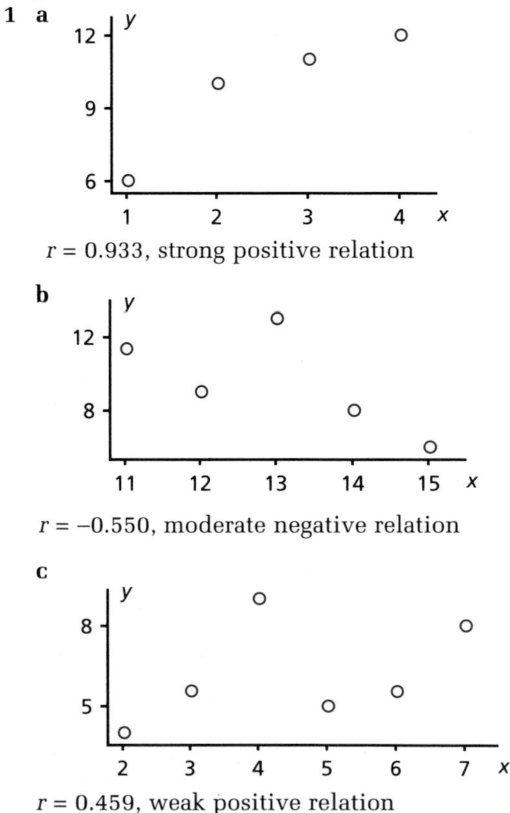

$r = 0.933$, strong positive relation

$r = -0.550$, moderate negative relation

$r = 0.459$, weak positive relation

d

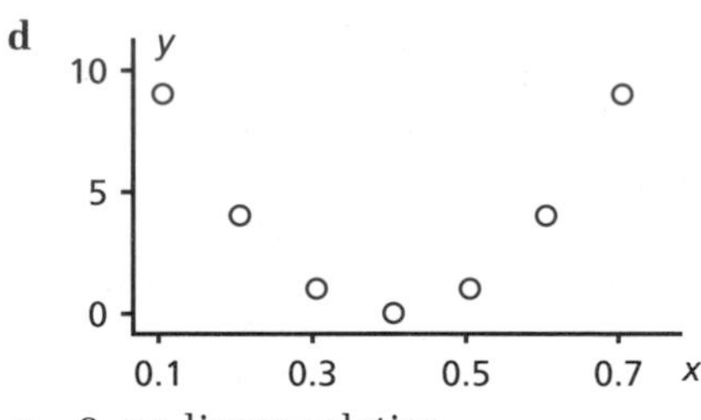

$r = 0$, no linear relation

2 **a** $S_{xy} = -89.275$, $S_{xx} = 408.41$, $S_{yy} = 33.9575$; $r = -0.758$
b a moderately strong negative correlation

3 **a** $S_{xy} = 293.5$, $S_{xx} = 2410.1$, $S_{yy} = 154.5$; $r = 0.481$ **b** a weak positive correlation

4 **a** $S_{xy} = 1298.427$, $S_{xx} = 1022.842$, $S_{yy} = 1759.25$; $r = 0.97$
b a very strong positive correlation

Page 115 Exercise 5.2B

1 **a** $r = 0.872$, a strong positive correlation
b $r = 0.982$, a very strong positive correlation
c $r = 0.872$, same as **a**, only units are different

2

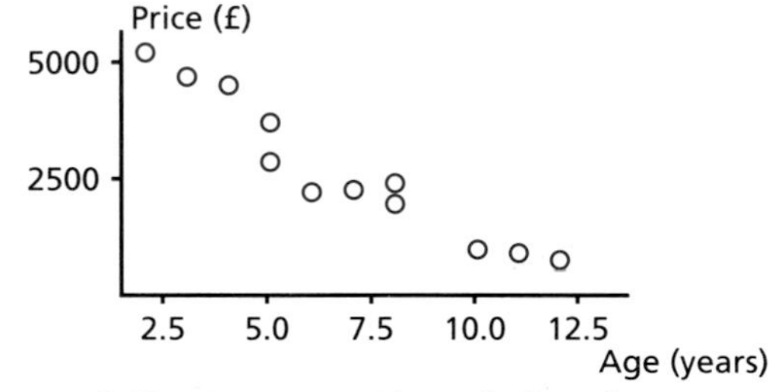

$r = -0.96$; strong negative relation, i.e. as age increases, price decreases, but notice a possible levelling off in the relationship for older cars

Page 117 Exercise 5.3B

1 **a** predictor: amount of revision; response: exam performance **b** predictor: amount of fertiliser; response: crop yield
c IQ influences both **d** predictor: number unemployed; response: amount spent on social security **e** predictor: number of cigarettes smoked; response: lung cancer rates **f** population size influences both
g age influences both **h** spurious correlation, time trend in each case

2 **a** $r = 0.852$, correlation becomes stronger
b $r = 0.443$, correlation becomes weaker
c Different kinds of outliers have a different effect. In **a** remaining points are more linear. In **b** remaining points are more spread. See scatter diagram.

3 **a** younger group $r = 0.631$;
older group $r = 0.988$
b Evidence suggests there may be a different and stronger relationship for older women. More scatter in data for younger women. More data required.

4 **a** $r = -0.331$ for whole data set
b Maybe Northern Ireland had special circumstances. $r = -0.822$ without Northern Ireland. There is a strong negative correlation between percentage unemployment and percentage spent on travel if Northern Ireland is excluded.

5 **a** $r = 0.626$ (boys), moderately strong positive correlation; $r =$ 0.474 (girls), weak positive correlation
b $r = 0.577$ (together), moderate positive correlation: the boys and girls do seem to have slightly different characteristics which are lost if the data are combined.

Page 121 Exercise 5.4

(Two points have been plotted for each regression line.)

1 **a/c**

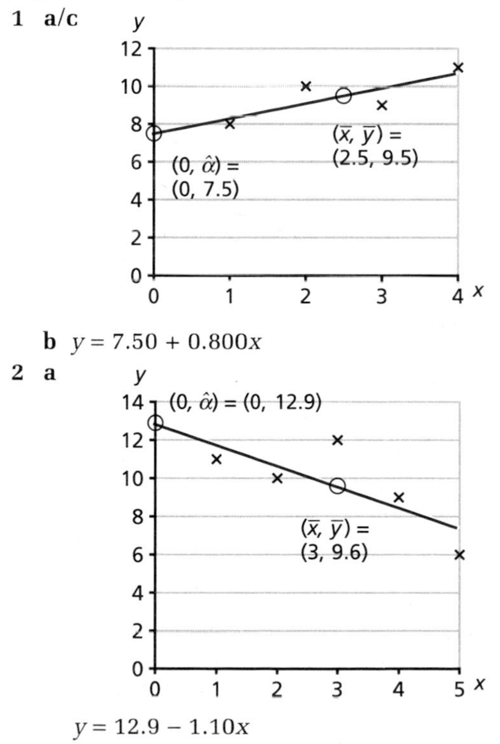

b $y = 7.50 + 0.800x$

2 **a**

$y = 12.9 - 1.10x$

b

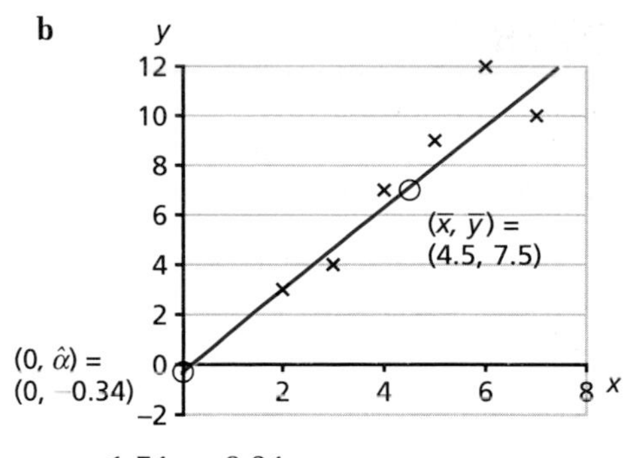

$y = 1.74x - 0.34$

Page 123 Exercise 5.5A

(Two points have been plotted for each regression line.)

1

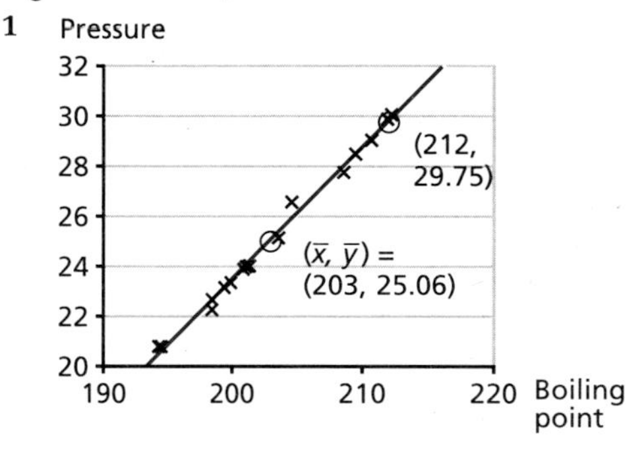

pressure = 0.521 boiling point − 80.7;
$\hat{y} = 29.752$ in. Hg; pressure increases at 0.521 in. Hg per F°.

2

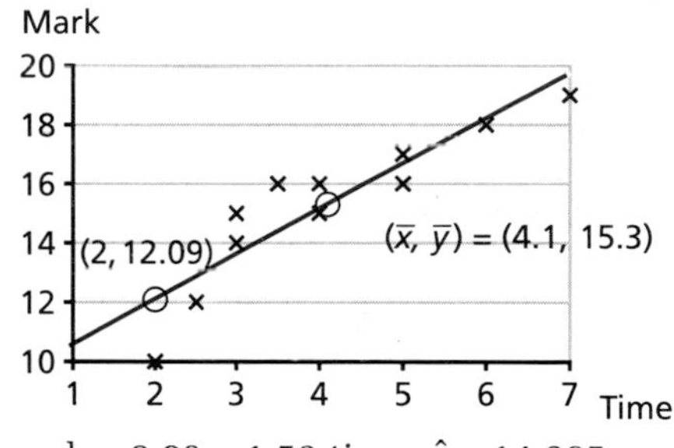

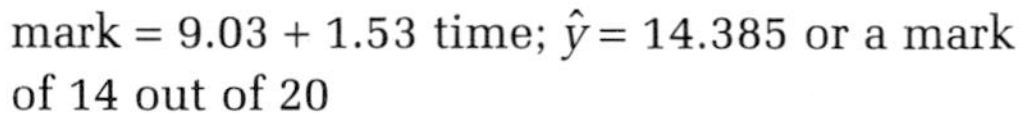

mark = 9.03 + 1.53 time; $\hat{y} = 14.385$ or a mark of 14 out of 20

3

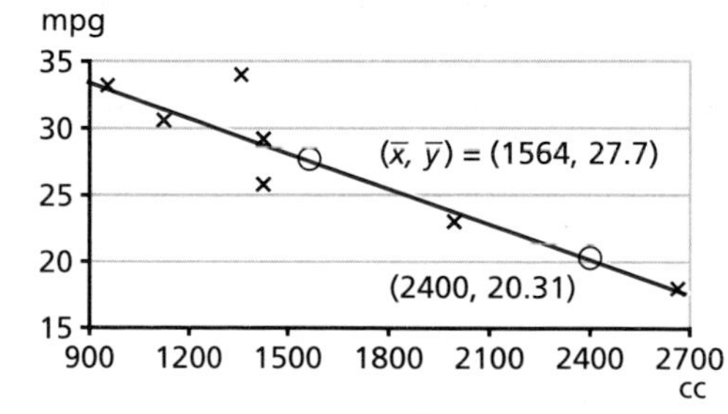

mpg = 41.91 − 0.009 cc; $\hat{y} = 20.31$ mpg; for an increase of 100 cc, a reduction of 0.9 mpg is expected.

Page 124 Exercise 5.5B

(Two points have been plotted for each regression line.)

1 a Correlation of size and price = 0.829; strong positive correlation

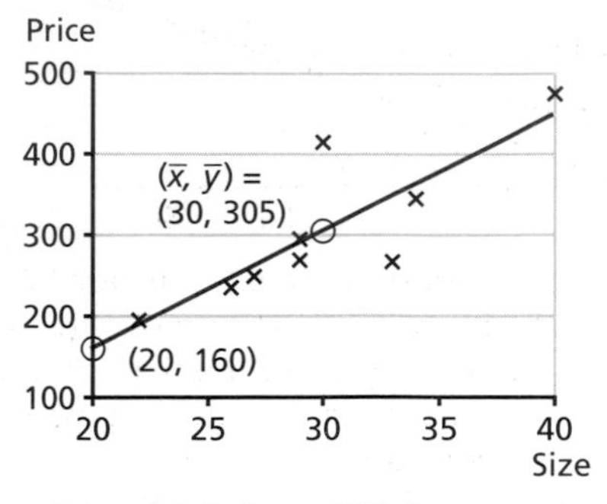

b price = 14.4 size − 128.3

c price increases at FF 14 400 per m^2

d FF 246 100

2 a Correlation of temp and litres = 0.907, i.e. very strong positive relation

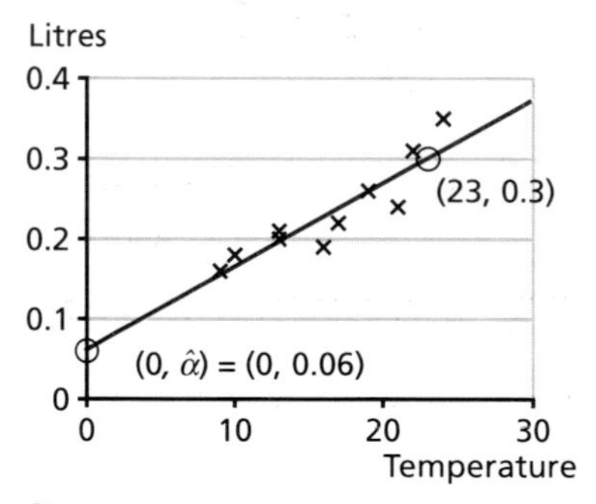

b litres = 0.0584 + 0.0106 temp

c average consumption when temperature is 23 °C is 0.302 litre

Page 125 Exercise 5.6B

1 1 With all boys included predictions will be a little high. 2 When the heavy boy is omitted, the regression line moves down the y-axis. Better predictions on the whole. 3 Removing the short boy reduces the gradient. 4 The best fitting line for most data in the height range 140–160 is given when both boys are excluded.

2 a With Northern Ireland: $y = 15.5 - 0.078x$; without Northern Ireland: $y = 17.04 - 0.238x$

b

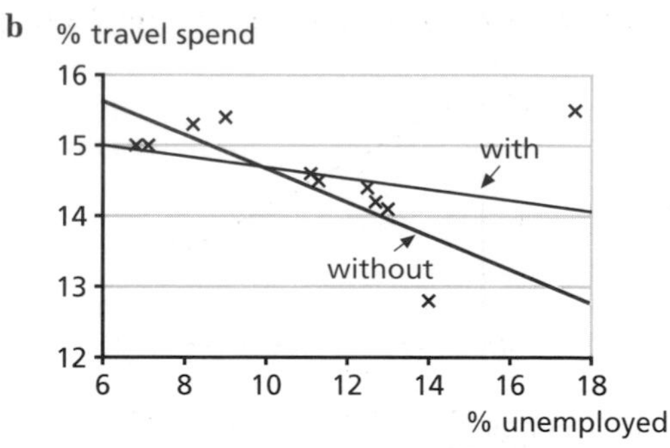

c (i) 14.33 (with), 13.47 (without) (ii) 13.94 (with), 12.28 (without). Omitting Northern Ireland gives a better line for describing the relationship between the other regions. Prediction for 20% unemployment requires extrapolation so is less reliable.

3 a no; road (km) = 0.38 + 1.27 crow (km)

b The relationship nearer the origin is likely to be different from the relationship in the given range.

c (i) 30.86 km (more reliable) (ii) 1.65 km

4 a sbp $y = 75.8 + 1.16$ age x (whole group); sbp $y = 85.6 + 0.940$ age x (younger group)

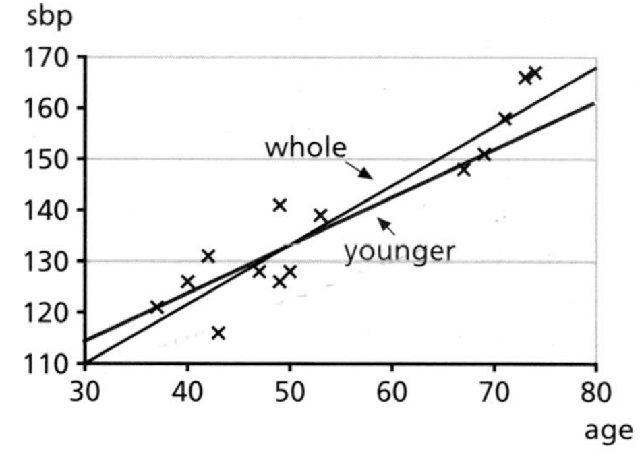

b (i) 127.9 (using regression equation for younger group) – the relationship is not particularly strong (ii) 174.4 (using regression equation for whole group) – the younger women's relation is not appropriate. Not a very reliable result because extrapolation is required. There is no evidence about the relationship above the age of 74 years.

Page 127 Chapter 5 Review

1 a (i)

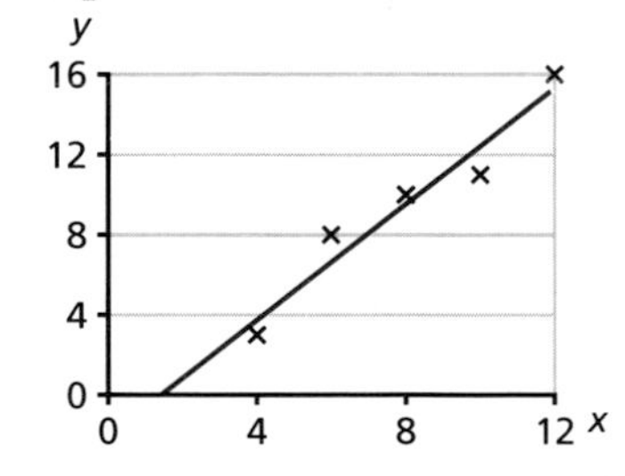

(ii) $r = 0.971$ (iii) $y = 1.45x - 2$ (iv) $\hat{y} = 5.25$

b (i)

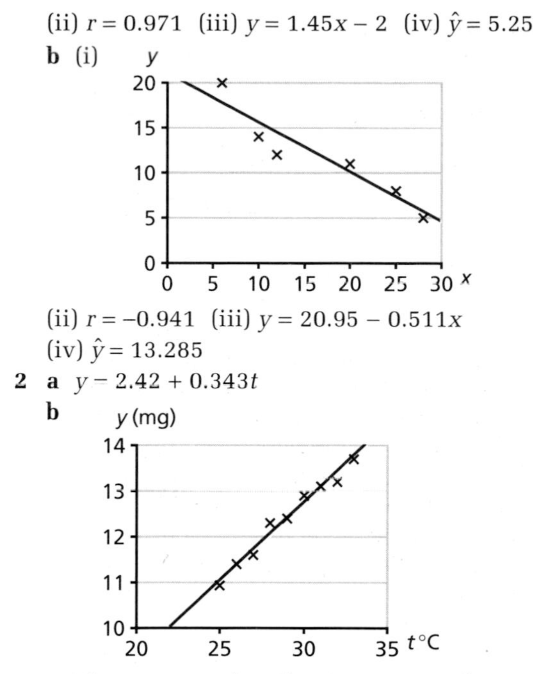

(ii) $r = -0.941$ (iii) $y = 20.95 - 0.511x$

(iv) $\hat{y} = 13.285$

2 **a** $y = 2.42 + 0.343t$

b

c The amount of antibiotic increases by 0.343 mg for every 1°C rise in the incubation temperature. **d** Average antibiotic present at 28 °C = 12.024 mg; average antibiotic present at 20 °C = 9.28 mg; prediction at 20 °C is extrapolation outside the range of the data.

3 **a** (i) For females: $r = 0.507$; % fat = 20.1 + 0.240 × age; a moderate positive relationship (ii) Removing outliers: $r = 0.609$; % fat = 12.7 + 0.363 age; a moderately strong positive relationship

(iii)

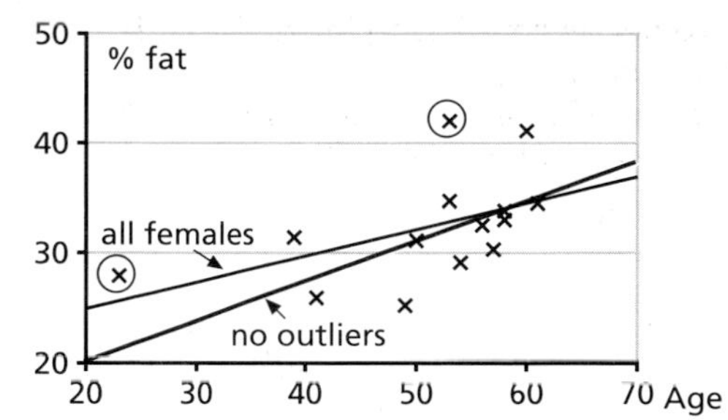

(iv) For a 30-year-old, predictions are 27.3% using all females, or 23.6% removing outliers. For a 60-year-old predictions are 34.5% using either line. Prediction for 30-year-old more difficult.

b For males: % fat = −9.16 + 0.813 age:

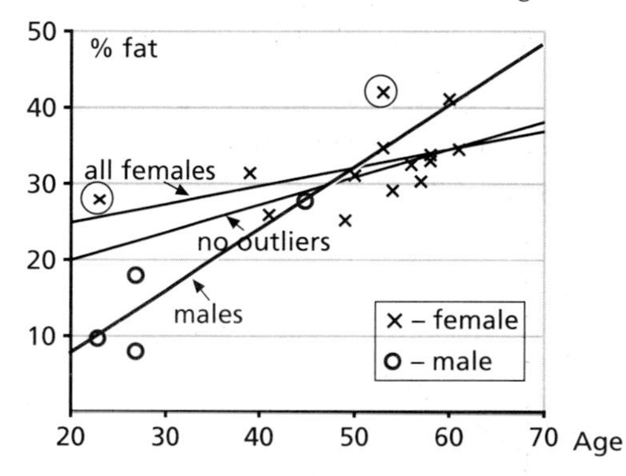

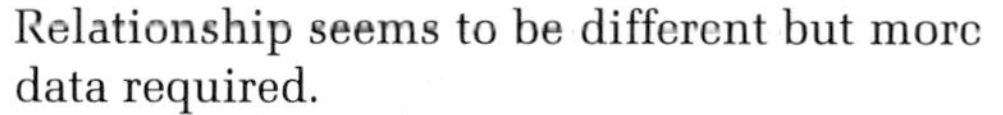

Relationship seems to be different but more data required.

Acknowledgements

Some of the data sets used in this book are taken from the following original sources. The publishers are grateful for permission to reproduce them. While every effort has been made to contact copyright holders, if any acknowledgement has been inadvertently omitted, the publishers will be pleased to make the necessary arrangements at the earliest opportunity.

Survival times in leukaemia
Bryson, M.C. and Siddiqui M.M. (1969) Survival times: some criteria for aging. *Journal of the American Statistical Association*, **64**, 1472-1483.

20 000 die throws
Wolf, R. (1882), *Vierteljahresschrift Naturforschende Gesellschaft in Zürich (Vierteljahrsschrift)*, **207**, 242.

Duration of pregnancy
Newell, D.J. (1964) Statistical aspects of the demand for maternity beds. *Journal of the Royal Statistical Society, Series A*, **127**, 1-33.

Strengths of glass fibres
Smith, R.L. and Naylor, J.C. (1987) A comparison of maximum likelihood and Bayesian estimators for the three-parameter Weibull distribution. *Applied Statistics*, **36**, 358-369, Table 1.

Births in Basel
Walser, P. (1969) Untersuchung über die Verteilung der Geburtstermine bei der mehrgebärenden Frau, *Helvetica Paediatrica Acta*, Suppl. XX ad vol. 24, fasc. 3, 1-30.

Scottish soldiers
Stigler, Stephen M. (1986) *The History of Statistics - The Measurement of Uncertainty before 1900*. Cambridge, Massachusetts: The Belknap Press of Harvard University Press, 208. From *The History of Statistics* by Stephen M. Stigler. Copyright © 1986 by the President and Fellows of Harvard College. Reprinted by permission of Harvard University Press.

Counting alpha-particles
Rutherford, E. and Geiger, M. (1910) The probability variations in the distribution of alpha-particles. *Philosophical Magazine, Series 6*, 20, 698-704.

Eruptions of the Old Faithful geyser
Azzalini, A. and Bowman, A.W. (1990) A look at some data on the Old Faithful geyser. *Journal of the Royal Statistical Society, Series C*, **39**, 357-366.

Road casualties on Fridays
Department of Transport (1987) *Road accidents in Great Britain 1986: the casualty report*, London: HMSO, Table 28. Crown copyright is reproduced with the permission of the Controller of Her Majesty's Stationery Office.

Unemployment and expenditure on motoring
Central Statistical Office (1989) *Regional trends 24*, London: HMSO, Tables 10.17 and 11.10. Crown copyright is reproduced with the permission of the Controller of Her Majesty's Stationery Office.

Circles Worksheet
Rouncefield, Mary, and Holmes, Peter (1989) *Practical Statistics*, Macmillan.
Crown copyright is reproduced with the permission of the Controller of Her Majesty's Stationery Office.

Borrowing library books
Burrell. Q.L. and Cane, V.R. (1982) The analysis of library data. *Journal of the Royal Statistical Society, Series A*, **145**, 439-471.

Cholesterol and behaviour type
Selvin, S. (1991) *Statistical analysis of epidemiological data*, New York: Oxford University Press, Table 2.1.

Caffeine and finger tapping
Draper, N.R. and Smith, H. (1981) *Applied regression analysis*, 2nd edition, New York: John Wiley & Sons, 425.

Butterfat
Sokal, R.R. and Rohlf, F.J. (1981) *Biometry*, 2nd edition, San Francisco: W.H. Freeman, 368.

Viral lesions on tobacco leaves
Youden, W.J. and Beale, H.P. (1934) *Contrib. Boyce Thompson Inst.*, **6**, 437.

Fun runners
Dale, G., Fleetwood, J.A., Weddell, A., Ellis, R.D. and Sainsbury, J.R.C. (1987) Beta endorphin: a factor in 'fun run' collapse? *British Medical Journal*, **294**, 1004.

Anorexia data
Brian Everitt (private communication by the author).

Distances in Sheffield
Gilchrist, W. (1984) *Statistical modelling*, Chichester: John Wiley & Sons, 5.

Finger ridges of identical twins
Newman, H.H., Freeman, F.N. and Holzinger, K.J. (1937) *Twins*, Chicago: University of Chicago Press.

Boiling points in the Alps
Atkinson, A.C. (1985) *Plots, Transformations and Regression*, Oxford: Clarendon Press, 4. By permission of Oxford University Press.

Sandflies
Christensen, H.A., Herrer, A. and Telford, S.R. (1972) Enzootic cutaneous leishmaniasis in Eastern Panama. 2. Entymological investigations. *Annals of tropical medicine and parasitology*, **66**, 55-66.

Subjective health assessment in 5 regions
Turral, K, (1992) *An analysis of 5 health and lifestyle surveys*. MSc dissertation, Southampton University, Faculty of Mathematics, Table 3.52, 43.

Smoking and motherhood
Freeman, D.H. (1987) *Applied Categorical Data Analysis*, New York: Marcel Dekker, 211.

Engine capacity and fuel consumption
The Open University (1983) *MDST242 Statistics in Society, Unit A3: Relationships*, 1st edition, Milton Keynes: The Open University, Figure 1.2.

Human age and fatness
Mazess, R.B., Peppler, W.W., and Gibbons, M. (1984) Total body composition by dual-photon (^{153}Gd) absorptiometry. *American Journal of Clinical Nutrition*, **40**, 834-839.

Age and systolic blood pressure
1992 CSYS Mathematics (Revised) Paper III Statistics, Scottish Examination Board. By permission of the Scottish Qualifications Authority.

Lean meat content from backfat thickness in pigs.
Dr G. E. Thomas, University of Dundee.

Incubation temperature and amount of antibiotic.
Dr G. E. Thomas, University of Dundee.